Aquatic and Riparian Weeds of the West

Joseph M. DiTomaso
Evelyn A. Healy

Sponsored by the California Weed Science Society

University of California
Agriculture and Natural Resources

Publication 3421

For information about ordering this publication, contact

University of California
Agriculture and Natural Resources
Communication Services
6701 San Pablo Avenue, 2nd Floor
Oakland, California 94608-1239

Telephone 1-800-994-8849
(510) 642-2431
FAX (510) 643-5470
E-mail: danrcs@ucdavis.edu
Visit the ANR Communication Services Web site at http://anrcatalog.ucdavis.edu

Publication 3421

 This publication has been anonymously peer reviewed for technical accuracy by University of California scientists and other qualified professionals. This review process was managed by the ANR Associate Editor for Pest Management.

ISBN 1-879906-59-7
Library of Congress Control Number: 2002107125

Contents

Acknowledgments vi
About This Book 2
Format of Plant Descriptions 4
How To Identify Plants Using This Book 6
Lists of Species Covered in This Book 8
    Species by Common Name 8
    Species by Scientific Name 12
    Species by Family 16
Shortcut Identification Tables 21
    Table 1. Plants completely or nearly completely submerged 21
    Table 2. Free-floating aquatic plants (roots in water column) 22
    Table 3. Plants with floating leaves and roots anchored in soil 22
    Table 4. Woody species 22
    Table 5. Plants spiny to the touch 23
    Table 6. Stem characteristics 23
    Table 7. Leaf characteristics 24
Key to Floating-Leaved and Submerged Aquatic Weeds 28
Key to Grasses or Grasslike Aquatic Weeds, Including Irises, Sedges,
Rushes, and Cattails 34
Key to *Potamogeton*, *Stuckenia* (Pondweeds), and *Ruppia* (Widgeongrass) Species 37
Floating-Leaved Aquatic Plants with Roots in the Water Column 40
    Ferns and Monocots 41
        Araceae (Arum Family)
            Waterlettuce 42
        Azollaceae (Mosquitofern Family)
            Mosquitofern 44
        Lemnaceae (Duckweed Family)
            Common duckweed 49
        Pontederiaceae (Pickerelweed Family)
            Water hyacinth 52
        Salviniaceae (Salvinia Family)
            Salvinia 57
Submerged or Floating-Leaved Aquatic Plants with Roots within the Soil Sediment . .62
    Algae 63
        Caulerpaceae (Caulerpa Family)
            Caulerpa 64
        Characeae (Stonewort Family)
            Chara • Nitella 66
        Cladophoraceae (Cladophora Family)
            Cladophora • Rhizoclonium 71
        Nostocaceae (Nostoc Family)
            Anabaena • Nostoc 74
    Ferns, Monocots, and Dicots 77
        Ceratophyllaceae (Hornwort Family)
            Coontail 78
        Haloragaceae (Watermilfoil Family)
            Parrotfeather • Eurasian watermilfoil 86
        Hydrocharitaceae (Waterweed Family)
            Hydrilla • Brazilian egeria • Common elodea 96
            Southern naiad 106

Contents

Nymphaeaceae (Waterlily Family)
Yellow pondlily 110
Mexican waterlily 114
Potamogetonaceae (Pondweed Family)
Pondweeds 118
Widgeongrass 128
Zannichelliaceae (Horned Pondweed Family)
Horned pondweed 132
Emerged Aquatic Plants 135
Monocots, Dicots, and Spore Producers 136
Alismataceae (Waterplantain Family)
Common waterplantain 137
Upright burhead 144
California arrowhead 147
Amaranthaceae (Pigweed Family)
Alligatorweed 152
Apiaceae (Carrot Family)
Giant hogweed 156
Floating pennywort 159
Asteraceae (Sunflower Family)
Seepwillow 162
Brassbuttons 165
Eclipta 168
Brassicaceae (Mustard Family)
Perennial pepperweed 171
Cyperaceae (Sedge Family)
Smallflower umbrella sedge • Lovegrass sedge 176
Creeping spikerush 184
Hardstem bulrush 189
Elaeagnaceae (Oleaster Family)
Russian olive 199
Equisetaceae (Horsetail Family)
Field horsetail • Scouringrush 202
Fabaceae (Pea or Bean Family)
Rough jointvetch 207
White sweetclover 211
Rattlebush 214
Iridaceae (Iris Family)
Yellowflag iris 221
Lamiaceae (Mint Family)
Pennyroyal 224
Lythraceae (Loosestrife Family)
Purple ammannia • Indian toothcup 228
Purple loosestrife • Hyssop loosestrife 237
Onagraceae (Evening Primrose Family)
Creeping waterprimrose 249
Poaceae (Grass Family)
Giant reed 254
Junglerice • Barnyardgrass .263
Bearded sprangletop • Mexican sprangletop 276
Dallisgrass • Knotgrass 281
Harding grass 290
Rabbitfoot polypogon 297
Smooth cordgrass 305

Polygonaceae (Buckwheat Family)
Swamp smartweed • Pale smartweed • Ladysthumb 314
Curly dock • Broadleaf dock 329
Pontederiaceae (Pickerelweed Family)
Ducksalad • Monochoria 342
Rosaceae (Rose Family)
Himalaya blackberry • Cutleaf blackberry 348
Salicaceae (Willow Family)
Coyote willow • Goodding's black willow •
Red willow • Arroyo willow 353
Scrophulariaceae (Figwort Family)
Eisen waterhyssop 359
Water speedwell 365
Tamaricaceae (Tamarisk Family)
Smallflower tamarisk • Saltcedar • Athel tamarisk 369
Typhaceae (Cattail Family)
Common cattail 378
Verbenaceae (Vervain Family)
Tall vervain • Seashore vervain .387

Appendix: Federally Listed Noxious Weeds in Aquatic Habitats 393
Glossary 396
Bibliography 412
Index 425
Authors and Contributors 442

Tables

Table 1. Plants completely or nearly completely submerged 21
Table 2. Free-floating aquatic plants (roots in water column) 22
Table 3. Plants with floating leaves and roots anchored in soil 22
Table 4. Woody species 22
Table 5. Plants spiny to the touch 23
Table 6. Stem characteristics 23
Table 7. Leaf characteristics 24
Table 8. Submersed aquatic plants with linear leaves 109
Table 9. Pondweeds (*Potamogeton* spp. and *Stuckenia* spp.) and widgeongrass
(*Ruppia* spp.): All leaves submersed and sessile 130
Table 10. Pondweeds (*Potamogeton* spp.): At least some leaves floating, stalked, and
ovate to elliptic 131
Table 11. Waterplantain (*Alisma* spp.), upright burhead (*Echinodorus berteroi*), and
arrowhead (*Sagittaria* spp.) commonly found as rice weeds 143
Table 12. Bulrushes (*Scirpus* spp.) 198
Table 13. Barnyardgrass and related *Echinochloa* species 275
Table 14. Canarygrass (*Phalaris*) species associated with aquatic sites 296
Table 15. *Polypogon* species 304
Table 16. Cordgrass (*Spartina*) species 313
Table 17. Smartweed (*Polygonum*) species 328
Table 18. Dock (*Rumex*) species 341
Table 19. Common willows (*Salix* spp.) 358

Acknowledgments

We would like to thank the many individuals who helped in the production of this book, including Pat Akers, Dr. Lars Anderson, Dr. Debra Ayres, Dorothy Brandon, Robin Breckenridge, Brenda Brinton, Dave Cheetham, Peter Connors, Dr. Clyde Elmore, Dr. Steve Enloe, Alison Fisher, Dr. Holly Forbes, Dr. Fred Hrusa, Guy Kyser, Jan Lowrey, Dr. Dan Marcum, Kathy Ann Miller, Byeong-Chul Moon, Dr. Joe Neal, Ross O'Connell, Jenifer Parsons, Carri Pirosko, Dr. Tim Prather, Dr. Mark Renz, Ramona Robison, Ernie Roncoroni Jr., Ernie Roncoroni Sr., Geoff Sainty, Kitty Schlosser, Dr. Dave Spencer, Dr. Don Strong, Melanie Allen Truan, Dr. Rick Uva, and Maria Winkler. We are particularly indebted to Chris Pirosko for collecting several of the submerged aquatic specimens for photography and Drs. Ellen Dean and Fred Hrusa for assisting in identifying many of our collections and providing important taxonomic information. Although the author photographed most of the images used in this text, we are very grateful to Suzanne Paisley for her photographic advice and assistance. Most important, we are fortunate to have had the opportunity to work with Jack Kelly Clark, who not only advised us on photographic equipment and techniques but also photographed most of the submerged aquatic species and the seeds.

We would also like to thank the many reviewers for their helpful comments, including Carl Bell, Robin Breckenridge, Matt Brooks, Mick Canevari, Deanne DiPietro, Alison Fisher, Mike Kelly, Bill Neill, Steve Orloff, Carri Pirosko, Chris Pirosko, Mona Robison, Jerry Schmierer, Richard Smith, Joel Trumbo, Peter Warner, Rob Wilson, Maria Winkler and Jack Williams, and Drs. Lars Anderson, Debra Ayres, Dave Cudney, Sue Donaldson, Tom Dudley, Clyde Elmore, Albert Fischer, Ted Foin, Doreen Gee, Jodie Holt, Fred Hrusa, Nelroy Jackson, Tom Lanini, Joe Neal, John Randall, Barry Rice-Meyers, Dave Spencer, Mark Systma, Carol Thornber, Cheryl Wilen, and Susan Williams.

We thank our parents for their inspiration and families and friends for their support, include the CSs for their help with identification of the genus *Agrostis,* Cynthia Gauthier for her patience, and the DiTomaso boys (Evan and John Paul), who had to patiently hold plants or wait for photographic sessions to be completed.

In addition, we are most grateful to the California Weed Science Society for their substantial financial contribution and sponsorship of this book. We also thank the Center for Pest Management Research and Extension, Pesticide Applicators Professional Association (PAPA), UC Division of Agriculture and Natural Resources, UC Integrated Pest Management Program, and the Smith-Lever IPM Project at the University of California. We also thank the Weed Research and Information Center, as well as the California Department of Food and Agriculture, for their financial assistance in the development of the text. Finally, we thank the University of California Division of Agriculture and Natural Resources Communication Services staff for working with the authors on the production and publication of this book.

Aquatic and Riparian Weeds of the West

About This Book

Aquatic and Riparian Weeds of the West is a practical guide to the identification and biology of submerged, floating-leaved, and emergent aquatic weeds in rice production fields (paddies), water use systems, and wildland areas in the western United States. We have defined the western states to include regions west of the Rocky Mountains: Montana, Wyoming, Colorado, New Mexico, Idaho, Utah, Arizona, Nevada, Washington, Oregon, and California. Each species was carefully researched to provide the most accurate and timely data possible. A bibliography of some of the most pertinent publications on these species is included at the end of this book.

The common names used in this book conform to those in *Composite List of Weeds*, to be published in 2003 by the Weed Science Society of America (WSSA). When a species was not included in the *Composite List of Weeds*, we used the most widely recognized common name. The scientific names are those we considered the most widely accepted by current taxonomic treatments. Synonyms of both common and scientific names are also included in the text and can also be found in the indexes. Five-letter Bayer codes (standardized abbreviation and computer code) were included when available from the *Composite List of Weeds*. We have also indicated when a particular species was listed on a federal or state noxious weed list or on an Exotic Pest Plant Council invasive weed list. The list of names and categories for the California Exotic Pest Plant Council was revised in late 2003. Current listings can be found at www.caleppc.org.

Rather than providing individual descriptions for each weed species, we grouped related species or morphologically similar species into a single description to allow for easier comparison. In addition to photographs and descriptions of the prominent weedy species, we have also included photographs and distinguishing characteristics of many morphologically similar or related species. In some cases these species are also weedy, although less common in distribution, but in other cases they are nonweedy native species. We have included some of the nonweedy natives to avoid potential misidentification and inadvertent damage to nontarget desirable species.

The book consists of 58 plant entries, including a full description of 89 species representing 36 plant families, and another 96 plants compared as similar species. There is at least one photograph of 171 aquatic plant species.

Although numerous algae can cause problems in aquatic systems, we have included only the most widespread and significant. Many emergent species can cause problems around aquatic systems, and not all could be covered in this book. We did, however, attempt to discuss emergent species we considered to be significant problems near aquatic habitats and systems, including nonnative invasive species of wildlands and important emerged plants that interfere with water use systems.

The main body of the book contains weed descriptions. It is divided into three parts: "Floating-Leaved Aquatic Plants with Roots in the Water Column"; "Submerged or Floating-Leaved Aquatic Plants with Roots within the Soil Sediment"; and "Emerged Aquatic Plants." Within the parts, families are divided into the algae and the ferns, monocots, dicots, and spore producers. These divisions are organized alphabetically by scientific family name and then genus. On the first page of each plant group, the broad taxonomic group (algae, fern, monocot, dicot) and the family name appear at the upper left of the page; the growth form and problematic habitat appear at the upper right of the page. On subsequent pages for that plant group, the common name of the plant or plants in the group appears at the top of the page (see "Format of Plant Descriptions," below).

The format of the text is similar to that in *Weeds of the Northeast* (Cornell University Press, 1997), coauthored by Rick Uva, Joe Neal, and Joe DiTomaso. The text includes not only detailed descriptions of the morphological character-istics of each main species but also information on the distribution, habitat, post-senescence characteristics, propagation and phenology, management considera-tions that favor or discourage survival, and characteristics that allow distinguish-ing between other similar or related species (see "Format of Plant Descriptions," below). The symbol ± is used to mean "about" and indicates variability in the given characteristic; numbers in parentheses, as in "12(15) cm wide," indicate occasional variability to the parenthetical number. Phrases or words in **bold** indi-cate important characteristics in the identification of that species. Where a par-ticular genus or group contains many difficult-to-distinguish weedy species, we have included tables comparing important characteristics. Distribution informa-tion was more difficult to obtain for most western states than for California, and, consequently, detailed information is provided only for California. Regional des-ignation in California is according to the *Jepson Manual*, edited by J. C. Hickman (University of California Press, 1993).

Three separate lists of the species covered in the text are provided, beginning on page 8. These lists are organized by common, scientific, and family name and give the page number where the discussion of each species begins. The book also contains quick identification tables for groups that share similar, unusual, or rel-atively uncommon characteristics. Three keys have also been provided, including a key to floating-leaved and submerged aquatic weeds; a key to grasses or grasslike emergent aquatic weeds; and keys to the *Potamogeton, Stuckenia,* and *Ruppia* species. Because there are so many emergent species in and around aquat-ic habitats, we did not include a key to this group. The emergent species includ-ed in this book are those we considered the most problematic in wildlands, rice production areas, or water use systems.

The text employs certain technical botanical terms in describing the species. To assist in understanding these technical terms, we have included an illustrated glossary. Measurements are given in metric units; aid in conversion can be found on the inside back cover of the book. The two indexes at the end of the book include one for currently accepted common and scientific names used in the text and one for synonyms of common and scientific names.

Although we have taken every precaution to ensure that the information provided is accurate and the identifications are correct, there may be instances where inaccuracies escaped our notice. Should a reader find an error in the text, please contact Joe DiTomaso at the Weed Science Program, Robbins Hall, University of Californa, Davis CA, 95616.

Format of Plant Descriptions

(Note: Every entry may not contain all categories of descriptions.)

Plant category: Family name (Family common name)　　　　Growth form; problem site

Common name [*Scientific name* and author] [Bayer code]

Noxious Weed Lists: Federal Noxious Weed List, or states where the species is listed as noxious in the western United States, including associated list. Also includes species listed by the California Exotic Pest Plant Council (CalEPPC) as *Plants of Greatest Ecological Concern.*

Synonyms: Common and scientific names used in other texts or references but not considered as the commonly accepted names today.

General Information: Summary of the important aspects of the plant's life cycle, size, growth form, visual appearance, habitat, distribution, impact, method of introduction, and native environment and range. In cases where the plant can cause toxicity to humans or other animals, a brief description of the toxicology is included.

Seedling: Description of the vegetative characteristics of newly emerging perennials, as well as seedlings, including cotyledons and the first few leaves.

Mature Plant: Description of the vegetative characteristics of mature plants.

Roots and Underground Structures: Description of the root types and growth characteristics of annuals, biennials, and herbaceous and woody perennial species. In some algae, referred to as ROOTLIKE STRUCTURES.

Flowers: Flowering season and a description of flowering stems, inflorescence, and individual flowers and structures associated with flowers. When available, pollination method, self-compatibility, and flower timing are included.

Fruits and Seeds: Description of the size and type of fruit and seed.

Spikelets and Florets: Description of the reproductive structures of grasses.

Spore-Bearing Structures: Description of organisms that reproduce by spores, rather than flowers (e.g., horsetails, ferns).

Other Reproductive Structures: In some cases, other uncommon reproductive structures are described, such as turions.

Postsenescence Characteristics: Description of the weed either in the dormant stage or after the plant has died (annual or biennial) or foliage has senesced (perennials).

Habitat: Description of habitats where the species is typically found. This section may also include soil, nutrient, or exposure characteristics associated with the species.

Additional Ecological Aspects: Typically a comparison between the biology and ecology of the weedy species and native desirable species within the same habitat.

Distribution: Broad distribution range in the western United States, often including all of North America. More detailed distribution in California, including maximum elevation in which the species is found. When known, the world-wide distribution is also included.

Propagation and Phenology: Description of the methods of reproduction, seed dispersal, germination requirements and conditions, seed survival and longevity, and early establishment characteristics and requirements.

Management Favoring or Discouraging Survival: When available, cultural practices that can prevent establishment or management options that have proven effective or ineffective in controlling infestations. Because of the dynamic nature of weed control, specific recommendations are not included.

Similar Species: A description of species that resemble or are closely related to the main species described in the entry and characteristics that allow separation. In some cases, these include detailed descriptions given only here, whereas in other cases, they refer to similar species that are described in detail elsewhere in the text. Species described only here also include synonyms and the Bayer code (when available).

How To Identify Plants Using This Book

This book provides users with a number of resources to aid in identifying aquatic and riparian weeds. Although we expect that most users will leaf through the book until they see a photo that matches the plant of concern, there are other, perhaps faster, methods of identification. For example, if the plant of interest has an unusual characteristic, such as square stems, a whorled leaf arrangement, or arrow-shaped leaves, the plant can be identified by finding these characteristics in the shortcut identification tables on pages 21–27. Using these tables narrows the number of choices and, hopefully, saves time in correctly identifying a plant.

We have also included three keys to help in identification. The two main ones are the "Key to Floating-Leaved and Submerged Aquatic Weeds" (page 28) and "Key to Grasses or Grasslike Aquatic Weeds, Including Irises, Sedges, Rushes, and Cattails (page 34)." These keys are set up much like typical dichotomous keys, with occasionally three choices instead of the customary two. We have made every effort to include only vegetative characteristics to facilitate identification at any time during the growing season and not just during the sexual reproductive stages. In some grasses, reproductive structures were necessary to separate genera. Some steps in the keys end with a genus rather than with a particular species; in these cases, identification to species can be achieved by reading the individual entry for that genus. In many situations, we have included a plant in more than one place in the key. This was done to account for variability in the species or difficulty in separating a particular species based on that key step. The third key, "Key to *Potamogeton, Stuckenia* (Pondweeds), and *Ruppia* (Widgeongrass) Species" (page 37), is included to help separate these very similar submerged aquatic species. In this key, users will find that a generally easy-to-recognize vegetative characteristic could lead to two, three, or four possibilities. These similar species are then compared by several characteristics to help in their identification.

Some plant descriptions contain tables to assist in separating closely related species. These tables compare and contrast several characteristics, including life cycle and vegetative and reproductive characteristics. Rather than using standard dichotomous keys, these tables should allow users to compare related species based on the characteristics that may be available. Identification to species should be easy if the plant is at a stage where all characteristics are evident. However, if only a few vegetative characteristics are present, it is still possible to narrow the choices to one or two possible species.

Finally, the book includes two indexes. "Index to Common and Scientific Names" is an index to the currently accepted common and scientific names to the plants discussed in this book. The common names used in this book were those included in the most recent edition of the *Composite List of Weeds*, published by the Weed Science Society of America (2003 edition). However, we recognize that many other texts and taxonomists use other common names or recognize different scientific names as acceptable. Consequently, we have also included "Index to Synonyms of Common and Scientific Names," a more extensive index that indexes the other common and scientific names used for plants in the book.

We hope that the combination of color photos, text descriptions, keys, tables, and indexes will increase the accuracy and speed of aquatic and riparian weed identification.

Lists of Species Covered in This Book

Species by Common Name

Common name	Scientific name	Family	Page
alligatorweed	*Alternanthera philoxeroides*	Amaranthaceae	152
ammannia, purple	*Ammannia robusta*	Lythraceae	228
anabaena	*Anabaena* spp.	Nostocaceae	74
arrowhead, California	*Sagittaria montevidensis*	Alismataceae	147
arrowhead, Gregg	*Sagittaria longiloba*	Alismataceae	150
bahiagrass	*Paspalum notatum*	Poaceae	284
barnyardgrass	*Echinochloa crus-galli*	Poaceae	263
barnyardgrass, rough	*Echinochloa muricata*	Poaceae	270
bent, water	*Polypogon viridis* (= *Agrostis viridis*)	Poaceae	302
blackberry, cutleaf	*Rubus laciniatus*	Rosaceae	348
blackberry, elmleaf	*Rubus ulmifolius* var. *inermis*	Rosaceae	352
blackberry, Himalaya	*Rubus armeniacus* (= *R. discolor*)	Rosaceae	348
brassbuttons	*Cotula coronopifolia*	Asteraceae	165
bulrush, California	*Scirpus californicus*	Cyperaceae	191
bulrush, cosmopolitan	*Scirpus maritimus*	Cyperaceae	191
bulrush, hardstem	*Scirpus acutus* var. *occidentalis*	Cyperaceae	189
bulrush, ricefield	*Scirpus mucronatus*	Cyperaceae	193
bulrush, river	*Scirpus fluviatilis*	Cyperaceae	191
bulrush, southern	*Scirpus californicus*	Cyperaceae	191
bulrush, sturdy	*Scirpus robustus*	Cyperaceae	191
bulrush, tuberous	*Scirpus glaucus* (= *S. tuberosus*)	Cyperaceae	193
burhead, upright	*Echinodorus berteroi*	Alismataceae	144
canarygrass, Carolina	*Phalaris caroliniana*	Poaceae	293
canarygrass, reed	*Phalaris arundinacea*	Poaceae	292
canarygrass, short-spike	*Phalaris brachystachys*	Poaceae	293
cattail, common	*Typha latifolia*	Typhaceae	378
cattail, narrowleaf	*Typha angustifolia*	Typhaceae	384
cattail, southern	*Typha domingensis*	Typhaceae	384
caulerpa	*Caulerpa taxifolia*	Caulerpaceae	64
chara	*Chara* spp.	Characeae	66
cladophora	*Cladophora* spp.	Cladophoraceae	71
cockspur, gulf	*Echinochloa crus-pavonis*	Poaceae	270
coontail	*Ceratophyllum demersum*	Ceratophyllaceae	78
cordgrass, California	*Spartina foliosa*	Poaceae	308
cordgrass, common	*Spartina anglica*	Poaceae	311
cordgrass, dense-flowered	*Spartina densiflora*	Poaceae	310
cordgrass, salt-meadow	*Spartina patens*	Poaceae	310
cordgrass, smooth	*Spartina alterniflora*	Poaceae	305
cress, hoary	*Cardaria draba*	Brassicaceae	175
dallisgrass	*Paspalum dilatatum*	Poaceae	281
ditchgrass, spiral	*Ruppia cirrhosa*	Potamogetonaceae	128
dock, broadleaf	*Rumex obtusifolius*	Polygonaceae	329
dock, cluster	*Rumex conglomeratus*	Polygonaceae	338
dock, curly	*Rumex crispus*	Polygonaceae	329

Species by Common Name, cont.

Common name	Scientific name	Family	Page
dock, fiddleleaf	*Rumex pulcher*	Polygonaceae	340
dock, Kerner's	*Rumex kerneri*	Polygonaceae	340
dock, toothed	*Rumex dentatus*	Polygonaceae	338
duckmeat	*Spirodela* spp.	Lemnaceae	49
ducksalad	*Heteranthera limosa*	Pontederiaceae	342
duckweed	*Lemna* spp.	Lemnaceae	49
duckweed, giant	*Spirodela* spp.	Lemnaceae	49
eclipta	*Eclipta prostrata*	Asteraceae	168
egeria	*Egeria densa*	Hydrocharitaceae	96
egeria, Brazilian	*Egeria densa*	Hydrocharitaceae	96
elodea, Brazilian	*Egeria densa*	Hydrocharitaceae	96
elodea, common	*Elodea canadensis*	Hydrocharitaceae	96
fanwort	*Cabomba caroliniana*	Cabombaceae	80
fern, water	*Salvinia minima*	Salviniaceae	60
flatsedge, brown	*Cyperus fuscus*	Cyperaceae	182
flatsedge, redroot	*Cyperus erythrorhizos*	Cyperaceae	182
flatsedge, tall	*Cyperus eragrostis*	Cyperaceae	176
flatsedge, whitemargined	*Cyperus flavicomus*	Cyperaceae	183
floatingheart, yellow	*Nymphoides peltata*	Menyanthaceae	117
frogbit, smooth	*Limnobium laevigatum*	Hydrocharitaceae	55
Harding grass	*Phalaris aquatica*	Poaceae	290
hogweed, giant	*Heracleum mantegazzianum*	Apiaceae	156
horsetail, field	*Equisetum arvense*	Equisetaceae	202
horsetail, giant	*Equisetum telmateia* ssp. *braunii*	Equisetaceae	205
hydrilla	*Hydrilla verticillata*	Hydrocharitaceae	96
indigobush	*Amorpha fruticosa*	Fabaceae	219
iris, yellowflag	*Iris pseudacorus*	Iridaceae	221
jointvetch, rough	*Aeschynomene rudis*	Fabaceae	207
junglerice	*Echinochloa colona*	Poaceae	263
kelp, Japanese	*Undaria pinnatifida*	Alariaceae	64
knotgrass	*Paspalum distichum*	Poaceae	281
ladysthumb	*Polygonum persicaria*	Polygonaceae	314
loosestrife, California	*Lythrum californicum*	Lythraceae	247
loosestrife, dotted	*Lysimachia punctata*	Primulaceae	248
loosestrife, European wand	*Lythrum virgatum*	Lythraceae	247
loosestrife, garden	*Lysimachia vulgaris*	Primulaceae	247
loosestrife, hyssop	*Lythrum hyssopifolium*	Lythraceae	237
loosestrife, purple	*Lythrum salicaria*	Lythraceae	237
loosestrife, spatulaleaf	*Lythrum portula*	Lythraceae	245
loosestrife, threebract	*Lythrum tribracteatum*	Lythraceae	245
marshweed	*Limnophila* ×*ludoviciana*	Scrophulariaceae	82
mint, apple	*Mentha suaveolens*	Lamiaceae	226
monochoria	*Monochoria vaginalis*	Pontederiaceae	342
mosquitofern	*Azolla* spp.	Azollaceae	44
naiad, grassy	*Najas graminea*	Hydrocharitaceae	105, 107

Species by Common Name, cont.

Common name	Scientific name	Family	Page
naiad, hollyleaf	*Najas marina*	Hydrocharitaceae	108
naiad, southern	*Najas guadalupensis*	Hydrocharitaceae	106
nitella	*Nitella* spp.	Characeae	66
nostoc	*Nostoc* spp.	Nostocaceae	74
olive, Russian	*Elaeagnus angustifolia*	Elaeagnaceae	199
parrotfeather	*Myriophyllum aquaticum*	Haloragaceae	86
parsnip, cow	*Heracleum lanatum*	Apiaceae	158
pennyroyal	*Mentha pulegium*	Lamiaceae	224
pennywort, floating	*Hydrocotyle ranunculoides*	Apiaceae	159
pepperweed, perennial	*Lepidium latifolium*	Brassicaceae	171
pepperwort, hairy	*Marsilea vestita*	Marsileaceae	45
polypogon, Chilean	*Polypogon australis*	Poaceae	302
polypogon, ditch	*Polypogon interruptus*	Poaceae	301
polypogon, Mediterranean	*Polypogon maritimus*	Poaceae	301
polypogon, rabbitfoot	*Polypogon monspeliensis*	Poaceae	297
polypogon, streambank	*Polypogon elongatus*	Poaceae	302
pondlily, yellow	*Nuphar polysepala*	Nymphaeaceae	110
pondweed, American	*Potamogeton nodosus*	Potamogetonaceae	118
pondweed, curlyleaf	*Potamogeton crispus*	Potamogetonaceae	118
pondweed, flatstem	*Potamogeton zosteriformis*	Potamogetonaceae	127
pondweed, floatingleaf	*Potamogeton natans*	Potamogetonaceae	118
pondweed, horned	*Zannichellia palustris*	Zannichelliaceae	132
pondweed, Illinois	*Potamogeton illinoensis*	Potamogetonaceae	118
pondweed, largeleaf	*Potamogeton amplifolius*	Potamogetonaceae	127
pondweed, leafy	*Potamogeton foliosus*	Potamogetonaceae	118
pondweed, ribbonleaf	*Potamogeton epihydrus*	Potamogetonaceae	127
pondweed, Richardson's	*Potamogeton richardsonii*	Potamogetonaceae	127
pondweed, sago	*Stuckenia pectinatus* (= *Potamogeton pectinatus*)	Potamogetonaceae	118
pondweed, small	*Potamogeton pusillus*	Potamogetonaceae	118
pondweed, threadleaf	*Stuckenia filiformis* (= *Potamogeton filiformis*)	Potamogetonaceae	127
pondweed, variable	*Potamogeton gramineus*	Potamogetonaceae	127
pondweed, waterthread	*Potamogeton diversifolius*	Potamogetonaceae	127
pondweed, whitestem	*Potamogeton praelongus*	Potamogetonaceae	127
rattlebush	*Sesbania punicea*	Fabaceae	214
ravennagrass	*Saccharum ravennae*	Poaceae	261
redstem	*Ammannia coccinea*	Lythraceae	228
reed, common	*Phragmites australis*	Poaceae	260
reed, giant	*Arundo donax*	Poaceae	254
rhizoclonium	*Rhizoclonium* spp.	Cladophoraceae	71
saltcedar	*Tamarix ramosissima*	Tamaricaceae	369
salvinia	*Salvinia* spp.	Salviniaceae	57
salvinia, giant	*Salvinia molesta*	Salviniaceae	57
scouringrush	*Equisetum hyemale* ssp. *affine*	Equisetaceae	202
scouringrush, smooth	*Equisetum laevigatum*	Equisetaceae	205
sedge, lovegrass	*Cyperus eragrostis*	Cyperaceae	176

Species by Common Name, cont.

Common name	Scientific name	Family	Page
sedge, smallflower umbrella	*Cyperus difformis*	Cyperaceae	176
seepwillow	*Baccharis salicifolia*	Asteraceae	162
sesbania, hemp	*Sesbania exaltata*	Fabaceae	218
smartweed, dotted	*Polygonum punctatum*	Polygonaceae	327
smartweed, marshpepper	*Polygonum hydropiper*	Polygonaceae	327
smartweed, mild	*Polygonum hydropiperoides*	Polygonaceae	327
smartweed, pale	*Polygonum lapathifolium*	Polygonaceae	314
smartweed, Pennsylvania	*Polygonum pensylvanicum*	Polygonaceae	327
smartweed, swamp	*Polygonum amphibium* var. *emersum*	Polygonaceae	314
smartweed, water	*Polygonum amphibium* var. *stipulaceum*	Polygonaceae	315
spearmint	*Mentha spicata*	Lamiaceae	226
speedwell, American	*Veronica americana*	Scrophulariaceae	368
speedwell, chain	*Veronica catenata*	Scrophulariaceae	367
speedwell, European	*Veronica beccabunga*	Scrophulariaceae	367
speedwell, water	*Veronica anagallis-aquatica*	Scrophulariaceae	365
spikerush, blunt	*Eleocharis obtusa*	Cyperaceae	185
spikerush, creeping	*Eleocharis macrostachya*	Cyperaceae	184
spikerush, dwarf	*Eleocharis parvula*	Cyperaceae	185
spikerush, needle	*Eleocharis acicularis*	Cyperaceae	185
spongeplant	*Limnobium laevigatum*	Hydrocharitaceae	55
sprangles, water	*Salvinia minima*	Salviniaceae	60
sprangletop, bearded	*Leptochloa fascicularis*	Poaceae	276
sprangletop, Mexican	*Leptochloa uninervia*	Poaceae	276
sweetclover, white	*Melilotus albus*	Fabaceae	211
tamarisk, athel	*Tamarix aphylla*	Tamaricaceae	369
tamarisk, Chinese	*Tamarix chinensis*	Tamaricaceae	377
tamarisk, French	*Tamarix gallica*	Tamaricaceae	377
tamarisk, smallflower	*Tamarix parviflora*	Tamaricaceae	369
toothcup	*Rotala ramosior*	Lythraceae	233
toothcup, Indian	*Rotala indica*	Lythraceae	228
tule	*Scirpus acutus* var. *occidentalis*	Cyperaceae	189
vaseygrass	*Paspalum urvillei*	Poaceae	284
vervain, seashore	*Verbena litoralis*	Verbenaceae	387
vervain, tall	*Verbena bonariensis*	Verbenaceae	387
water hyacinth	*Eichhornia crassipes*	Pontederiaceae	52
water sprangles	*Salvinia minima*	Salviniaceae	60
waterbuttercup, white	*Ranunculus aquatilis*	Ranunculaceae	84
watergrass, early	*Echinochloa oryzoides*	Poaceae	271
watergrass, late	*Echinochloa oryzicola*	Poaceae	270
watergrass, late	*Echinochloa phyllopogon*	Poaceae	271
waterhyssop, creeping	*Bacopa repens*	Scrophulariaceae	362
waterhyssop, disc	*Bacopa rotundifolia*	Scrophulariaceae	362
waterhyssop, Eisen	*Bacopa eisenii*	Scrophulariaceae	359
waterhyssop, Monnier	*Bacopa monnieri*	Scrophulariaceae	361
waterlettuce	*Pistia stratiotes*	Araceae	42
waterlily, fragrant	*Nymphaea odorata*	Nymphaeaceae	117

Species by Common Name, cont.

Common name	Scientific name	Family	Page
waterlily, Mexican	*Nymphaea mexicana*	Nymphaeaceae	114
watermeal	*Wolffia* spp.	Lemnaceae	49
watermilfoil, Eurasian	*Myriophyllum spicatum*	Haloragaceae	86
watermilfoil, northern	*Myriophyllum sibiricum*	Haloragaceae	82, 93
watermilfoil, western	*Myriophyllum hippuroides*	Haloragaceae	93
watermilfoil, whorled	*Myriophyllum verticillatum*	Haloragaceae	93
waterplantain, common	*Alisma plantago-aquatica*	Alismataceae	137
waterplantain, lanceleaved	*Alisma lanceolatum*	Alismataceae	142
waterprimrose, creeping	*Ludwigia peploides*	Onagraceae	249
waterprimrose, Uruguay	*Ludwigia hexapetala*	Onagraceae	253
waterpurslane	*Ludwigia palustris*	Onagraceae	253
watershield	*Brasenia schreberi*	Cabombaceae	111
whitetop, hairy	*Cardaria pubescens*	Brassicaceae	175
whitetop, lens-podded	*Cardaria draba* ssp. *chalepensis*	Brassicaceae	175
widgeongrass	*Ruppia maritima*	Potamogetonaceae	128
willow, Arroyo	*Salix lasiolepis*	Salicaceae	353
willow, coyote	*Salix exigua*	Salicaceae	353
willow, Goodding's black	*Salix gooddingii*	Salicaceae	353
willow, red	*Salix laevigata*	Salicaceae	353
willow, weeping	*Salix babylonica*	Salicaceae	358

Species by Scientific Name

Scientific name	Common name	Family	Page
Aeschynomene rudis	rough jointvetch	Fabaceae	207
Alisma lanceolatum	lanceleaved waterplantain	Alismataceae	142
Alisma plantago-aquatica	common waterplantain	Alismataceae	137
Alternanthera philoxeroides	alligatorweed	Amaranthaceae	152
Ammannia coccinea	redstem	Lythraceae	228
Ammannia robusta	purple ammannia	Lythraceae	228
Amorpha fruticosa	indigobush	Fabaceae	219
Anabaena spp.	anabaena	Nostocaceae	74
Arundo donax	giant reed	Poaceae	254
Azolla spp.	mosquitofern	Azollaceae	44
Baccharis salicifolia	seepwillow	Asteraceae	162
Bacopa eisenii	Eisen waterhyssop	Scrophulariaceae	359
Bacopa monnieri	Monnier waterhyssop	Scrophulariaceae	361
Bacopa repens	creeping waterhyssop	Scrophulariaceae	362
Bacopa rotundifolia	disc waterhyssop	Scrophulariaceae	362
Brasenia schreberi	watershield	Cabombaceae	111
Cabomba caroliniana	fanwort	Cabombaceae	80
Cardaria draba	hoary cress	Brassicaceae	175
Cardaria draba ssp. *chalepensis*	lens-podded whitetop	Brassicaceae	175
Cardaria pubescens	hairy whitetop	Brassicaceae	175
Caulerpa taxifolia	caulerpa	Caulerpaceae	64
Ceratophyllum demersum	coontail	Ceratophyllaceae	78

Species by Scientific Name, cont.

Scientific name	Common name	Family	Page
Chara spp.	chara	Characeae	66
Cladophora spp.	cladophora	Cladophoraceae	71
Cotula coronopifolia	brassbuttons	Asteraceae	165
Cyperus difformis	smallflower umbrella sedge	Cyperaceae	176
Cyperus eragrostis	lovegrass sedge or tall flatsedge	Cyperaceae	176
Cyperus erythrorhizos	redroot flatsedge	Cyperaceae	182
Cyperus flavicomus	whitemargined flatsedge	Cyperaceae	183
Cyperus fuscus	brown flatsedge	Cyperaceae	182
Echinochloa colona	junglerice	Poaceae	263
Echinochloa crus-galli	barnyardgrass	Poaceae	263
Echinochloa crus-pavonis	gulf cockspur	Poaceae	270
Echinochloa muricata	rough barnyardgrass	Poaceae	270
Echinochloa oryzicola	late watergrass	Poaceae	270
Echinochloa oryzoides	early watergrass	Poaceae	271
Echinochloa phyllopogon	late watergrass	Poaceae	271
Echinodorus berteroi	upright burhead	Alismataceae	144
Eclipta prostrata	eclipta	Asteraceae	168
Egeria densa	Brazilian elodea, Brazilian egeria, egeria	Hydrocharitaceae	96
Eichhornia crassipes	water hyacinth	Pontederiaceae	52
Elaeagnus angustifolia	Russian olive	Elaeagnaceae	199
Eleocharis acicularis	needle spikerush	Cyperaceae	185
Eleocharis macrostachya	creeping spikerush	Cyperaceae	184
Eleocharis obtusa	blunt spikerush	Cyperaceae	185
Eleocharis parvula	dwarf spikerush	Cyperaceae	185
Elodea canadensis	common elodea	Hydrocharitaceae	96
Equisetum arvense	field horsetail	Equisetaceae	202
Equisetum hyemale ssp. *affine*	scouringrush	Equisetaceae	202
Equisetum laevigatum	smooth scouringrush	Equisetaceae	205
Equisetum telmateia ssp. *braunii*	giant horsetail	Equisetaceae	205
Heracleum lanatum	cow parsnip	Apiaceae	158
Heracleum mantegazzianum	giant hogweed	Apiaceae	156
Heteranthera limosa	ducksalad	Pontederiaceae	342
Hydrilla verticillata	hydrilla	Hydrocharitaceae	96
Hydrocotyle ranunculoides	floating pennywort	Apiaceae	159
Iris pseudacorus	yellowflag iris	Iridaceae	221
Lemna spp.	duckweed	Lemnaceae	49
Lepidium latifolium	perennial pepperweed	Brassicaceae	171
Leptochloa fascicularis	bearded sprangletop	Poaceae	276
Leptochloa uninervia	Mexican sprangletop	Poaceae	276
Limnobium laevigatum	spongeplant or smooth frogbit	Hydrocharitaceae	55
Limnophila ×*ludoviciana*	marshweed	Scrophulariaceae	82
Ludwigia hexapetala	Uruguay waterprimrose	Onagraceae	253
Ludwigia palustris	waterpurslane	Onagraceae	253
Ludwigia peploides	creeping waterprimrose	Onagraceae	249

Species by Scientific Name, cont.

Scientific name	Common name	Family	Page
Lysimachia punctata	dotted loosestrife	Primulaceae	248
Lysimachia vulgaris	garden loosestrife	Primulaceae	247
Lythrum californicum	California loosestrife	Lythraceae	247
Lythrum hyssopifolium	hyssop loosestrife	Lythraceae	237
Lythrum portula	spatulaleaf loosestrife	Lythraceae	245
Lythrum salicaria	purple loosestrife	Lythraceae	237
Lythrum tribracteatum	threebract loosestrife	Lythraceae	245
Lythrum virgatum	European wand loosestrife	Lythraceae	247
Marsilea vestita	hairy pepperwort	Marsileaceae	45
Melilotus albus	white sweetclover	Fabaceae	211
Mentha pulegium	pennyroyal	Lamiaceae	224
Mentha spicata	spearmint	Lamiaceae	226
Mentha suaveolens	apple mint	Lamiaceae	226
Monochoria vaginalis	monochoria	Pontederiaceae	342
Myriophyllum aquaticum	parrotfeather	Haloragaceae	86
Myriophyllum hippuroides	western watermilfoil	Haloragaceae	93
Myriophyllum sibiricum	northern watermilfoil	Haloragaceae	82, 93
Myriophyllum spicatum	Eurasian watermilfoil	Haloragaceae	86
Myriophyllum verticillatum	whorled watermilfoil	Haloragaceae	93
Najas graminea	grassy naiad	Hydrocharitaceae	105, 107
Najas guadalupensis	southern naiad	Hydrocharitaceae	106
Najas marina	hollyleaf naiad	Hydrocharitaceae	108
Nitella spp.	nitella	Characeae	66
Nostoc spp.	nostoc	Nostocaceae	74
Nuphar polysepala	yellow pondlily	Nymphaeaceae	110
Nymphaea mexicana	Mexican waterlily	Nymphaeaceae	114
Nymphaea odorata	fragrant waterlily	Nymphaeaceae	117
Nymphoides peltata	yellow floatingheart	Menyanthaceae	117
Paspalum dilatatum	dallisgrass	Poaceae	281
Paspalum distichum	knotgrass	Poaceae	281
Paspalum notatum	bahiagrass	Poaceae	284
Paspalum urvillei	vaseygrass	Poaceae	284
Phalaris aquatica	Harding grass	Poaceae	290
Phalaris arundinacea	reed canarygrass	Poaceae	292
Phalaris brachystachys	short-spike canarygrass	Poaceae	293
Phalaris caroliniana	Carolina canarygrass	Poaceae	293
Phragmites australis	common reed	Poaceae	260
Pistia stratiotes	waterlettuce	Araceae	42
Polygonum amphibium var. emersum	swamp smartweed	Polygonaceae	314
Polygonum amphibium var. stipulaceum	water smartweed	Polygonaceae	315
Polygonum hydropiper	marshpepper smartweed	Polygonaceae	327
Polygonum hydropiperoides	mild smartweed	Polygonaceae	327
Polygonum lapathifolium	pale smartweed	Polygonaceae	314
Polygonum pensylvanicum	Pennsylvania smartweed	Polygonaceae	327
Polygonum persicaria	ladysthumb	Polygonaceae	314
Polygonum punctatum	dotted smartweed	Polygonaceae	327
Polypogon australis	Chilean polypogon	Poaceae	302
Polypogon elongatus	streambank polypogon	Poaceae	302

Species by Scientific Name, cont.

Scientific name	Common name	Family	Page
Polypogon interruptus	ditch polypogon	Poaceae	301
Polypogon maritimus	Mediterranean polypogon	Poaceae	301
Polypogon monspeliensis	rabbitfoot polypogon	Poaceae	297
Polypogon viridis (= *Agrostis viridis*)	water bent	Poaceae	302
Potamogeton amplifolius	largeleaf pondweed	Potamogetonaceae	127
Potamogeton crispus	curlyleaf pondweed	Potamogetonaceae	118
Potamogeton diversifolius	waterthread pondweed	Potamogetonaceae	127
Potamogeton epihydrus	ribbonleaf pondweed	Potamogetonaceae	127
Potamogeton foliosus	leafy pondweed	Potamogetonaceae	118
Potamogeton gramineus	variable pondweed	Potamogetonaceae	127
Potamogeton illinoensis	Illinois pondweed	Potamogetonaceae	118
Potamogeton natans	floatingleaf pondweed	Potamogetonaceae	118
Potamogeton nodosus	American pondweed	Potamogetonaceae	118
Potamogeton praelongus	whitestem pondweed	Potamogetonaceae	127
Potamogeton pusillus	small pondweed	Potamogetonaceae	118
Potamogeton richardsonii	Richardson's pondweed	Potamogetonaceae	127
Potamogeton zosteriformis	flatstem pondweed	Potamogetonaceae	127
Ranunculus aquatilis	white waterbuttercup	Ranunculaceae	84
Rhizoclonium spp.	rhizoclonium	Cladophoraceae	71
Rotala indica	Indian toothcup	Lythraceae	228
Rotala ramosior	toothcup	Lythraceae	233
Rubus armeniacus (= *R. discolor*)	Himalaya blackberry	Rosaceae	348
Rubus laciniatus	cutleaf blackberry	Rosaceae	348
Rubus ulmifolius var. *inermis*	elmleaf blackberry	Rosaceae	352
Rumex conglomeratus	cluster dock	Polygonaceae	338
Rumex crispus	curly dock	Polygonaceae	329
Rumex dentatus	toothed dock	Polygonaceae	338
Rumex kerneri	Kerner's dock	Polygonaceae	340
Rumex obtusifolius	broadleaf dock	Polygonaceae	329
Rumex pulcher	fiddleleaf dock	Polygonaceae	340
Ruppia cirrhosa	spiral ditchgrass	Potamogetonaceae	128
Ruppia maritima	widgeongrass	Potamogetonaceae	128
Saccharum ravennae	ravennagrass	Poaceae	261
Sagittaria longiloba	Gregg arrowhead	Alismataceae	150
Sagittaria montevidensis	California arrowhead	Alismataceae	147
Salix babylonica	weeping willow	Salicaceae	358
Salix exigua	coyote willow	Salicaceae	353
Salix gooddingii	Goodding's black willow	Salicaceae	353
Salix laevigata	red willow	Salicaceae	353
Salix lasiolepis	Arroyo willow	Salicaceae	353
Salvinia minima	water fern, water sprangles	Salviniaceae	60
Salvinia molesta	giant salvinia	Salviniaceae	57
Salvinia spp.	salvinia	Salviniaceae	57
Scirpus acutus var. *occidentalis*	hardstem bulrush, tule	Cyperaceae	189
Scirpus californicus	California or southern bulrush	Cyperaceae	191
Scirpus fluviatilis	river bulrush	Cyperaceae	191

Species by Scientific Name, cont.

Scientific name	Common name	Family	Page
Scirpus glaucus (= *S. tuberosus*)	tuberous bulrush	Cyperaceae	193
Scirpus maritimus	cosmopolitan bulrush	Cyperaceae	191
Scirpus mucronatus	ricefield bulrush	Cyperaceae	193
Scirpus robustus	sturdy bulrush	Cyperaceae	191
Sesbania exaltata	hemp sesbania	Fabaceae	218
Sesbania punicea	rattlebush	Fabaceae	214
Spartina alterniflora	smooth cordgrass	Poaceae	305
Spartina anglica	common cordgrass	Poaceae	311
Spartina densiflora	dense-flowered cordgrass	Poaceae	310
Spartina foliosa	California cordgrass	Poaceae	308
Spartina patens	salt-meadow cordgrass	Poaceae	310
Spirodela spp.	giant duckweed, duckmeat	Lemnaceae	49
Stuckenia filiformis (= *Potamogeton filiformis*)	threadleaf pondweed	Potamogetonaceae	127
Stuckenia pectinatus (= *Potamogeton pectinatus*)	sago pondweed	Potamogetonaceae	118
Tamarix aphylla	athel tamarisk	Tamaricaceae	369
Tamarix chinensis	Chinese tamarisk	Tamaricaceae	377
Tamarix gallica	French tamarisk	Tamaricaceae	377
Tamarix parviflora	smallflower tamarisk	Tamaricaceae	369
Tamarix ramosissima	saltcedar	Tamaricaceae	369
Typha angustifolia	narrowleaf cattail	Typhaceae	384
Typha domingensis	southern cattail	Typhaceae	384
Typha latifolia	common cattail	Typhaceae	378
Undaria pinnatifida	Japanese kelp	Alariaceae	64
Verbena bonariensis	tall vervain	Verbenaceae	387
Verbena litoralis	seashore vervain	Verbenaceae	387
Veronica americana	American speedwell	Scrophulariaceae	368
Veronica anagallis-aquatica	water speedwell	Scrophulariaceae	365
Veronica beccabunga	European speedwell	Scrophulariaceae	367
Veronica catenata	chain speedwell	Scrophulariaceae	367
Wolffia spp.	watermeal	Lemnaceae	49
Zannichellia palustris	horned pondweed	Zannichelliaceae	132

Species by Family

Family	Scientific name	Common name	Page
Alariaceae	*Undaria pinnatifida*	Japanese kelp	64
Alismataceae	*Alisma lanceolatum*	lanceleaved waterplantain	142
Alismataceae	*Alisma plantago-aquatica*	common waterplantain	137
Alismataceae	*Echinodorus berteroi*	upright burhead	144
Alismataceae	*Sagittaria longiloba*	Gregg arrowhead	150
Alismataceae	*Sagittaria montevidensis*	California arrowhead	147
Amaranthaceae	*Alternanthera philoxeroides*	alligatorweed	152
Apiaceae	*Heracleum lanatum*	cow parsnip	158
Apiaceae	*Heracleum mantegazzianum*	giant hogweed	156
Apiaceae	*Hydrocotyle ranunculoides*	floating pennywort	159
Araceae	*Pistia stratiotes*	waterlettuce	42

Species by Family, cont.

Family	Scientific name	Common name	Page
Asteraceae	*Baccharis salicifolia*	seepwillow	162
Asteraceae	*Cotula coronopifolia*	brassbuttons	165
Asteraceae	*Eclipta prostrata*	eclipta	168
Azollaceae	*Azolla* spp.	mosquitofern	44
Brassicaceae	*Cardaria draba*	hoary cress	175
Brassicaceae	*Cardaria draba* ssp. *chalepensis*	lens-podded whitetop	175
Brassicaceae	*Cardaria pubescens*	hairy whitetop	175
Brassicaceae	*Lepidium latifolium*	perennial pepperweed	171
Cabombaceae	*Cabomba caroliniana*	fanwort	80
Cabombaceae	*Brasenia schreberi*	watershield	111
Caulerpaceae	*Caulerpa taxifolia*	caulerpa	64
Ceratophyllaceae	*Ceratophyllum demersum*	coontail	78
Characeae	*Chara* spp.	chara	66
Characeae	*Nitella* spp.	nitella	66
Cladophoraceae	*Cladophora* spp.	cladophora	71
Cladophoraceae	*Rhizoclonium* spp.	rhizoclonium	71
Cyperaceae	*Cyperus difformis*	smallflower umbrella sedge	176
Cyperaceae	*Cyperus eragrostis*	lovegrass sedge or tall flatsedge	176
Cyperaceae	*Cyperus erythrorhizos*	redroot flatsedge	182
Cyperaceae	*Cyperus flavicomus*	whitemargined flatsedge	183
Cyperaceae	*Cyperus fuscus*	brown flatsedge	182
Cyperaceae	*Eleocharis acicularis*	needle spikerush	185
Cyperaceae	*Eleocharis macrostachya*	creeping spikerush	184
Cyperaceae	*Eleocharis obtusa*	blunt spikerush	185
Cyperaceae	*Eleocharis parvula*	dwarf spikerush	185
Cyperaceae	*Scirpus acutus* var. *occidentalis*	hardstem bulrush, tule	189
Cyperaceae	*Scirpus californicus*	California or southern bulrush	191
Cyperaceae	*Scirpus fluviatilis*	river bulrush	191
Cyperaceae	*Scirpus glaucus* (= *S. tuberosus*)	tuberous bulrush	193
Cyperaceae	*Scirpus maritimus*	cosmopolitan bulrush	191
Cyperaceae	*Scirpus mucronatus*	ricefield bulrush	193
Cyperaceae	*Scirpus robustus*	sturdy bulrush	191
Elaeagnaceae	*Elaeagnus angustifolia*	Russian olive	199
Equisetaceae	*Equisetum arvense*	field horsetail	202
Equisetaceae	*Equisetum hyemale* ssp. *affine*	scouringrush	202
Equisetaceae	*Equisetum laevigatum*	smooth scouringrush	205
Equisetaceae	*Equisetum telmateia* ssp. *braunii*	giant horsetail	205
Fabaceae	*Aeschynomene rudis*	rough jointvetch	207
Fabaceae	*Amorpha fruticosa*	indigobush	219
Fabaceae	*Melilotus albus*	white sweetclover	211
Fabaceae	*Sesbania exaltata*	hemp sesbania	218
Fabaceae	*Sesbania punicea*	rattlebush	214
Haloragaceae	*Myriophyllum aquaticum*	parrotfeather	86
Haloragaceae	*Myriophyllum hippuroides*	western watermilfoil	93
Haloragaceae	*Myriophyllum sibiricum*	northern watermilfoil	82, 93
Haloragaceae	*Myriophyllum spicatum*	Eurasian watermilfoil	86
Haloragaceae	*Myriophyllum verticillatum*	whorled watermilfoil	93

Species by Family, cont.

Family	Scientific name	Common name	Page
Hydrocharitaceae	*Egeria densa*	Brazilian elodea, Brazilian egeria, egeria	96
Hydrocharitaceae	*Elodea canadensis*	common elodea	96
Hydrocharitaceae	*Hydrilla verticillata*	hydrilla	96
Hydrocharitaceae	*Limnobium laevigatum*	spongeplant or smooth frogbit	55
Hydrocharitaceae	*Najas graminea*	grassy naiad	105, 107
Hydrocharitaceae	*Najas guadalupensis*	southern naiad	106
Hydrocharitaceae	*Najas marina*	hollyleaf naiad	108
Iridaceae	*Iris pseudacorus*	yellowflag iris	221
Lamiaceae	*Mentha pulegium*	pennyroyal	224
Lamiaceae	*Mentha spicata*	spearmint	226
Lamiaceae	*Mentha suaveolens*	apple mint	226
Lemnaceae	*Lemna* spp.	duckweed	49
Lemnaceae	*Spirodela* spp.	giant duckweed, duckmeat	49
Lemnaceae	*Wolffia* spp.	watermeal	49
Lythraceae	*Ammannia coccinea*	redstem	228
Lythraceae	*Ammannia robusta*	purple ammannia	228
Lythraceae	*Lythrum californicum*	California loosestrife	247
Lythraceae	*Lythrum hyssopifolium*	hyssop loosestrife	237
Lythraceae	*Lythrum portula*	spatulaleaf loosestrife	245
Lythraceae	*Lythrum salicaria*	purple loosestrife	237
Lythraceae	*Lythrum tribracteatum*	threebract loosestrife	245
Lythraceae	*Lythrum virgatum*	European wand loosestrife	247
Lythraceae	*Rotala indica*	Indian toothcup	228
Lythraceae	*Rotala ramosior*	toothcup	233
Marsileaceae	*Marsilea vestita*	hairy pepperwort	45
Menyanthaceae	*Nymphoides peltata*	yellow floatingheart	117
Nostocaceae	*Anabaena* spp.	anabaena	74
Nostocaceae	*Nostoc* spp.	nostoc	74
Nymphaeaceae	*Nuphar polysepala*	yellow pondlily	110
Nymphaeaceae	*Nymphaea mexicana*	Mexican waterlily	114
Nymphaeaceae	*Nymphaea odorata*	fragrant waterlily	117
Onagraceae	*Ludwigia hexapetala*	Uraguay waterprimrose	253
Onagraceae	*Ludwigia palustris*	waterpurslane	253
Onagraceae	*Ludwigia peploides*	creeping waterprimrose	249
Poaceae	*Arundo donax*	giant reed	254
Poaceae	*Echinochloa colona*	junglerice	263
Poaceae	*Echinochloa crus-galli*	barnyardgrass	263
Poaceae	*Echinochloa crus-pavonis*	gulf cockspur	270
Poaceae	*Echinochloa muricata*	rough barnyardgrass	270
Poaceae	*Echinochloa oryzicola*	late watergrass	270
Poaceae	*Echinochloa oryzoides*	early watergrass	271
Poaceae	*Echinochloa phyllopogon*	late watergrass	271
Poaceae	*Leptochloa fascicularis*	bearded sprangletop	276
Poaceae	*Leptochloa uninervia*	Mexican sprangletop	276
Poaceae	*Paspalum dilatatum*	dallisgrass	281
Poaceae	*Paspalum distichum*	knotgrass	281
Poaceae	*Paspalum notatum*	bahiagrass	284
Poaceae	*Paspalum urvillei*	vaseygrass	284
Poaceae	*Phalaris aquatica*	Harding grass	290
Poaceae	*Phalaris arundinacea*	reed canarygrass	293

Species by Family, cont.

Family	Scientific name	Common name	Page
Poaceae	*Phalaris brachystachys*	short-spike canarygrass	293
Poaceae	*Phalaris caroliniana*	Carolina canarygrass	293
Poaceae	*Phragmites australis*	common reed	260
Poaceae	*Polypogon australis*	Chilean polypogon	302
Poaceae	*Polypogon elongatus*	streambank polypogon	302
Poaceae	*Polypogon interruptus*	ditch polypogon	301
Poaceae	*Polypogon maritimus*	Mediterranean polypogon	301
Poaceae	*Polypogon monspeliensis*	rabbitfoot polypogon	297
Poaceae	*Polypogon viridis (= Agrostis viridis)*	water bent	302
Poaceae	*Saccharum ravennae*	ravennagrass	261
Poaceae	*Spartina alterniflora*	smooth cordgrass	305
Poaceae	*Spartina anglica*	common cordgrass	311
Poaceae	*Spartina densiflora*	dense-flowered cordgrass	310
Poaceae	*Spartina foliosa*	California cordgrass	308
Poaceae	*Spartina patens*	salt-meadow cordgrass	310
Polygonaceae	*Polygonum amphibium* var. *emersum*	swamp smartweed	314
Polygonaceae	*Polygonum amphibium* var. *stipulaceum*	water smartweed	315
Polygonaceae	*Polygonum hydropiper*	marshpepper smartweed	327
Polygonaceae	*Polygonum hydropiperoides*	mild smartweed	327
Polygonaceae	*Polygonum lapathifolium*	pale smartweed	314
Polygonaceae	*Polygonum pensylvanicum*	Pennsylvania smartweed	327
Polygonaceae	*Polygonum persicaria*	ladysthumb	314
Polygonaceae	*Polygonum punctatum*	dotted smartweed	327
Polygonaceae	*Rumex conglomeratus*	cluster dock	338
Polygonaceae	*Rumex crispus*	curly dock	329
Polygonaceae	*Rumex dentatus*	toothed dock	338
Polygonaceae	*Rumex kerneri*	Kerner's dock	340
Polygonaceae	*Rumex obtusifolius*	broadleaf dock	329
Polygonaceae	*Rumex pulcher*	fiddleleaf dock	340
Pontederiaceae	*Eichhornia crassipes*	water hyacinth	52
Pontederiaceae	*Heteranthera limosa*	ducksalad	342
Pontederiaceae	*Monochoria vaginalis*	monochoria	342
Potamogetonaceae	*Potamogeton amplifolius*	largeleaf pondweed	127
Potamogetonaceae	*Potamogeton crispus*	curlyleaf pondweed	118
Potamogetonaceae	*Potamogeton diversifolius*	waterthread pondweed	127
Potamogetonaceae	*Potamogeton epihydrus*	ribbonleaf pondweed	127
Potamogetonaceae	*Potamogeton foliosus*	leafy pondweed	118
Potamogetonaceae	*Potamogeton gramineus*	variable pondweed	127
Potamogetonaceae	*Potamogeton illinoensis*	Illinois pondweed	118
Potamogetonaceae	*Potamogeton natans*	floatingleaf pondweed	118
Potamogetonaceae	*Potamogeton nodosus*	American pondweed	118
Potamogetonaceae	*Potamogeton praelongus*	whitestem pondweed	127
Potamogetonaceae	*Potamogeton pusillus*	small pondweed	118
Potamogetonaceae	*Potamogeton richardsonii*	Richardson's pondweed	127
Potamogetonaceae	*Potamogeton zosteriformis*	flatstem pondweed	127
Potamogetonaceae	*Ruppia cirrhosa*	spiral ditchgrass	128
Potamogetonaceae	*Ruppia maritima*	widgeongrass	128

Species by Family, cont.

Family	Scientific name	Common name	Page
Potamogetonaceae	*Stuckenia filiformis* (= *Potamogeton filiformis*)	threadleaf pondweed	127
Potamogetonaceae	*Stuckenia pectinatus* (= *Potamogeton pectinatus*)	sago pondweed	118
Primulaceae	*Lysimachia punctata*	dotted loosestrife	248
Primulaceae	*Lysimachia vulgaris*	garden loosestrife	247
Ranunculaceae	*Ranunculus aquatilis*	white waterbuttercup	84
Rosaceae	*Rubus armeniacus* (= *R. discolor*)	Himalaya blackberry	348
Rosaceae	*Rubus laciniatus*	cutleaf blackberry	348
Rosaceae	*Rubus ulmifolius* var. *inermis*	elmleaf blackberry	352
Salicaceae	*Salix babylonica*	weeping willow	358
Salicaceae	*Salix exigua*	coyote willow	353
Salicaceae	*Salix gooddingii*	Goodding's black willow	353
Salicaceae	*Salix laevigata*	red willow	353
Salicaceae	*Salix lasiolepis*	Arroyo willow	353
Salviniaceae	*Salvinia minima*	water fern, water sprangles	60
Salviniaceae	*Salvinia molesta*	giant salvinia	57
Salviniaceae	*Salvinia* spp.	salvinia	57
Scrophulariaceae	*Bacopa eisenii*	Eisen waterhyssop	359
Scrophulariaceae	*Bacopa monnieri*	Monnier waterhyssop	361
Scrophulariaceae	*Bacopa repens*	creeping waterhyssop	362
Scrophulariaceae	*Bacopa rotundifolia*	disc waterhyssop	362
Scrophulariaceae	*Limnophila* ×*ludoviciana*	marshweed	82
Scrophulariaceae	*Veronica americana*	American speedwell	368
Scrophulariaceae	*Veronica anagallis-aquatica*	water speedwell	365
Scrophulariaceae	*Veronica beccabunga*	European speedwell	367
Scrophulariaceae	*Veronica catenata*	chain speedwell	367
Tamaricaceae	*Tamarix aphylla*	athel tamarisk	369
Tamaricaceae	*Tamarix chinensis*	Chinese tamarisk	377
Tamaricaceae	*Tamarix gallica*	French tamarisk	377
Tamaricaceae	*Tamarix parviflora*	smallflower tamarisk	369
Tamaricaceae	*Tamarix ramosissima*	saltcedar	369
Typhaceae	*Typha angustifolia*	narrowleaf cattail	384
Typhaceae	*Typha domingensis*	southern cattail	384
Typhaceae	*Typha latifolia*	common cattail	378
Verbenaceae	*Verbena bonariensis*	tall vervain	387
Verbenaceae	*Verbena litoralis*	seashore vervain	387
Zannichelliaceae	*Zannichellia palustris*	horned pondweed	132

Shortcut Identification Tables

Identification of plants can be simplified when species have characteristics that are easily observed in the vegetative stage. The following tables consider many characteristics common to aquatic weed species. The grasses and cattails have been omitted from these tables. For more specific information and photographs, see the page number listed after each species.

Table 1. Plants completely or nearly completely submerged

Scientific name	Common name	Family	Page
Algae			
Anabaena spp.	anabaena (freshwater blue-green algae)	Nostocaceae	74
Caulerpa taxifolia	caulerpa (marine algae)	Caulerpaceae	64
Chara spp.	chara (freshwater algae)	Characeae	66
Cladophora spp.	cladophora (freshwater filamentous algae)	Cladophoraceae	71
Nitella spp.	nitella (freshwater algae)	Characeae	66
Nostoc spp.	nostoc (freshwater blue-green algae)	Nostocaceae	74
Rhizoclonium spp.	rhizoclonium (freshwater filamentous algae)	Cladophoraceae	71
Monocots			
Egeria densa	Brazilian elodea, Brazilian egeria, egeria	Hydrocharitaceae	96
Eleocharis acicularis	needle spikerush	Cyperaceae	185
Eleocharis parvula	dwarf spikerush	Cyperaceae	185
Elodea canadensis	common elodea	Hydrocharitaceae	96
Hydrilla verticillata	hydrilla	Hydrocharitaceae	96
Najas spp.	naiad or waternymph	Hydrocharitaceae	105
Potamogeton crispus	curlyleaf pondweed	Potamogetonaceae	118
Potamogeton foliosus	leafy pondweed	Potamogetonaceae	118
Potamogeton illinoensis	Illinois pondweed	Potamogetonaceae	118
Potamogeton pusillus	small pondweed	Potamogetonaceae	118
Ruppia spp.	widgeongrass	Potamogetonaceae	128
Stuckenia pectinatus (= Potamogeton pectinatus)	sago pondweed	Potamogetonaceae	118
Zannichellia palustris	horned pondweed	Zannichelliaceae	132
Dicots			
Cabomba caroliniana	fanwort	Cabombaceae	80
Ceratophyllum demersum	coontail	Ceratophyllaceae	78
Limnophila ×ludoviciana	marshweed	Scrophulariaceae	82
Myriophyllum aquaticum (more emergent than others in this group)	parrotfeather	Haloragaceae	86
Myriophyllum spicatum	Eurasian watermilfoil	Haloragaceae	86

Table 2. Free-floating aquatic plants (roots in water column)

Scientific name	Common name	Family	Page
Ferns			
Azolla spp.	mosquitofern	Azollaceae	44
Salvinia molesta	giant salvinia	Salviniaceae	57
Monocots			
Eichhornia crassipes	water hyacinth	Pontederiaceae	52
Lemna spp.	duckweed	Lemnaceae	49
Limnobium laevigatum	spongeplant or smooth frogbit	Hydrocharitaceae	55
Pistia stratiotes	waterlettuce	Araceae	42
Spirodela spp.	giant duckweed, duckmeat	Lemnaceae	49
Wolffia spp.	watermeal	Lemnaceae	49

Table 3. Plants with floating leaves and roots anchored in soil

Scientific name	Common name	Family	Page
Ferns			
Marsilea vestita	hairy pepperwort	Marsileaceae	45
Monocots			
Potamogeton amplifolius	largeleaf pondweed	Potamogetonaceae	127
Potamogeton gramineus	variable pondweed	Potamogetonaceae	127
Potamogeton illinoensis	Illinois pondweed	Potamogetonaceae	118
Potamogeton natans	floatingleaf pondweed	Potamogetonaceae	118
Potamogeton nodosus	American pondweed	Potamogetonaceae	118
Dicots			
Brasenia schreberi	watershield	Cabombaceae	111
Hydrocotyle ranunculoides	floating pennywort	Apiaceae	159
Ludwigia peploides	creeping waterprimrose	Onagraceae	249
Nuphar polysepala	yellow pondlily	Nymphaeaceae	110
Nymphaea mexicana	Mexican waterlily	Nymphaeaceae	114
Nymphaea odorata	fragrant waterlily	Nymphaeaceae	117
Nymphoides peltata	yellow floatingheart	Menyanthaceae	117
Polygonum amphibium var. *stipulaceum*	water smartweed	Polygonaceae	314

Table 4. Woody species

Scientific name	Common name	Family	Page
Dicots			
Amorpha fruticosa	indigobush	Fabaceae	219
Baccharis salicifolia	seepwillow	Asteraceae	162
Elaeagnus angustifolia	Russian olive	Elaeagnaceae	199
Rubus spp.	blackberry	Rosaceae	348
Salix spp.	willow	Salicaceae	353
Sesbania punicea	rattlebush	Fabaceae	214
Tamarix spp.	saltcedar or tamarisk	Tamaricaceae	369

Table 5. Plants spiny to the touch

Scientific name	Common name	Family	Page
Monocots			
Najas marina	hollyleaf naiad	Hydrocharitaceae	108
Dicots			
Ceratophyllum demersum	coontail	Ceratophyllaceae	78
Elaeagnus angustifolia	Russian olive	Elaeagnaceae	199
Rubus spp.	blackberry	Rosaceae	348

Table 6. Stem characteristics

Scientific name	Common name	Family	Page
A. Square or angled stems			
Dicots			
Ammannia spp. (or angled)	purple ammannia, redstem	Lythraceae	228
Lythrum salicaria	purple loosestrife	Lythraceae	237
Mentha pulegium	pennyroyal	Lamiaceae	224
Rotala spp.	toothcup	Lythraceae	228
Rubus spp.	blackberry	Rosaceae	348
Verbena spp.	vervain	Verbenaceae	387
Veronica spp. (some species)	speedwell	Scrophulariaceae	365
B. Triangular stems			
Monocots			
Cyperus difformis	smallflower umbrella sedge	Cyperaceae	176
Cyperus eragrostis	lovegrass sedge or tall flatsedge	Cyperaceae	176
Cyperus erythrorhizos	redroot flatsedge	Cyperaceae	182
Cyperus flavicomus	whitemargined flatsedge	Cyperaceae	183
Cyperus fuscus	brown flatsedge	Cyperaceae	182
Scirpus fluviatilis	river bulrush	Cyperaceae	191
Scirpus glaucus	tuberous bulrush	Cyperaceae	193
Scirpus maritimus	cosmopolitan bulrush	Cyperaceae	191
Scirpus mucronatus	ricefield bulrush	Cyperaceae	193
Scirpus robustus	sturdy bulrush	Cyperaceae	191
Scripus californicus	California or southern bulrush	Cyperaceae	191
C. Stems green, appearing leafless			
Monocots			
Eleocharis spp.	spikerush	Cyperaceae	184
Scirpus acutus	hardstem bulrush, tule	Cyperaceae	189
Scripus californicus	California or southern bulrush	Cyperaceae	191

Table 7. Leaf characteristics

Scientific name	Common name	Family	Page
A. Leaf arrangement			
1. Opposite leaves			
Monocots			
Najas spp.	naiad or waternymph	Hydrocharitaceae	105
Zannichellia palustris	horned pondweed	Zannichelliaceae	132
Dicots			
Alternanthera philoxeroides	alligatorweed	Amaranthaceae	152
Ammannia spp.	purple ammannia, redstem	Lythraceae	228
Bacopa spp.	waterhyssop	Scrophulariaceae	359
Cabomba caroliniana	fanwort	Cabombaceae	80
Eclipta prostrata	eclipta	Asteraceae	168
Lysimachia spp.	loosestrife	Primulaceae	247
Lythrum spp. (some alternate in *L. hyssopifolium* and *L. tribracteatum*)	loosestrife	Lythraceae	247
Mentha pulegium	pennyroyal	Lamiaceae	224
Nymphoides peltata (opposite on flowering stem only)	yellow floatingheart	Menyanthaceae	117
Rotala spp.	toothcup	Lythraceae	228
Verbena spp.	vervain	Verbenaceae	387
Veronica anagallis-aquatica	water speedwell	Scrophulariaceae	365
2. Leaves or branches whorled (>2 per node) or appearing whorled			
Algae			
Chara spp.	chara (freshwater algae)	Characeae	
Nitella spp.	nitella (freshwater algae)	Characeae	66
Ferns or fernlike			
Equisetum arvense	field horsetail	Equisetaceae	202
Equisetum telmateia ssp. *braunii*	giant horsetail	Equisetaceae	205
Monocots			
Egeria densa	Brazilian elodea, Brazilian egeria, egeria	Hydrocharitaceae	96
Elodea canadensis	common elodea	Hydrocharitaceae	96
Hydrilla verticillata	hydrilla	Hydrocharitaceae	96
Najas spp. (usually opposite)	naiad or waternymph	Hydrocharitaceae	105
Dicots			
Ceratophyllum demersum	coontail	Ceratophyllaceae	78
Limnophila ×*ludoviciana*	marshweed	Scrophulariaceae	82
Lysimachia spp.	loosestrife	Primulaceae	247
Lythrum salicaria	purple loosestrife	Lythraceae	237
Myriophyllum spp.	parrotfeather, watermilfoil	Haloragaceae	86

Table 7. Leaf characteristics, cont.

Scientific name	Common name	Family	Page
B. Leaf division			
1. Trifoliolate (3 leaflets), pinnately or palmately divided or compound			
Ferns			
Marsilea vestita	hairy pepperwort	Marsileaceae	45
Dicots			
Aeschynomene rudis	rough jointvetch	Fabaceae	207
Amorpha fruticosa	indigobush	Fabaceae	219
Heracleum mantegazzianum	giant hogweed	Apiaceae	156
Melilotus albus	white sweetclover	Fabaceae	211
Myriophyllum spp.	parrotfeather, watermilfoil	Haloragaceae	86
Rubus spp.	blackberry	Rosaceae	348
Sesbania punicea	rattlebush	Fabaceae	214
2. Finely dissected leaves (narrow leaf segments)			
Dicots			
Cabomba caroliniana	fanwort	Cabombaceae	80
Ceratophyllum demersum	coontail	Ceratophyllaceae	78
Myriophyllum aquaticum	parrotfeather	Haloragaceae	86
Myriophyllum spicatum	Eurasian watermilfoil	Haloragaceae	86
Ranunculus aquatilis	white waterbuttercup	Ranunculaceae	84
3. Forked, branched leaves			
Dicots			
Cabomba caroliniana	fanwort	Cabombaceae	80
Ceratophyllum demersum	coontail	Ceratophyllaceae	78
Limnophila ×*ludoviciana*	marshweed	Scrophulariaceae	82
Ranunculus aquatilis	white waterbuttercup	Ranunculaceae	84
C. Leaf shape			
1. Leaves round, ovate, or horseshoe-shaped			
Monocots			
Eichhornia crassipes	water hyacinth	Pontederiaceae	52
Dicots			
Bacopa eisenii	Eisen waterhyssop	Scrophulariaceae	359
Bacopa rotundifolia	disc waterhyssop	Scrophulariaceae	362
Brasenia schreberi (peltate leaf, shield-shaped)	watershield	Cabombaceae	111
Hydrocotyle ranunculoides	floating pennywort	Apiaceae	159
Nymphaea mexicana	Mexican waterlily	Nymphaeaceae	114
Nymphaea odorata	fragrant waterlily	Nymphaeaceae	117
Nymphoides peltata	yellow floatingheart	Menyanthaceae	117

Table 7. Leaf characteristics, cont.

Scientific name	Common name	Family	Page
2. Leaves heart-shaped			
Monocots			
Echinodorus berteroi	upright burhead	Alismataceae	144
Monochoria vaginalis	monochoria	Pontederiaceae	342
Potamogeton natans	floatingleaf pondweed	Potamogetonaceae	118
Dicots			
Nuphar polysepala	yellow pondlily	Nymphaeaceae	110
Nymphoides peltata	yellow floatingheart	Menyanthaceae	117
3. Leaves arrow-shaped			
Monocots			
Sagittaria longiloba	Gregg arrowhead	Alismataceae	150
Sagittaria montevidensis	California arrowhead	Alismataceae	147
D. Leaf base			
1. Leaves sessile			
Monocots			
Egeria densa	Brazilian elodea, Brazilian egeria, egeria	Hydrocharitaceae	96
Elodea canadensis	common elodea	Hydrocharitaceae	96
Hydrilla verticillata	hydrilla	Hydrocharitaceae	96
Najas spp.	naiad or waternymph	Hydrocharitaceae	105
Pistia stratiotes	waterlettuce	Araceae	42
Potamogeton crispus	curlyleaf pondweed	Potamogetonaceae	118
Potamogeton foliosus	leafy pondweed	Potamogetonaceae	118
Potamogeton pusillus	small pondweed	Potamogetonaceae	118
Stuckenia pectinatus (= *Potamogeton pectinatus*)	sago pondweed	Potamogetonaceae	118
Zannichellia palustris	horned pondweed	Zannichelliaceae	132
Dicots			
Ammannia spp.	purple ammannia, redstem	Lythraceae	228
Bacopa spp.	waterhyssop	Scrophulariaceae	359
Cotula coronopifolia	brassbuttons	Asteraceae	165
Eclipta prostrata	eclipta	Asteraceae	168
Lysimachia spp.	loosestrife	Primulaceae	247
Lythrum spp.	loosestrife	Lythraceae	247
Mentha pulegium (subsessile)	pennyroyal	Lamiaceae	224
Rotala spp.	toothcup	Lythraceae	228
Tamarix spp.	saltcedar or tamarisk	Tamaricaceae	359
Verbena spp.	vervain	Verbenaceae	387
Veronica spp.	speedwell	Scrophulariaceae	367

Table 7. Leaf characteristics, cont.

Scientific name	Common name	Family	Page
2. Leaves with obvious sheath at base			
Fernlike			
Equisetum spp. (lack leaves)	horsetail or scouringrush	Equisetaceae	202
Monocots			
Grasses, sedges and cattails		Cyperaceae,	176
		Poaceae,	254
		Typhaceae	378
Iris pseudacorus	yellowflag iris	Iridaceae	221
Najas guadalupensis	southern naiad	Hydrocharitaceae	106
Potamogeton spp.	pondweeds	Potamogetonaceae	118
Ruppia spp.	widgeongrass	Potamogetonaceae	128
Dicots			
Cotula coronopifolia	brassbuttons	Asteraceae	165
Heracleum mantegazzianum	giant hogweed	Apiaceae	156
Polygonum spp.	smartweeds	Polygonaceae	314
Rumex spp.	docks	Polygonaceae	329

Key to Floating-Leaved and Submerged Aquatic Weeds

This key is to aquatic weeds that contain most of their plant parts under water or floating on the surface of the water. It does not include marine, filamentous, and blue-green algae, or weeds that are primarily emergent, including many broadleaf species, grasses, sedges, rushes, or cattails.

Page

1. Entire plant or majority of leaf blades floating at water surface or emerged above water

2. Roots free floating in water column when plants mature

3. Plant body without obvious leaves, stems or stem branches (which may be flattened and leaflike) <2 cm in length or width

4. Stems not leaflike, many-times-branched (>10 branches), each branch covered with tiny (often reddish) segments; roots per branch numerous
Azolla spp. (mosquitofern) [**common natives**] . . .44

4. Stems flattened and leaflike, solitary or in clusters of two to many; roots per branch numerous or not

5. Roots >2 per plant segment
Spirodela spp. (giant duckweed) [**occasional natives**] 49

5. Roots 0–1 per plant segment

6. Roots 1 per plant segment
Lemna spp. (duckweed) [**common natives**] 49

6. Roots absent from all plant segments
Wolffia spp. (watermeal) [**uncommon natives**] . . .49

3. Obvious leaves present

7. Leaves hairless or nearly so

8. Petiole extremely swollen
Eichhornia crassipes (water hyacinth) [**common non-native**] 52

8. Petiole not swollen
Limnobium laevigatum (spongeplant or smooth frog-bit) [**uncommon non-native**] 55

7. Leaves with obvious hairs either on upper or lower leaf surface

    9. Leaves without obvious nerves or veins; upper leaf surface with hairs that look like eggbeaters when viewed at 10× magnification
        Salvinia molesta (giant salvinia)
        [**uncommon non-native**] 57

    9. Leaves with obvious multiple nerves or veins running parallel to the midrib; hairs of lower leaf surface velvety
        Pistia stratiotes (waterlettuce)
        [**uncommon non-native**] 42

2. Roots anchored in soil at maturity, not free floating

  10. Leaves divided into leaflets or segments

    11. Leaflets 4, originating from one point (palmate) at tip of long stalk
        Marsilea vestita (hairy pepperwort)
        [**occasional native**] 45

    11. Leaflets pinnately divided or lobed with many segments; aerial portions of stem erect above water surface, not floating

      12. Leaves above water glaucous or gray-green
         Myriopyllum aquaticum (parrotfeather)
         [**common non-native**] 86

      12. Leaves above water green
         Myriophyllum verticillatum (whorled watermilfoil)
         or *Myriophyllum hippuroides* (western watermilfoil)
         [**uncommon natives**] 93

  10. Leaves simple, not divided into leaflets or obvious segments

    13. Leaves with petiole attached in center of blade, shieldlike (peltate)
        Brasenia schreberi (watershield)
        [**occasional native**] 111

    13. Leaves with petiole attached at base, not in center of blade

      14. Mature leaves >12 cm long and >8 cm wide

        15. Leaf blade longer than wide, heart-shaped, not round; flowers yellow with <10 petals
           Nuphar polysepala (yellow pondlily)
           [**occasional native**] 110

        15. Leaf blade roundish to horseshoe-shaped; flowers white, yellow, or pink, petals >10

16. Flowers yellow
Nymphaea mexicana (Mexican waterlily)
[**rare non-native**] 114

16. Flowers white or pink to red
Nymphaea odorata (fragrant waterlily)
[**uncommon non-native**] 117

14. Mature leaves <12 cm long and <8 cm wide

17. Leaf blade round or heart-shaped in outline

18. Leaf blade with toothed to lobed margin
Hydrocotyle ranunculoides (floating pennywort)
[**occasional native**] 159

18. Leaf blade margin entire (not toothed)
Nymphoides peltata (yellow floatingheart)
[**uncommon non-native**] 117

17. Leaf blade not round or heart-shaped

19. Leaves lacking sheath at base of petiole, veins of leaf blades obvious and pinnate along midvein; leaves and stems floating on water surface or emerged; flowers yellow when present (>1 cm diam)

20. Leaves opposite; petals absent
Ludwigia palustris (waterpurslane)
[**occasional native**] 253

20. Leaves alternate; petals conspicuously yellow
Ludwigia peploides (creeping waterprimrose)
[**common native or non-native**] 249

19. Leaves with sheath at base, veins not conspicuous, if so, parallel with midvein; leaves not emerged, always floating on water surface; flowers not yellow (<1 cm diam)

21. Flowers pink to red; transparent stipules encircling the stem above each node
Polygonum amphibium var. *stipulaceum* (water smartweed) [**occasional native**] 315

21. Flowers greenish; stipules sometimes fused to petiole, resembling a stipular sheath but not enclosing the stem
Potamogeton **spp.**, *Stuckenia* **spp.**, or *Ruppia* **spp.** (see *Potamogeton, Stuckenia,* and *Ruppia* spp. key) 37

1. **Leaves normally either all submerged or with emergent leaves only at the branch tips; leaf blades not predominately floating horizontally at the water surface**

22. Branches or leaves whorled (>2 per node)

23. Each branch of a whorl also bearing whorls of branches
Nitella spp. (nitella) [**common natives**] 66

23. Each branch of a whorl not bearing branches

24. Each branch or leaf of a whorl deeply divided into linear segments

25. Segments (of leaves) pinnately arranged along a central axis, individual pinnate segments not rebranched

26. Stems entirely submerged

27. Pinnate leaf segments usually <26, generally not paired; turions often present; distinct black scales lacking or with two distinct scales at inflorescence nodes; stems erect near water surface
Myriophyllum sibiricum (northern watermilfoil) [**occasional native**] .82, 93

27. Pinnate leaf segments usually >28, paired; no turions present; 2–3 distinct black scales at inflorescence nodes; stems lie parallel to water surface
Myriophyllum spicatum (Eurasian watermilfoil) [**common non-native**] 86

26. Stem tip emerged from water

28. Leaves above water glaucous or gray-green, similar to submerged leaves
Myriophyllum aquaticum (parrotfeather) [**common non-native**] 86

28. Leaves above water green, smaller than submerged leaves, bracteate
Myriophyllum verticillatum (whorled watermilfoil) or *Myriophyllum hippuroides* (western watermilfoil) [**uncommon natives**] 93

25. Branch or leaf segments either not pinnately arranged along a central axis or if so, pinnate segments variously rebranched

29. Margin of leaf segments toothed, rough to the touch
Ceratophyllum demersum (coontail) [**common native**] 78

29. Margin of leaf segments not toothed or rough to the touch

30. Leaves arranged in a whorl of >2 per stem node; branch (leaf) segments pinnately arranged but then variously rebranched *Limnophila* ×*ludoviciana* (marshweed) [**rare non-native**] 82

30. Leaves 2 per node, rarely 3; branch (leaf) segments regularly and extensively dichotomously (2-forked) rebranched *Cabomba caroliniana* (fanwort) [**occasional non-native**] .80

24. Each branch or leaf of a whorl not deeply divided into linear segments

31. Branches very narrow, firm to the touch, skunk or garlic odor present *Chara* **spp.** (chara) [**common natives**] 66

31. Branches either not narrow and firm, skunk or garlic odor not present

32. Leaves prickly or spiny to the touch *Najas marina* (hollyleaf naiad) [**occasional native**] 108

32. Leaves not prickly or spiny to the touch

33. Branches (leaves) opposite or in a whorl of 3 per node

34. Leaves of a whorl threadlike, <2 mm wide, fruit attached in lower leaf axils *Zannichellia palustris* (horned pondweed) [**common native**] 132

34. Leaves of a whorl lanceolate or oblong, >2 mm wide, fruit on long stalks *Elodea canadensis* (common elodea) [**common native**] 96

33. Branches (leaves) of a whorl generally >3 per node

35. Leaf margin generally "conspicuously" toothed, sometimes with prickles on the midrib of the lower leaf surface; stipule appendages orange, deeply divided (difficult to see); tubers present in fall *Hydrilla verticillata* (hydrilla) [**uncommon non-native**] .96

35. Leaf margin generally inconspicuously toothed, never with prickles on midrib of lower leaf surface; stipule appendage absent; no tubers
Egeria densa (Brazilian egeria, Brazilian elodea, egeria) [**common non-native**] 96

22. Branches or leaves 2 or less at a node (opposite or alternate, not whorled)

36. Branches or leaves 2 per node (opposite)

37. Branches (leaves) dissected into numerous linear segments dichotomously branched
Cabomba caroliniana (fanwort)
[**occasional non-native**] .80

37. Branches (leaves) not divided into linear segments

38. Leaf margins obviously very spiny to the touch
Najas marina (hollyleaf naiad)
[**occasional native**] 108

38. Leaf margins may have small spines, but not obviously spiny to the touch

39. Leaf margins lacking teeth, 3–5 sessile fruits per flowering node
Zannichellia palustris (horned pondweed)
[**common native**] 132

39. Leaf margins toothed, 1–2 sessile fruits per flowering node

40. Leaf sheath appendage obvious, rounded to pointed
Najas graminea (grassy naiad)
[**uncommon non-native**] 105, 107

40. Leaf sheath lacking an appendage
Najas guadalupensis (southern naiad)
[**common native**] 106

36. Branches or leaves 1 per node (alternate)

41. Branches (leaves) divided in many linear segments
Ranunculus aquatilis (white waterbuttercup)
[**occasional native**] 84

41. Branches (leaves) not divided
Potamogeton **spp.,** *Stuckenia* **spp.,** or *Ruppia* **spp.** (see *Potamogeton, Stuckenia,* and *Ruppia* spp. key) 37

Key to Grasses or Grasslike Aquatic Weeds, Including Irises, Sedges, Rushes, and Cattails

Page

1. **Stems triangular in cross-section**

    2. Leaves absent or not obvious

          Scirpus californicus (California or southern bulrush) **[occasional native]** 191

    2. Leaves obviously present

        3. Bracts of flower structures (spikelets) in 2 rows giving the structure a flattened appearance

              Cyperus **spp.** (sedges) **[common natives and non-natives]** 176

        3. Bracts of flowering structures (spikelets) spirally arranged giving the structure a cylindrical or conical appearance

              Scirpus **spp.** (bulrushes) **[common natives and some non-natives]** 191

1. **Stems round or flattened, not triangular**

    4. Leaves lacking or not obvious

        5. Plants <1 m tall

              Eleocharis **spp.** (spikerushes) **[common natives]** 184

        5. Plants >1 m tall

              Scirpus acutus (hardstem bulrush, tule); *Scirpus californicus* similar but with triangular stem near top **[common native]** 189

    4. Leaves obvious (grasses or cattails)

        6. Leaves lacking a ligule at junction of blade and sheath

            7. Plants >1.5 m tall

                  Typha **spp.** (cattails) **[common natives]** 378

            7. Plants <1.5 m tall

               8. Annual, grass, leaves not strongly keeled

                    Echinochloa **spp.** (watergrasses, barnyardgrass, junglerice) **[common non-natives]** 263

8. Rhizomatous perennial, non-grass, leaves strongly keeled
Iris pseudacorus (yellowflag iris)
[occasional non-native] 221

6. Leaves with ligule at junction of blade and sheath

9. Reedlike plants, >2 m tall

10. Base of blade with long (5–10 mm) tawny-colored hairs near collar
Saccharum ravennae (ravennagrass)
[uncommon non-native] 261

10. Base of blade lacking hairs or with hairs <5 mm long and not tawny colored

11. Collar at junction of blade and sheath auriculate (extended), collar-blade attachment at a high angle (about 40°) with stem, ligule hairs short, $\frac{1}{10}$ the length of the membranous part of the ligule, membranous part about 1 mm, leaf width >2 cm
Arundo donax (giant reed)
[common non-native] .254

11. Collar lacking auricle-like extension, collar-blade attachment at low angle (about 20°) with stem, membranous part of ligule about 0.5 mm long, ligule hairs often longer than the membranous part, leaf blade <2 cm wide
Phragmites australis (common reed) [occasional native, non-native in some areas] 260

9. Plants <2 m tall (except in *Phalaris arundinacea* [reed canarygrass])

12. Inflorescence branches inconspicuous, inflorescence appearing as narrow spike

13. Spikelets one-sided on appressed branches, nearly always in saline water of marine habitats
Spartina spp. (cordgrasses)
[mainly occasional non-natives] 305

13. Spikelets not one-sided, branches not appressed to the main stem (rachis)

14. Glume awns >1 mm, lemma length <2.5 mm
Polypogon spp. (polypogons)
[common non-natives] .297

14. Glume awns absent, lemma >3 mm long
Phalaris spp. (canarygrasses)
[common native and non-natives] 290

12. Inflorescence branches conspicuous, not appearing as a spike

15. Inflorescence branches diverging from the central stem (rachis), individual branches spikelike, spikelets one-sided, awnless or with awns <3 mm

16. Spikelets with >1 fertile floret (>1 seed per spikelet) *Leptochloa* **spp.** (sprangletops) [**common natives**] 276

16. Spikelet with only 1 fertile floret (1 seed per spikelet) *Paspalum* **spp.** (dallisgrass, knotgrass, bahiagrass and vaseygrass) [**common natives and non-natives**] 281

15. Inflorescence a panicle, spikelets with awns >3 mm *Polypogon viridis* (= *Agrostis viridis*) (water bent) [**occasional native**] 302

Key to *Potamogeton, Stuckenia* (Pondweeds), and *Ruppia* (Widgeongrass) Species

All *Potamogeton* and *Stuckenia* species are native to the western United States, except *Potamogeton crispus* (curlyleaf pondweed), which is native to Eurasia. Pondweeds and widgeongrass are important components of wildland aquatic habitats and are considered weedy only in irrigation systems and other water use areas. Although all the species in this key have been reported as weedy problems in some areas of the United States, many are rarely encountered in the western states and almost never pose a problem. The frequency of encountering a particular pondweed or widgeongrass is indicated in bold. This key should assist in the separation of species within this difficult genus. For additional details and tables comparing numerous characteristics see the *Potamogeton* spp. and *Ruppia* spp. on pages 118 and 128. Note that there are three choices for step 1.

1. **Leaves submerged, linear, with no distinct flattened blade (generally submerged leaves only)**

> *P. diversifolius* (waterthread pondweed): Small elliptical floating leaves (<4 cm long) with petioles half as long may be present; stipules fused ⅓ to ½ the length; submerged leaves sessile, <10 cm long, <1.5 mm wide, sheath <1 cm long [**uncommon native**]

> *Stuckenia pectinatus* (= *Potamogeton pectinatus*) (sago pondweed): Tubers present; branches many-times forked, especially near top of plant; no floating leaves; submerged leaves <10 cm long, <1 mm wide; leaf tips acute; stipules fused most of the length; achenes 3–4.5 mm long [**common native**]

> *Stuckenia filiformis* (= *Potamogeton filiformis*) (threadleaf pondweed): No floating leaves; submerged leaves 10–18 cm long, 0.5–2 mm wide; leaf tips blunt or notched; stipules fused most of the length; achenes 2–3 mm long [**rare native**]

> *Ruppia* **spp.** (widgeongrass): No floating leaves; leaves opposite, with toothed margin, <10 cm long; sheaths open most of the length; inflorescence an umbel on axillary stalk (*R. maritima* 2–25 mm long, straight; *R. cirrhosa* 30–300 mm long, coiled or twisted) [**occasional natives**]

1. Leaves submerged, straplike or ribbonlike (floating leaves present or absent)

2. All leaves submerged

3. Leaves wavy

P. crispus (curlyleaf pondweed): Leaf margins serrated; leaves to 8 cm long, 5–8 mm wide; stipules <1 cm long [**common non-native**]

P. richardsonii (Richardson's or clasping leaf pondweed): Leaf margins entire; leaves sessile, 2–12 cm long, 1–3 cm wide, clasping the stem by the cordate base; stipules <2 cm long [**uncommon native**]

P. praelongus (whitestem pondweed): Stems whitish; leaf margins entire; boat-shaped leaf tips; not as curly as the above two; leaves longer, to 20 cm, 10–30 mm wide; stipules whitish, 3–10 cm long [**rare native**]

3. Leaves not wavy

P. foliosus (leafy pondweed): Stems round; leaves sessile, 2–8 cm long, 1–2.5 mm wide; main veins 3 (5); stipules wrapped around stem, no glands at nodes [**occasional native**]

P. pusillus (small pondweed): Stems round; leaves sessile, 1–7 cm long, 0.5–2 mm wide; main veins 3 (5); stipules wrapped around stem, pair of glands at leaf nodes [**occasional native**]

P. zosteriformis (flatstem pondweed): Stems flat; leaves sessile, 10–20 cm long, 3–5 mm wide; main veins numerous, >9; stipules free [**rare native**]

2. Leaves submerged and floating, well developed

P. gramineus (variable pondweed): Stems with many short branches; floating leaves elliptic, <6 cm long, 1–3 cm wide, petiole longer than blade; submerged leaves lanceolate to linear, tapered at base with pointed tip, 2–11 cm long, ± 1 cm wide [**uncommon native**]

P. epihydrus (ribbonleaf pondweed): Floating leaves narrowly obovate to elliptic, 3–8 cm long, 1.5–3.5 cm wide on petioles about the length of blade; submerged leaves linear, to 25 cm long, <1 cm wide, with netlike band along midrib [**rare native**]

1. Leaves floating and/or submerged, elliptic or lanceolate

4. Leaves floating and submerged, well developed

5. Submerged leaves narrow (<2 mm)

P. natans (floatingleaf pondweed): Floating leaves elliptic, usually heart-shaped at base, <10 cm long, <6 cm wide; petiole longer than blade; blade at right angle to stalk; submerged leaves <50 cm long, 1–2 mm wide [**common native**]

P. nodosus (American pondweed): Floating leaves elliptic, 5–12 cm long, 1.5–4 cm wide, gradually taper at base; petiole longer than blade, submerged leaves lanceolate to narrowly elliptic, 10–30 cm long, 1–3 cm wide, on petiole 2–10 cm long [common native]

5. Submerged leaves well developed (>2 mm wide)

   6. Submerged leaves 2–12 mm wide, sessile; stipules <4 cm long, free, persisting

      P. gramineus (variable pondweed): Stems with many short branches; floating leaves elliptic, <6 cm long, 1–3 cm wide, petioles longer than blade; submerged leaves lanceolate to linear, tapered at base with pointed tip, 2–11 cm long, ± 1 cm wide [uncommon native]

      P. epihydrus (ribbonleaf pondweed): Floating leaves narrowly obovate to elliptic, 3–8 cm long, 1.5–3.5 cm wide on petioles about the length of blade; stems few-branched or simple; submerged leaves linear, 5–25 cm long, with netlike band along midrib [rare native]

   6. Submerged leaves 1–7 cm wide, generally petiolated (esp. above); stipules 3–10 cm long, breaking apart with age

      P. amplifolius (largeleaf pondweed): Submerged leaves lanceolate to ovate, curved, folded along midvein, sessile or short-petiolated; floating leaves with 30–50 parallel veins [uncommon native]

      P. nodosus (American pondweed): Submerged leaves lanceolate to narrowly elliptic, 10–30 cm long, 1–3 cm wide, not curved or folded along midvein, upper submerged leaves on long petioles, 2–10 cm long; floating leaves with <30 parallel veins; floating leaves elliptic, 5–12 cm long, 1.5–4 cm wide, gradually taper at base, petiole longer than blade [common native]

      P. illinoensis (Illinois pondweed): Submerged leaves lanceolate, sesssile or with short petiole, <3 cm long, blades <20 cm long, <5 cm wide, 9–19 longitudinal veins and conspicuous cross-veins; base of leaf blade not clasping stem; floating leaves (when present) similar [occasional native]

4. Leaves submerged (rarely floating)

      P. illinoensis (Illinois pondweed): Submerged leaves lanceolate, sesssile or with short petiole, <3 cm long, blades <20 cm long, <5 cm wide, 9–19 longitudinal veins and conspicuous cross-veins; base of leaf blade not clasping stem; floating leaves (when present) similar [occasional native]

      P. praelongus (whitestem pondweed): Zigzag stem; leaves 7–30 cm long, 1.5–2.5 cm wide, >5 longitudinal veins with fine cross-veins; no petiole; base of leaves clasping stem, boat-shaped leaf tip, no floating leaves [rare native]

      P. richardsonii (Richardson's or clasping leaf pondweed): Stems straight; no petiole; base of leaves cordate, margins crinkly near tip, tip not boat-shaped [uncommon native]

Floating-Leaved Aquatic Plants with Roots in the Water Column

Ferns and Monocots

Waterlettuce (*Pistia stratiotes* L.) [PIIST]

NOXIOUS WEED LISTS: California: Q list

SYNONYMS: pistie; tropical duckweed

GENERAL INFORMATION: Floating perennial with **stolons** and **leaves in a basal rosette**. Under favorable conditions, large, dense colonies can develop. Dense colonies may reduce water oxygen concentration, pH levels, and light penetration and displace desirable aquatic vegetation, colonies can also impede water flow, provide habitat for mosquitoes, increase the deposition of silt, and interfere with recreational activities. Waterlettuce is a state-listed noxious weed in Florida, but it is much less problematic in California and Arizona. Plants sequester heavy metals. However, roots are often killed in heavily polluted water. Where species coexist, waterlettuce is typically displaced by **water hyacinth** (*Eichhornia crassipes* (Mart.) Solms) and may increase when water hyacinth is reduced. Waterlettuce is commonly sold as a pond or aquarium ornamental and is used medicinally in Asia. It is widely distributed in tropical regions and was probably introduced into the southeastern United States from tropical South America. Two biocontrol agents, a weevil (*Neohydronomus affinis*) and a moth (*Namangana pectinicornis*), have been released in Florida.

SEEDLING: Cotyledon deeply 2-lobed, ± 1 mm long. A few adventitious roots grow from base of cotyledon. First leaf broadly ovate, base ± heart-shaped, tip broad, slightly indented to squared, pubescent, emerges from between the lobes of the cotyledon, usually cupped at first, later flat. Seed coat remains attached to the seedling during the second-leaf stage.

MATURE PLANT: Stem short, cormlike, develops **stolons** to 60 cm long. Leaves in **basal rosettes**, pale grayish- to yellowish-green, densely covered with **soft velvety hairs**, sessile, **obovate to ± wedge-shaped**, with 4–12 parallel veins, to 15 cm long, 5 cm wide, tips **squared to slightly indented**. Leaf tissue contains air spaces and is ± stiffly spongy to touch.

ROOTS: Numerous, dense, pendant from stem to ± 80 cm long, unbranched, feathery, with long slender root hairs. Plants occasionally weakly root in mud.

FLOWERS: Spikes inconspicuous among leaves, mostly surrounded by and fused near the base to a larger bract (spathe), consist of several minute whorled male flowers at the tip and 1 female flower mostly hidden below. Spathe whitish, pubescent, to 20 mm long, constricted between male and female flowers. Stamens sessile, 2–8 per male flower. Pistil (ovary) 1-chambered. Insect-pollinated. Self-compatible.

FRUITS AND SEEDS: Berries green, 5–8 mm diameter, contain several seeds. Seeds oblong, truncate at both ends, with a depression at the apex, ± 2 mm long, ± 1 mm wide, brown at maturity, surface wrinkled, coat thick.

HABITAT: Still or slow-moving water in ponds, lakes, ditches, irrigation channels, and rice fields. Usually killed by freezing temperatures. Often inhabits nutrient-rich water. Grows best in tropical to subtropical climates.

DISTRIBUTION: Arizona and California in the eastern Sonoran Desert (Colorado River drainage), to 50 m. Southeastern United States. Expected to expand range.

PROPAGATION AND PHENOLOGY: Reproduces vegetatively from stolons with daughter offsets and by seed. Berries, seeds, and offsets disperse primarily with water and human activities. Seeds require an after-ripening period of about 4–6 weeks and can survive a period of dry conditions or freezing temperatures. Seeds contain an air chamber and float for a period before sinking to the sediment. Germination occurs submerged at temperatures above 20°C, but optimally at 25°C, and light is required. Seedlings float to the surface when the first leaf emerges. Plants grow rapidly, typically producing stolons with offsets within ± 1 month. Stolons fragment to release offsets.

MANAGEMENT FAVORING OR DISCOURAGING SURVIVAL: Mechanical harvesting can help control dense colonies.

SIMILAR SPECIES: Waterlettuce is unlikely to be confused with other floating aquatic plants.

Waterlettuce (*Pistia stratiotes*) plants floating in a pond.   J. M. DiTomaso

Mosquitofern (*Azolla* spp.)

Synonyms: azolla; fairy moss; water fern; water velvet

General Information: Small **free-floating aquatic ferns** that often occur in colonies. **Mosquitoferns** are **annual to perennial** depending on environmental conditions. Upper leaf lobes are typically colonized by the nitrogen-fixing cyanobacterium *Anabaena azollae*. **Pacific mosquitofern** (*Azolla filiculoides* Lam.) and **Mexican mosquitofern** (*Azolla mexicana* C. Presl) are native species that occur in many western states. Native mosquitoferns are consumed by wildlife, especially waterfowl, and are usually a desirable component of natural aquatic communities. Such populations may fluctuate greatly from year to year. However, dense colonies can become a nuisance in certain situations by excluding other aquatic vegetation, encouraging the growth of algae, interfering with livestock drinking, and clogging water pumps. In native habitat, however, mosquitofern provides breeding habitat for aquatic insects important to fisheries. Mosquitoferns are sometimes sold as aquarium or pond ornamentals. **Pinnate mosquitofern** (*Azolla pinnata* R.Br.) [AZOPI] is listed as a federal noxious weed. It is not naturalized in the United States at publication time, although it may be cultivated as an aquarium plant. In East Asia, mosquitofern is used as livestock feed and as a nitrogen source in rice fields. The genus *Azolla* consists of fewer than 10 species worldwide and is sometimes included in the Salviniaceae. Species identification often requires microscopic examination of female sporangia and leaves.

Mature Plant: Entire plant fan- to deltoid-shaped, **to ± 5 cm long**. Stems floating, pinnately branched. Leaves alternate, sessile, **scalelike, 0.5–1.5 mm long**, **2-lobed, overlapping in 2 rows** and hiding stem. Upper lobe emergent, thick, pouched, green to reddish. Lower lobe submerged, whitish, thinner and larger than upper lobe. Young plants are gray to green but turn red to brown with age and season.

Roots: Simple, slender, whitish, pendant from stems, turning darker with age.

Sporocarps: Plants usually produce male and female sporangia. Sporangia mostly occur in pairs in the axils of first leaves on older stems. Sporangia roundish, female 0.2–0.4 mm diameter, male 1.2–2 mm diameter.

Habitat: On still water or mud in ponds, small lakes, slow-moving streams and channels, ditches, rice fields, and sloughs. Often grow in eutrophic water. Do not tolerate saline water.

Distribution:

Pacific mosquitofern: Throughout California, except desert regions, to 1600 m. Oregon, Washington, Nevada, Arizona.

Mexican mosquitofern: Throughout California, except desert regions, to 1600 m. Oregon, Washington, Utah, Colorado, Nevada, Arizona, New Mexico.

Propagation and Phenology: Reproduce vegetatively from stem fragments and by spores. Fragments and spores disperse primarily with water, but also by human activities and by clinging to the feet or feathers of birds. Colonies typically enlarge rapidly during the warm months and diminish during the cool months.

MANAGEMENT FAVORING OR DISCOURAGING SURVIVAL: Careless disposal of pond or aquarium contents can introduce plants to previously uninhabited areas. Manual or mechanical harvesting can help control troublesome colonies.

SIMILAR SPECIES: Plants in the duckweed family (duckweeds [*Lemna, Spirodela* spp.] and watermeal [*Wolffia* spp.]) typically exist in floating colonies and may be confused with mosquitofern at first glance. However, duckweeds and watermeal **lack pinnately branched stems** and have leaflike stems **solitary**, **paired**, or in **rosettelike clusters of 2–10**.

Although not resembling mosquitofern or salvinia, **hairy pepperwort** (*Marsilea vestita* Hook. & Grev. ssp. *vestita*, synonyms: hairy water-clover; *Marsilea oligospora* Goodd., *Marsilea mucronata* A. Braun) [MASMU] is a **native aquatic perennial fern** with slender **creeping rhizomes** in the pepperwort family

Pond with dense Pacific mosquitofern (*Azolla filiculoides*) population.   W. J. McHenry

Pacific mosquitofern (*Azolla filiculoides*) in a pond.   J. M. DiTomaso

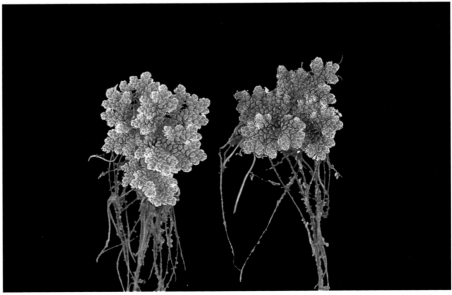

Two color forms of Pacific mosquitofern (*Azolla filiculoides*).   J. K. Clark

Marsileaceae. Its roots are embedded within the soil substrate. Hairy pepperwort has **floating** to emersed **palmate-compound leaves** with **4 leaflets** that resemble those of terrestrial sorrel (*Oxalis* spp.) or clover (*Trifolium* spp.). Foliage is ± covered with deciduous hairs. Hairy pepperwort is a desirable component of aquatic plant communities in natural areas but is occasionally weedy in drainage or irrigation ditches. Hairy pepperwort inhabits ponds, vernal pools, shallow marshy places, ditches, and flood basins in all western states. It occurs throughout most of California, except the Mojave Desert, Great Basin, North Coast, western North Coast Ranges, and eastern South Coast Ranges, to 2200 m.

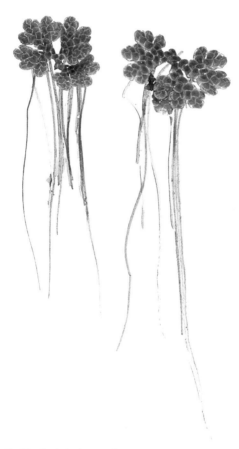

Pacific mosquitofern (*Azolla filiculoides*) plant with roots.   J. K. CLARK

Emergent leaves of hairy pepperwort (*Marsilea vestita* ssp. *vestita*).   J. M. DiTomaso

Floating leaves of hairy pepperwort (*Marsilea vestita* ssp. *vestita*).   J. M. DiTomaso

Common duckweed (*Lemna minor* L.) [LEMMI] and relatives

SYNONYMS: common duckweed: water lentil; *Hydrophace minor* (L.) Bubani; *Lemna minor* L. var *minima* Chev.; *Lenticula minor* (L.) Scop.

GENERAL INFORMATION: Very small floating perennials, often growing in clusters and forming dense colonies. In irrigation canals they can clog filters, and in ponds with high organic matter duckweeds can grow rapidly and cover the surface in a very short time. The Lemnaceae in the western United States includes 3 genera of similar plants that often grow together and can be troublesome under certain conditions. These are **duckweed** (*Lemna* spp.), **duckmeat or giant duckweed** (*Spirodela* spp.), and **watermeal** (*Wolffia* spp.). All species are **native** in the western states, and most are widespread in other areas of the United States and elsewhere. Common duckweed, duckmeat, and a few other species occur nearly worldwide. Species identification can be difficult, requiring magnification and sometimes examination of fruits or chemical analysis. Common duckweed is used as animal feed in Asia and in bioassays to detect water pollution levels since it can sequester certain pollutants. Duckweeds are common in the aquarium and ornamental pond trade. All duckweed, duckmeat, and watermeal species are a valuable food source for wildlife, especially waterfowl.

MATURE PLANT: Fronds (plant body) leaflike, not differentiated into stem and leaf, typically in pairs or trios, **flat, slightly obovate, to ± 5 mm long, symmetric at base and tip**, glossy, green, smooth, with **3–5 veins** visible with back-lighting and magnification. Margins smooth. Under surface sometimes purplish. Daughter fronds bud from a marginal pouch on each side at the base of the parent frond.

ROOTS: Typically **1 per frond**, simple, to 3 cm long or more. Root cap rounded.

Common duckweed (*Lemna minor*) in an irrigation ditch.　　　　　J. M. DITOMASO

Common duckweed

FLOWERS: Minute, single but resemble 2–3 unisexual flowers in 2 marginal pouches on each side of a frond, enclosed by a membranous sheath.

FRUITS AND SEEDS: Fruits minute, achene- or utricle-like, ovoid, ribbed, contain 1(–3) seed(s). The fruit wall (pericarp) decomposes to release seed. Seeds ovoid, ± 1 mm long, ± 0.5 mm wide, whitish, with 10–16 longitudinal ribs.

HABITAT: Ponds, lakes, slow-moving streams, ditches, and canals, sometimes on mud. Inhabits freshwater with intermediate to high nutrient levels. Tolerates a broad pH range and heavy shade. Grows best under warm conditions.

DISTRIBUTION: All western states. Throughout California to 2000 m. Occurs nearly worldwide.

PROPAGATION AND PHENOLOGY: Reproduces vegetatively by budding and some-times **by seed.** During the warm season the rate of budding can be very high, with each plant producing a daughter plant about every 3 days. Plants and seeds disperse with water, human activities, and by clinging to the feet, fur, and feath-ers of animals. Some members of the Lemnaceae, particularly duckmeat and watermeal species, develop minute winter buds (turions) that separate from the

Duckweed *(Lemna minuscula)* floating in a pond.   J. M. DITOMASO

Individual duckweed *(Lemna minuscula)* plants.   J. K. CLARK

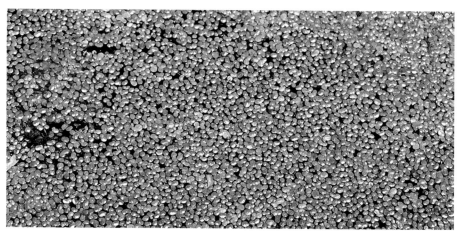

Giant duckweed (*Spirodela polyrrhiza*) floating in a pond.   J. M. DiTOMASO

Individual giant duckweed (*Spirodela polyrrhiza*) plants.   J. M. DiTOMASO

mother fronds and sink to the sediment. As the water warms in spring, the buds float to the surface.

MANAGEMENT FAVORING OR DISCOURAGING SURVIVAL: Manual or mechanical removal can help control troublesome colonies.

SIMILAR SPECIES: Duckmeat is distinguished by having **fronds to 10 mm long, typically with 2–16 roots and 7–15 veins.** Duckmeat fronds usually occur in pairs or small clusters of 3–5. Duckmeat occurs in all western states. **Watermeal** has **spherical to ovoid or cylindrical fronds to ± 1 mm long** that **lack roots** and **veins.** Watermeal fronds typically exist in unequal pairs. Watermeal occurs in California, Oregon, Washington, Idaho, Montana, Colorado, and Utah. Mosquitofern (*Azolla* spp.) often grows with duckweed, duckmeat, and watermeal, but it is easily distinguished by having **pinnately branched stems** with **overlapping scalelike leaves.** Refer to the **Mosquitofern** entry (page 44) for more information.

Water hyacinth (*Eichhornia crassipes* (Mart.) Solms) [EICCR]

Noxious Weed Lists: Arizona: Restricted Noxious Weed; California: C, CalEPPC: A-2

Synonyms: *Eichhornia speciosa* Kunth; *Heteranthera formosa* Miq.; *Piaropus crassipes* (Mart.) Raf.; *Pontederia crassipes* Mart.; others

General Information: Noxious floating perennial with stolons and emergent leaves to ± 40 cm tall. Water hyacinth occurs nearly worldwide in tropical to warm temperate regions and is considered one of the most serious aquatic weeds, especially in tropical regions. Under favorable conditions, it has an extremely high growth rate and is difficult to control. Populations expand rapidly, forming dense mats that can produce high quantities of dry matter. Floating mats clog waterways; alter water oxygen levels, temperature, and pH; provide mosquito habitat; and displace native aquatic vegetation and wildlife. In some places, water hyacinth is utilized as green manure to produce methane gas or is processed into a component of animal feeds, paper, particle board, activated carbon, and other products. Water hyacinth removes pollutants from water, including sewage, heavy metals, and chlorinated hydrocarbons, and is useful in waste treatment systems. Introduced from tropical South America (Brazil) as an aquatic ornamental. Two crown/petiole-boring weevils (*Neochetina bruchi, Neochetina eichhorniae*) and a stem-boring moth (*Sameodes albiguttalis*) have been released as biocontrol agents in California. Only *Neochetina eichhorniae* has become established to a limited extent, and control of water hyacinth has been poor. Control of water hyacinth with these insects has been much more successful in the southeastern states. The fungal pathogen *Cercospora rodmanii* is host-specific to water hyacinth and may be suitable for use as a commercial bioherbicide, although it has not yet been registered.

Water hyacinth *(Eichhornia crassipes)* infestation in an irrigation canal.   J. M. DiTomaso

Whole plant and floating roots of water hyacinth (*Eichhornia crassipes*).   J. M. DiTOMASO

SEEDLING: Most often observed rooted in mud along shorelines where the water level fluctuates or on floating or beached mats of decomposing water hyacinth. Seedlings detach from roots and float if they become submerged. Cotyledon glabrous, ± oval, parallel-veined, ± 1 mm long, on a sheathing stalk 2–3 mm long. First and subsequent leaves glabrous, linear-lanceolate, 8–15 mm long, 1–2 mm wide, on a sheathing stalk 2–4 mm long.

MATURE PLANT: Floating, sometimes rooted in mud, typically **linked to other plants by stolons** from a thick erect stem. Foliage glabrous, variable. Leaves ± basal, floating, and emersed. Blades obovate to lanceolate, to 12(15) cm wide, bases sometimes ± heart-shaped. Stalks spongy, to 30 cm long or more, usually **inflated** in younger plants and ± tapered in older plants.

ROOTS: Pendant, feathery, dark, to 1 m long or more.

FLOWERS: June–October. **Spikes** sometimes panicle-like, on **stalks taller than leaves** (to ± 50 cm), consist of (1)3–35 showy **bisexual** flowers. Perianth (petals and/or sepals) **pale blue, lilac**, or **white**, funnel-shaped, 6-lobed, slightly irregular, 4–6 cm wide. Upper lobe **enlarged**, with a **central yellow blotch surrounded by darker blue.** Ovary **superior.** Style short, medium, or long relative to stamens (heterostylous). Insect-pollinated.

FRUITS AND SEEDS: Capsules membranous, narrowly oblong, with a persistent style at the apex, 10–15 mm long, 3-chambered, contain numerous seeds. Seeds ovoid, 1–1.5 mm long, longitudinally ribbed.

POSTSENESCENCE CHARACTERISTICS: Frost can kill foliage, but stem bases often survive and develop new foliage the following spring.

HABITAT: Ponds, sloughs, channels, streams, and lakes, in still or slow-moving water. Plants grow best in warm, high-nutrient (eutrophic) water at pH 4–8. Tolerates acidity levels as low as pH 3. Does not tolerate salinity above ± 1.6%.

DISTRIBUTION: Arizona and California in the Central Valley, San Francisco Bay region, South Coast, Peninsular Ranges, to 200 m. Southern and eastern United States. Nearly worldwide.

PROPAGATION AND PHENOLOGY: Reproduces vegetatively from stolons and by seeds. Vegetative parts and seeds disperse primarily with water and human activities. Seeds also disperse by clinging to the feet or feathers of birds. Vegetative reproduction is rapid under favorable conditions, with plant numbers often doubling in ± 5 days. New plants can flower in 3–4 weeks. After flowering, stalks

Water hyacinth (*Eichhornia crassipes*) inflorescence.

J. M. DITOMASO

Swollen basal region of water hyacinth (*Eichhornia crassipes*) leaf.　　　J. M. DITOMASO

bend over and may become submerged. Seeds mature submersed or emersed. Seed production peaks during the middle of the flowering season. In the western United States, the European honey bee (*Apis mellifera*) is the primary pollinator, and seed production in the Central Valley appears to be roughly half that of tropical populations. Seeds sink to the substrate upon release from capsules. Seeds typically germinate in spring. Germination requirements appear variable. Seeds of some populations require an after-ripening period of about 3 months, and light may be important. A temperature of ± 20°–35°C usually enhances germination. Seeds maintained under wet conditions often germinate better than those that became dry for a period. In temperate regions, seeds have been reported to survive up to 15–20 years in dried mud.

MANAGEMENT FAVORING OR DISCOURAGING SURVIVAL: Construction of dams can create still water conditions that are favorable to water hyacinth establishment. Mechanical harvesting, herbicide treatments, and biocontrol agents can help control infestations. Integrated management utilizing these techniques is more likely to successfully control persistent infestations.

SIMILAR SPECIES: Sponge plant or **smooth frogbit** (*Limnobium laevigatum* (Humb. & Bonpl. ex Willd.) Heine, synonym: *Limnobium spongia* (Bosc) L.C. Rich ex Steud ssp. *laevigatum* (Humb. & Bonpl. ex Willd.) Lowden) is a **floating to rooted stoloniferous perennial** in the waterweed family (Hydrocharitaceae) with foliage that may be confused with that of water hyacinth. Smooth frogbit has a juvenile form of partly submersed rosettes with thick, spongy, floating, ovate to spatula-shaped leaves, usually with rounded tips and on inflated stalks. Juvenile rosettes gradually develop into mature clumps to 50 cm tall, with leathery, emergent, broadly elliptic leaves on noninflated stalks. Unlike water hyacinth, smooth frogbit typically has juvenile leaves and sometimes mature leaves with a patch or disc of (± purplish) **honeycomb-like spongy tissue** (aerenchyma) on the **lower**

Smooth frogbit (*Limnobium laevigatum*) young plants attached to stolon.   D.W. KRATVILLE

surfaces. At maturity, small **solitary** or paired **unisexual white flowers** with **inferior ovaries** on stalks up to **± 1/3 the height of the leaves** may develop in spring or summer. Capsules are fleshy, **berrylike**, obovoid to ellipsoid, 4–13 mm long, and 2–5 mm in diameter. Seeds are ellipsoidal, ± 1 mm long, and covered with **hairs** to 0.2 mm long. In California, **smooth frogbit** has escaped cultivation as a pond ornamental in some coastal areas (Alameda and Riverside Cos.). Introduced from tropical to subtropical Central and South America. Smooth frogbit is sometimes considered a subspecies of **American frogbit** (*Limnobium spongia* (Bosc) L.C. Rich ex Steud) [LIMSP], a native perennial of the southern and eastern United States. However, American and smooth frogbit have distinct ranges and differ in floral characteristics and leaf shape. American frogbit is not known to occur in any western states.

Smooth frogbit (*Limnobium laevigatum*) plants.   D.W. KRATVILLE

Smooth frogbit (*Limnobium laevigatum*) plant with mature leaves.   D.W. KRATVILLE

Salvinia (a complex consisting of *Salvinia auriculata* Aubl. [SAVAU], *Salvinia molesta* D.S. Mitch. [SAVMO], *Salvinia biloba* Raddi, *Salvinia herzogii* de la Sota)

Noxious Weed Lists: Federal Noxious Weed; California: Q list; Arizona: Prohibited Noxious Weed

Synonyms: African pyle or payal; aquarium watermoss; butterfly fern; eared watermoss; giant salvinia; karibaweed; koi kandy; *Salvinia hispida* Kunth; *Salvinia natans* auct. non (L.) All.; *Salvinia rotundifolia* Willd.

General Information: A complex of closely related **perennial floating aquatic ferns** that are difficult to distinguish from one another. **Giant salvinia** (*Salvinia molesta*) is often grown as an aquatic ornamental, but it has escaped cultivation and become **noxious** in many regions worldwide. Depending on environmental conditions, plants exhibit a range of growth forms, from the primary invading form of open water, with small flat leaves, to the dense tertiary or mat form with large, crowded, folded leaves. Under favorable conditions giant salvinia can form dense mats more than 0.5 m thick that can completely cover the water surface. Thick mats can support other aquatic vegetation, and the lower part consists of dead plant material. Mats limit boat travel and recreational activities, increase flooding and stagnation, displace native vegetation and animals, and diminish water quality. Where it is carefully managed, giant salvinia has been used to remove excess nutrients and other pollutants from water. Dried plants make satisfactory mulch. Members of the salvinia complex are native to tropical South America. The salvinia weevil (*Cyrtobagus salviniae*) has been successfully used as a biocontrol agent for giant salvinia infestations in Africa, Australia, India, Indonesia, and elsewhere. The weevil was accidentally introduced into the southern United States. It will also feed on **Herzog salvinia** (*Salvinia herzogii* de la Sota). It is uncertain whether members of the salvinia complex other than giant salvinia could become noxious weeds outside their native range.

Mature Plant: Stems horizontal just below water surface, often simple in the primary form and much-branched in the tertiary form. Leaves 3-whorled, with 2 floating and 1 submerged. Floating leaf upper surfaces densely covered with water-resistant **eggbeater-shaped hairs 2–4 mm long that diverge into 4 branches near the top and fuse together at the tips**. Floating leaves of the primary form are flat, well spaced, ± oval with slightly lobed bases to obovate with wedge-shaped bases, 8–15 mm wide. Tips rounded or acute. Floating leaves of the tertiary form are densely crowded, tightly folded upward along the midvein, deeply 2-lobed at the tip, 25–60 mm wide when unfolded, typically broader than long. Floating leaves of the secondary form are intermediate to the primary and tertiary forms. Submerged leaves are rootlike.

Roots: True roots lacking. Submerged leaves function and appear as roots and are whitish, finely dissected into several filaments up to 2 cm long, with hairlike projections along the length. Submerged leaves are short in high-nutrient water but can grow to 10–15 cm long in nutrient-poor water. Experimental evidence suggests that submersed leaves may sometimes associate with nitrogen-fixing blue-green algae.

REPRODUCTIVE STRUCTURES: Variable. Some filaments of submerged leaves may develop chains or clusters of tiny ovoid spore-bearing structures (sporocarps) ± 1–3 mm in diameter.

POSTSENESCENCE CHARACTERISTICS: Partial plant death often stimulates dormant buds to develop.

HABITAT: Still and slow-moving waters of lakes, ponds, reservoirs, rivers, marshes, ditches, and rice fields. Grows best in nutrient-rich water in tropical climates. Tolerates mild temperate conditions, some salinity, and occasional frost but not prolonged periods of freezing temperatures. Dense mats do not develop at temperatures below 10°C.

DISTRIBUTION: Giant salvinia has escaped cultivation and is spreading in the southern United States, particularly Texas, and as far west as the lower Colorado River in Arizona and California. At publication time, populations have naturalized in the Colorado River drainage and have invaded some canals in the Sonoran Desert (Riverside and Imperial Cos., CA) and in San Luis Obispo County (CA). **Salvinia** species are sometimes offered for sale as an aquarium or pond ornamental. Introductions may be expected to persist wherever water hyacinth is established.

Giant salvinia (*Salvinia molesta*) in a pond.   D.W. KRATVILLE

Giant salvinia *(Salvinia molesta)* plant.   D.W. KRATVILLE

PROPAGATION AND PHENOLOGY: Reproduces vegetatively by stem fragments. Each node has up to 5 dormant buds. Older stems separate from nodes as more buds develop. Fragments disperse primarily with wind, water currents, flooding, and human activities. Some protected dormant buds of mat-form plants can survive dry conditions for long periods, up to 2 years in one case. *Salvinia molesta* and *S. herzogii* are functionally sterile hybrids that usually do not develop viable spores. The other 2 species can develop fertile spores. Under optimal conditions, giant salvinia plants can double their biomass in 2–3 days.

MANAGEMENT FAVORING OR DISCOURAGING SURVIVAL: Removing and destroying plant fragments from boat propellers, docking lines, fishing gear, and other equipment can help prevent the spread of salvinia. Dumping unwanted aquarium or pond ornamentals into natural areas can introduce salvinia into new areas.

SIMILAR SPECIES: Water sprangles or water fern (*Salvinia minima* Baker, synonyms: *Salvinia auriculata* auct. non Aubl.; *Salvinia rotundifolia* auct. non Willd.) is a non-problematic native species that occurs in New Mexico and other southern states. Unlike water sprangles and other innocuous *Salvinia* species, potentially noxious members of the salvinia complex have **eggbeater-shaped hairs, 2–4 mm long, on the upper surfaces of floating leaves.** These hairs are **easiest to see on young leaves** growing under sunny conditions. Hairs can become damaged on old leaves or may not develop on shaded plants.

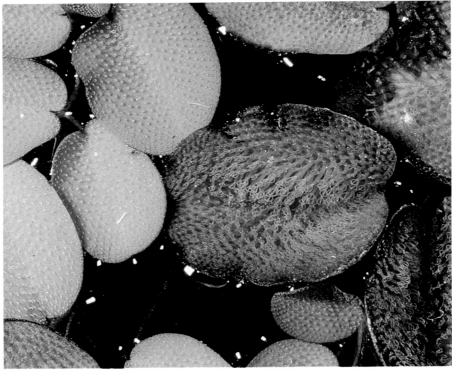

Giant salvinia (*Salvinia molesta*) plants with eggbeater-shaped hairs. J. M. DiTomaso

Eggbeater-shaped hairs of giant salvinia *(Salvinia molesta)*.
COURTESY USGS

Submerged or Floating-Leaved Aquatic Plants with Roots within the Soil Sediment

Algae

Caulerpa (*Caulerpa taxifolia* (Vahl) Agardh, Mediterranean strain)

NOXIOUS WEED LISTS: Federal Noxious Weed

GENERAL INFORMATION: Bright green marine alga with erect **fernlike fronds** to ± 65 cm long and anchored by **stolons** with rootlike rhizoids. The wild type of *Caulerpa taxifolia* is generally regarded as a noninvasive species of tropical waters. However, one plant of a strain cultured for aquarium use in Europe was released into the Mediterranean Sea in 1984. This clone has aggressively invaded thousands of hectares along the Mediterranean coast. Under suitable conditions, *Caulerpa* develops into vast colonies that densely cover all suitable substrates. Such colonies displace the natural flora and fauna of the area. *Caulerpa* has also invaded coastal waters near Sydney, Australia, and, has recently been discovered just north of San Diego, California. It is considered a significant threat to native California kelp because it occupies sites at the same water depths and light intensity. Consequently, an eradication program is in progress in California. *Caulerpa* tolerates cooler water and greater depth than the tropical wild type. *Caulerpa* species produce caulerpenyne, a toxic compound that prevents some species of mollusks, urchins, and fish from feeding on the plant. The toxin is not a threat to humans. The California legislature has made it illegal to sell, grow, or ship *Caulerpa taxifolia* and eight other *Caulerpa* species within the state. In other areas, however, they are still commercially available in the aquarium trade.

MATURE PLANT: Highly variable, **bright grass green**. Fronds erect, simple or few-branched, **flat, pinnately divided**, 5–65 cm long, 0.6–3 cm wide. **Divisions opposite, linear**, 4–12 mm long, narrow, often slightly curved or directed upward, **apex tapered to a minute ± spinelike tip** (mucronate), base slightly constricted.

ROOTLIKE STRUCTURES: Stolons green, creeping, to 3 m long or more, with up to 200 fronds. Rhoizoids clustered at the ends of short branchlets from the stolon. **Rhizoid branchlets (>1 cm long) usually spaced more than 1 cm apart on stolons**. Rhizoids rootlike, colorless.

HABITAT: Tropical and temperate coastal marine waters mostly to 40 m deep, but sometimes as deep as 150 m. Tolerates pollution and temperatures as low as 10°–15°C.

DISTRIBUTION: Rare in California to date. Agua Hedionda Lagoon, north of San Diego, and Huntington Harbor, Orange County, California.

PROPAGATION AND PHENOLOGY: Reproduces primarily vegetatively from stolon and frond fragments. Fragments disperse with human activities, such as boating, fishing, shipping, and releasing unwanted aquarium contents into the ocean. Small fragments can quickly grow into a new plant. One plant can develop into a colony that covers ± 7 m² within 1 year. Plants and fragments that remain moist can survive for up to 10 days out of water. Sexual reproduction has been observed in the invasive strain of *Caulerpa* only in the Mediterranean.

SIMILAR SPECIES: *Caulerpa* is unlikely to be confused with other green marine algae of the Pacific Coast. **Wakame** or **Japanese kelp** [*Undaria pinnatifida* (Harv.) Sur.; Alariaceae] is a **golden-brown kelp** with **flat broadly pinnate-lobed or pinnate-divided fronds to 2 m tall and to 1 m wide**. Mature fronds arise from a short stalk (stipe) that is sometimes hidden by a ± **spiral, lengthwise-folded spore-producing region** (sporophyll) **that resembles a blade**. Frond surfaces are randomly dotted with numerous small black pores (cryptostomata). Japanese kelp has an extended period of spore production and can release millions of motile spores (zoospores) that can remain active and motile for up to 2 days. It rapidly colonizes open or disturbed substrates and floating objects, including boats, where it can be dispersed long distances. Japanese kelp is adapted to temperate water temperatures and may be able to displace certain native kelp species in California coastal waters. Once spores attached to a substrate it can take 2 to 3 months before they become large enough to see (1–2 cm long recruit) and another 4 weeks to reach reproductive maturity. Although growth rates can be as rapid as 55 cm per week in late summer (September), they average about 4 cm per week. Japanese kelp typically inhabits the upper region of the sublittoral zone, from the low tide mark to ± 15 m deep, and it generally found in harbors and sheltered locations, growing on natural or artificial substrates. In some areas along the California coast, heavy grazing by the kelp crab (*Pugettia producta*) from February to June can reduce its survival, but in other areas little grazing has been observed. Japanese kelp was introduced from Japan, but it is also native to Southeast Asia. In Japan it is used as a food source, where it is a common ingredient of miso soup. It has been introduced to the coastal waters of France, Britain, Belgium, Spain, Italy, Argentina, and Australia, but it is most problematic in New Zealand. Along the west coast of North America it was first discovered in Ensenada, Mexico, in the late 1990s or 2000 and has since been discovered in several areas off the California coast, including Santa Catalina Island (42 km west of Los Angeles), Channel Islands (near Ventura), Santa Barbara, and Monterey Bay.

Wakame (*Undaria pinnatifida*) mature fronds with smaller recruit.

K. A. MILLER

Caulerpa taxifolia frond, branches, and rootlike structures.　　　　J. K. CLARK

Wakame (*Undaria pinnatifida*) mature frond attached to sea bed.

K. A. MILLER

Chara (*Chara* spp.)
Nitella (*Nitella* spp.)

SYNONYMS:

Chara: muskgrass; stonewort

Nitella: brittlewort; stonewort

GENERAL INFORMATION: Anchored green algae with whorled, branchlike filaments at the nodes of a central axis, to 30 cm long or more. Several species occur in various regions of the western United States. All are native. Chara and nitella provide food and cover for wildlife and are important components of natural aquatic ecosystems. These algae sometimes grow in rice fields and canals but are rarely of importance as weeds. At first glance, chara and nitella are easily mistaken for vascular aquatic plants.

MATURE PLANT: Submersed, anchored, fragments suspended. **Central axes regularly jointed, solid between nodes, with whorls of branches at each node.** Branches **simple,** sometimes with whorls or clusters of tiny bractlike branches at nodes (chara), or **forked 1 or more times** (nitella). **Leaves lacking.** *Chara* species

Cross-section of main stem of *Chara globularis* showing whorled arrangement of branches and sporangia.   J. K. CLARK

Chara sp. branches and reproductive structures.
J. K. CLARK

are typically coarse, gray-green, sometimes encrusted with carbonates, making plants rough to touch, and often have a garlic or skunklike odor. *Nitella* species are usually dark green, ± delicate, never encrusted with carbonates, and lack an unpleasant odor.

ROOTLIKE STRUCTURES: Plants are usually anchored to the substrate by well-developed, colorless rhizoids.

REPRODUCTIVE STRUCTURES: Minute, egg-containing structures (oogonia) are ellipsoid, sperm-containing structures (antheridia) are round. Oogonia develop at the nodes. Antheridia develop at the nodes below the oogonia in chara and at the ends of short branches within branch clusters in nitella.

Chara zeylonica stem section.

J. K. CLARK

HABITAT: Ponds, lakes, reservoirs, rivers, streams, bogs, canals, and rice fields. Some species inhabit brackish water. Chara often grows in hard water.

DISTRIBUTION: Throughout North America.

PROPAGATION AND PHENOLOGY: Reproduce vegetatively from fragmentation and sexually by egg cells and motile sperm. After fertilization, the zygote (oospore) remains dormant for a period before germination occurs.

SIMILAR SPECIES: Unlike vascular aquatic plants, chara and nitella **lack leaves** and have **solid, regularly jointed central axes** with **whorls of simple or forked branches at each node**.

Nitella sp. stem section.   J. K. CLARK

Nitella furcata stem section.   J. M. DiTOMASO

Nitella clavata stem section.   J. M. DiTOMASO

Nitella flexilis stem section.   J. K. C<small>LARK</small>

Nitella gracilis stem section.   J. K. C<small>LARK</small>

Cladophora (*Cladophora* spp.)
Rhizoclonium (*Rhizoclonium* spp.)

GENERAL INFORMATION: Common **filamentous green algae** that typically anchor to a substrate with rhizoidlike filaments. Cladophora often forms long, trailing mats. Rhizoclonium grows entangled with other algal species or forms short, thick mats. Both can become abundant under eutrophic conditions.

MATURE PLANT: Cells of filaments **cylindrical** (rectangular in longitudinal section), joined end to end, of **uniform size and shape**, contain **few to many nuclei.** Cell walls often thick and distinctly layered. Chloroplasts consist of **interconnected thickenings that form a netlike (reticulate) pattern.**

Cladophora: Filaments **branched, often treelike.** Branches **often branched again, usually consist of more than 1 cell**, usually directed toward the plant body apex.

Rhizoclonium: Filaments delicate, **unbranched or few-branched.** Branches **short, not branched again, often consist of 1 cell, usually spreading or curved toward the filament base.**

HABITAT: Ponds, lakes, rivers, streams, canals, and ditches. Both groups grow in still or flowing waters and often inhabit alkaline, saline, or eutrophic waters. Cladophora is common in fast-flowing water.

DISTRIBUTION: Throughout the United States and much of the world.

PROPAGATION AND PHENOLOGY: Reproduce vegetatively by fragmentation and by swimming zoospores, each with 2 or 4 flagella.

Cladophora infestation in a pond.   J. M. DITOMASO

SIMILAR SPECIES: There are numerous species of filamentous green algae, many of which can be problematic under certain conditions. However, cladophora and rhizoclonium are among the most common with all of the following characteristics: unbranched or branched filaments that consist of **uniform cylindrical cells, more than 1 nucleus per cell, chloroplasts that form a netlike or reticulate pattern, and zoospores with 2 or 4 flagella.**

Cladophora infestation.   G. SAINTY

Microscopic view of *Rhizoclonium* sp.   J. A. SONNEMAN

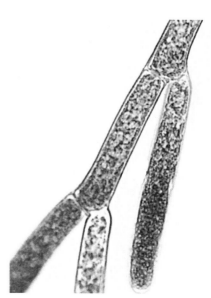

Microscopic view of *Cladophora* sp.   J. A. SONNEMAN

Anabaena (*Anabaena* spp.)
Nostoc (*Nostoc* spp.)

GENERAL INFORMATION: Widespread **filamentous blue-green algae** (cyanobacteria). Anabaena and nostoc species are sometimes troublesome in ponds, lakes, and other controlled aquatic systems when conditions lead to large blooms. Both groups fix atmospheric nitrogen; thus, blooms often occur when phosphate levels are high. Certain free-floating anabaena species produce a highly **toxic** cocainelike alkaloid. Animals and humans that drink water with a large algal bloom of toxic anabaena species can develop moderate to fatal respiratory and gastrointestinal problems.

MATURE PLANT: Both groups have short, **unbranched filaments**. Cells **lack a distinct nucleus and chloroplasts** and have a blue-green, gray, purplish, or brownish pigment distributed throughout the cells, often more dense near the cell walls.

Anabaena: Filaments straight, curved, or coiled, consist of **bead- or barrel-shaped cells randomly interspersed with usually solitary, conspicuously larger, differently shaped cells** (heterocysts). Filaments exist singly and free-floating or attached to a substrate, or in **soft, slimy** (mucilaginous) **colonies without a distinct shape** and attached to a substrate.

Nostoc: Filaments curved or contorted, consist of **bead-shaped cells randomly interspersed with usually solitary, slightly larger, paler cells with thicker cell walls**. Filaments always exist within **elastic, gelatinous colonies that are**

Anabaena sp. infestation in a pond.   G. SAINTY

74

enclosed within a firm skin or tegument and have a distinct globular shape. Colonies are free-floating or attached to a substrate and vary in size from microscopic to ± 10 cm diameter. Small colonies often form minute free-floating blue-green balls.

HABITAT: Ponds, lakes, ditches, slow-flowing canals, rivers, and streams. Nostoc attached to a substrate can grow in faster flowing water than anabaena.

DISTRIBUTION: Throughout the United States and most of the world.

PROPAGATION AND PHENOLOGY: Reproduce by cell division (fission) and by spores.

SIMILAR SPECIES: There are numerous species of freshwater algae, including blue-green algae. Other species can also be problematic on occasion. However, anabaena and nostoc are among the most common associated with algae blooms. Of the many blue-green algae species, only *Anabaena* and *Nostoc* species have **unbranched filaments that consist of bead- or barrel-shaped cells randomly interspersed with usually solitary, larger, differently shaped cells.**

Microscopic view of *Anabaena* sp.   G. SAINTY

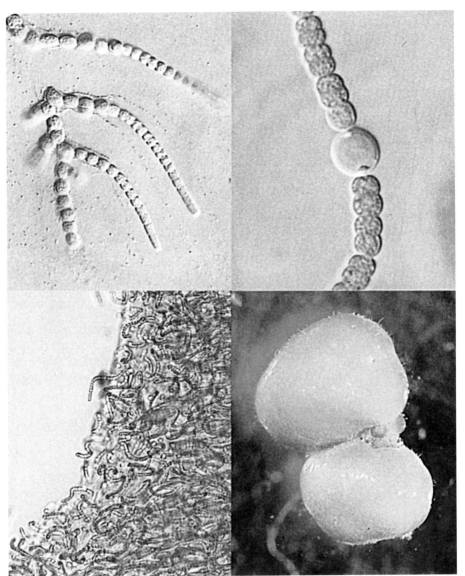

Microscopic views of *Nostoc* sp.

J. A. Sonneman

Ferns, Monocots, and Dicots

Coontail (*Ceratophyllum demersum* L.) [CEYDE]

SYNONYMS: hornwort; *Ceratophyllum apiculatum* Cham.; *Ceratophyllum asperum* Lam.; *Ceratophyllum cornutum* Rich. ex S.F. Gray; *Ceratophyllum demersum* L. vars. *apiculatum* (Cham.) Asch. and *oxyacanthum* (Cham.) K. Schum.; *Ceratophyllum oxyacanthum* Cham.; *Ceratophyllum tricuspidatum* Dumort.; *Ceratophyllum tuberculatum* Cham.; *Ceratophyllum unicorne* Dumort.; *Dichotophyllum demersum* (L.) Moench.

GENERAL INFORMATION: Submersed annual to perennial with firm, forked bottle-brush-like leaves and stems to 2.5 m long. Plants lack roots and exist free-floating or anchored to the substrate by specialized buried stems. Coontail is considered a native in many areas of the world. In natural areas, plants provide food and shelter for wildlife and are a desirable component of aquatic habitats. However, plants may develop dense subsurface mats in high-nutrient waters, channels, and controlled aquatic systems. Mats can inhibit water flow, block intake screens of water pumps, interfere with recreational activities, and create mosquito habitat. Plants are sometimes sold as an aquarium or pond ornamental.

SEEDLING: Young seedlings detach from the soil substrate when stems are ± 8 cm long.

MATURE PLANT: Stems slender, branched, with only 1 branch per node, usually fragment easily. Leaves **sessile**, (3)5–12-**whorled** at nodes, 1–2.5 cm long, ± **firm**, **filament-like**, mostly **forked 2–3 times**, olive-green to dark green. Margins **conspicuously small-toothed**. Turions (overwintering buds) consist of dense clusters of ± scalelike leaves at the stem tips.

ROOTS AND UNDERGROUND STRUCTURES: Roots are lacking in mature plants and embryos. Specialized buried stems (rhizoid shoots) anchor plants and are finely divided. Plants absorb nutrients directly from the water.

FLOWERS: June–October. Flowers submerged, sessile, ± 1 mm long, **solitary in 1 leaf axil per whorl, unisexual, male and female flowers develop on the same plant** (monoecious). Perianth parts thin, 8–13, linear, fused at the base. Stamens 5–20(30). Ovary superior, 1-chambered, with a persistent style. Water-pollinated. Anthers detach and float just below the water surface before releasing pollen, which sinks down to the female flowers below. Pollination is most likely to occur in still water.

FRUITS AND SEEDS: Fruits achene- or nutlike, dark, ellipsoid, ± 5 mm long, with a persistent spinelike style at the apex and often with 2 spines at the base. Fruit surface smooth to tubercled. Fruits do not open to release the single seed.

HABITAT: Ponds, slow-flowing streams, and ditches. Temperate to tropical regions. Tolerates low light levels and some turbidity but not salinity. Grows best in high-nutrient water, 2.5–5 m deep, with a neutral to slightly alkaline pH and at a temperature of ± 30°C.

DISTRIBUTION: Throughout the United States, including all western states. Throughout California to 2000 m. Nearly worldwide.

PROPAGATION AND PHENOLOGY: Reproduces vegetatively by turions and stem fragments and by seed. Fruits and turions sink to the bottom when separated from the parent plant. Fruits and vegetative parts disperse to greater distances with water or substrate movement, human activities, and by clinging to the fur, feathers, or feet of animals. In cold-winter areas, plants typically develop turions and few to no seeds. Plants remain green and typically sink to the bottom over win-

Coontail (*Ceratophyllum demersum*) plants.

W. J. McHenry

ter. In warm-temperate to subtropical regions, plants continue to grow slowly through winter and produce seeds and turions. Seeds subjected to a short dry period appear to have increased germination when conditions become favorable. Seeds and turions germinate in spring.

SIMILAR SPECIES: Fanwort or cabomba (*Cabomba caroliniana* A. Gray) [CABCA] is a **submersed rooted to free-floating perennial** in the watershield family (Cabombaceae). Unlike coontail, fanwort has **opposite** leaves on **short stalks** and **without toothed margins**. Submersed leaves are **palmately dissected** and **fan-shaped**. Sometimes a few small floating leaves develop when plants flower. Floating leaves are 1–3 cm long, ± narrowly elliptic, with the stem attached at the center (peltate) and one end shallowly forked. Fanwort inhabits tropical to

Coontail (*Ceratophyllum demersum*) stem section.   J. K. CLARK

temperate regions, grows rooted in the substrate or free-floating, and grows best in slightly acidic water. Fanwort occurs in southwestern Washington, Oregon, and California in the Sacramento River Delta, to 50 m deep. It is designated as a B list noxious weed in Washington and Oregon. This species has not been reported in California floras and has recently been designated a Q list noxious weed. Fanwort is commonly utilized as an aquarium ornamental and is considered a noxious weed in parts of Australia. Introduced from the eastern United States, often with discarded aquarium contents.

Cross-section of coontail (*Ceratophyllum demersum*) stem with whorled, branched, and toothed leaves.   W. J. McHENRY

Coontail (*Ceratophyllum demersum*) male flowers in leaf axil.   J. M. DiTOMASO

Marshweed (*Limnophila ×ludoviciana*) is a very uncommon submerged aquatic in the family Scrophulariaceae. It closely resembles fanwort and can be distinguished by having whorled leaves similar to coontail. Unlike coontail, it lacks the toothed margins on the leaf division. Marshweed was introduced from Asia and is found only in irrigation ditches of rice fields in Butte County, California.

Eurasian watermilfoil (*Myriophyllum spicatum* L.) [MYPSP] and **northern water-milfoil** (*Myriophyllum sibiricum* V. Komarov) [MYPSE] may also be confused

Fanwort (*Cabomba caroliniana*) in a pond.   D.W. KRATVILLE

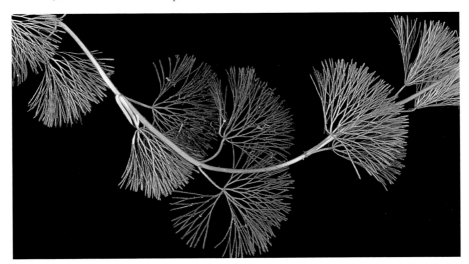

Fanwort (*Cabomba caroliniana*) stem section.   J. K. CLARK

Marshweed *(Limnophila* ×*ludoviciana)* stem section.   J. K. CLARK

Marshweed *(Limnophila* ×*ludoviciana)* infestation in a rice irrigation ditch.   J. M. DITOMASO

with coontail. Eurasian and northern watermilfoil are distinguished by having **pinnate-dissected leaves**. Refer to the **Parrotfeather** and **Eurasian Watermilfoil** entry (page 86) for more information.

White waterbuttercup (*Ranunculus aquatilis* L. [RANTR]) is a rooted to free-floating, ± mat-forming **submersed native perennial** in the buttercup family (Ranunculaceae) that is sometimes weedy in irrigation ditches. Unlike the other species described above, white waterbuttercup has **alternate** fan-shaped dissected

Dense population of white waterbuttercup (*Ranunculus aquatilis*) in a stream.   J. M. DiTomaso

Dissected leaves and flowers of white waterbuttercup (*Ranunculus aquatilis*).   J. M. DiTomaso

leaves. Flowers are floating or emergent and consist of 5 sepals, 5 white petals with or without a yellow base, numerous pistils, and 10 or more stamens. White waterbuttercup occurs in all western states and throughout California, except in deserts and on the Channel Islands, to 2900 m. White waterbuttercup is composed of a complex of intergrading varieties or subspecies that occur throughout much of North America. Botanists have interpreted the relationships within the complex in many ways, leading to much taxonomic confusion.

Dissected leaves and flower of white waterbuttercup (*Ranunculus aquatilis*).   J. M. DITOMASO

White waterbuttercup (*Ranunculus aquatilis*) seeds.   J. K. CLARK

Parrotfeather (*Myriophyllum aquaticum* (Vell. Conc.) Verdc.) [MYPBR]

Eurasian watermilfoil (*Myriophyllum spicatum* L.) [MYPSP]

NOXIOUS WEED LISTS:

Parrotfeather: Washington: B list, Wetland & Aquatic Weed Quarantine; CalEPPC: B

Eurasian watermilfoil: Oregon: B list; Washington: B list, Wetland & Aquatic Weed Quarantine; CalEPPC: A-1

SYNONYMS:

Parrotfeather: Brazilian watermilfoil; parrotfeather watermilfoil; thread-of-life; *Enydria aquatica* Vell.; *Myriophyllum brasiliense* Cambess.; *Myriophyllum proserpinacoides* Gillies ex Hook. & Arn.

Eurasian watermilfoil: spike watermilfoil

GENERAL INFORMATION: Noxious perennials with **rhizomes** and **finely dissected whorled submersed leaves**. Both species can develop colonies that form large subsurface or surface mats. Mats impede water flow, interfere with boat traffic and recreational activities, create mosquito habitat, and displace native aquatic vegetation.

Parrotfeather: Plants usually **emersed** with stems to 5 m long, sometimes semi-terrestrial on mud banks. Mats sometimes detach and become floating. Parrotfeather primarily inhabits warm temperate to tropical regions nearly worldwide and is not as widespread as Eurasian watermilfoil. Introduced from South America as an aquarium plant and pond ornamental in the late 1800s or early 1900s.

Eurasian watermilfoil: Plants typically **submersed** with stems to 4(7) m long, becoming **emersed only while flowering** or after stream or canal drawdown when moisture is still present. Unlike submersed leaves, **emersed leaves are bractlike**, developing just below each whorl of flowers. Eurasian watermilfoil primarily inhabits temperate regions in the Northern Hemisphere but also occurs in some subtropical to tropical areas. It is a serious aquatic weed in numerous countries and is also a state-listed noxious weed in Florida, North and South Carolina, and South Dakota. Eurasian watermilfoil can successfully compete with hydrilla (*Hydrilla verticillata* (L.f.) Royle) in freshwater. Its introduction is unclear; it has been suggested that it was accidentally introduced to the Chesapeake Bay area in the late 1800s from Eurasia and northern Africa, probably with shipping ballast. However, more recent information indicates that early identifications were probably the native northern watermilfoil (*Myriophyllum sibiricum* V. Komarov) and that Eurasian watermilfoil was actually first introduced near Maryland around 1942, possibly through the aquarium trade.

SEEDLING: Seedlings rarely encountered.

Parrotfeather (*Myriophyllum aquaticum*) infestation in an irrigation canal.   J. M. DiTomaso

Parrotfeather: Only populations within the native range have been observed to develop seeds.

Eurasian watermilfoil: Cotyledons narrowly linear, ± 12 mm long, tips rounded. First leaves opposite, dissected into 3 narrowly linear divisions, short-stalked. Subsequent leaves pinnately dissected into narrowly linear divisions. First and subsequent leaves ± 8 mm long.

MATURE PLANT: Foliage glabrous. Stems simple or branched, fragment easily, root at lower nodes. Submersed leaves 3–6-whorled per node, **pinnately dissected into linear lobes.** The number of lobe divisions per leaf and lobe thickness is often used to distinguish species. However, this characteristic is highly variable, depending on environmental conditions.

Parrotfeather: Stems light gray-green to reddish, to 5 mm in diameter at the base. **Emersed leaves resemble submerged leaves but are slightly thicker and not as finely dissected.** Leaves typically **light gray-green,** mostly 5–6-whorled, 1.5–3(4) cm long, with a **flattened midrib** that is broader than the lobes. Lobes alternate to opposite, typically 20–30 per leaf, to 7 mm long.

Eurasian watermilfoil: Regionally variable. Stems mostly branch near the water surface. Stems and growing tips often red-tinged. Internodes on mature portions of stems often 2–3 cm long. Submersed leaves usually 4-whorled, 1–3 cm long, midrib ± equal in width to the lobes, dark green to brown. Lobes mostly **opposite,** usually **more than 28 (14 pairs) per leaf,** to 10 mm long. Emersed leaves **develop only below flower whorls** (see below). Unlike northern watermilfoil (*Myriophyllum sibiricum*), **Eurasian watermilfoil does not develop turions** (specialized buds with toughened leaves that survive through winter) in fall.

ROOTS AND UNDERGROUND STRUCTURES: Rhizomes creeping, branched, produce numerous fibrous roots at nodes. Stems develop fine adventitious roots at lower nodes and on stem fragments.

FLOWERS: Flowers mostly unisexual. Sepals, petals 4. Female flowers lack petals. Stigmas 4. Male flowers have ephemeral petals and a vestigial ovary. Stamens 8. Mode of pollination controversial. Wind- and/or insect-pollination may be important.

Parrotfeather: Spring–early summer, mostly April–July. **Male and female flowers develop on separate plants** (dioecious). Cultivated and naturalized plants are typically female in California and elsewhere. Flowers **solitary in the axils** of middle to upper submersed and emersed leaves. Sepals translucent-white, ± 1.5 mm long. Female flowers sessile, ± 1.5 mm long. Stigmas white, feathery (plumose). Male flowers usually short-stalked, with petals ± 4 mm long.

Eurasian watermilfoil: June–September. **Male and female flowers develop on the same plant** (monoecious). **Spikes terminal, emersed,** initially erect, 4–8 cm long. Flowers pinkish, whorled, with **emersed bractlike leaves just below each whorl.** Bractlike leaves opposite, **1–3 mm long,** lanceolate, smooth-margined to finely toothed. Upper flowers male, lower female. Transitional flowers sometimes bisexual. Stigmas and petals of male flowers pinkish. Stigmas mature before stamens. **Stems below spikes nearly double in thickness** and **bend to position spikes horizontally** on the water surface as fruits mature. Stem nodes of spikes often have dark hydathodes (minute subsurface glandlike structures that passively secrete water).

Parrotfeather (*Myriophyllum aquaticum*) in a canal.   J. M. DiTOMASO

FRUITS AND SEEDS: Fruits 4-ribbed or grooved, ultimately break apart into 4 one-seeded nutlets.

Parrotfeather: Fruits narrowly ovoid, ± 2 mm long. Fruits are not known to develop in California and most other places where plants have been introduced.

Parrotfeather (*Myriophyllum aquaticum*) stem section with female flowers.   J. M. DiTOMASO

Eurasian watermilfoil (*Myriophyllum spicatum*) infestation in a pond.　　　J. M. DiTomaso

Eurasian watermilfoil (*Myriophyllum spicatum*) stems.
W. J. McHenry

Inflorescence of Eurasian watermilfoil
(*Myriophyllum spicatum*). J. M. DiTomaso

Eurasian watermilfoil: Fruiting spikes horizontal. Fruits nearly spherical, 2–3 mm long, surface roughened with projections. At maturity, fruits detach and float for a period before sinking.

HABITAT: Ponds, lakes, rivers, streams, canals, and ditches. Usually in still or slow-moving water, but occasionally found in faster-moving water of streams and rivers.

Parrotfeather: Grows best in tropical regions, can survive freezing conditions by becoming dormant. Typically grows in shallow water (to 1.5 m deep). Tolerates soft to very hard water and a pH range of 5.5–9. Does not tolerate brackish water. Requires high light conditions.

Eurasian watermilfoil: Inhabits a wide range of environmental conditions. Often grows in hard alkaline water to 3 m deep, but can grow in water up to 8 m deep if it is very clear with high light penetration. Tolerates a broad pH range (5.4–11), brackish water, and sandy to acid-peat substrates. Plants either die back to the root crowns over winter or remain green.

DISTRIBUTION:

Parrotfeather: Arizona, Idaho, Washington west of the Cascade Range, Oregon, and California in the North Coast, Cascade Range foothills, central-western region, and South Coast, to 500 m. Southern and eastern United States.

Eurasian watermilfoil: Probably occurs in every state except possibly South Dakota. Most recently it was discovered in Colorado. In California it is found in

Cross-section of Eurasian watermilfoil (*Myriophyllum spicatum*) stem. Note leaf segments >28.

J. K. CLARK

Northern watermilfoil (*Myriophyllum sibiricum*) flowering in a pond.   J. M. DiTOMASO

Cross-section of northern watermilfoil (*Myriophyllum sibiricum*) stem (two smaller sections on right) and Eurasian watermilfoil (*Myriophyllum spicatum*) stem (larger section on left). Note leaf segments <26 on northern watermilfoil.   J. M. DiTOMASO

the central-western region, San Joaquin Valley, and southern Sacramento Valley, and both the California and Nevada sides of Lake Tahoe, to 150 m.

PROPAGATION AND PHENOLOGY: Reproduce vegetatively by rhizomes, stem fragments, and axillary buds. Stem fragments disperse with water, by clinging to the feet or feathers of water birds, and with human activities such as boating, mechanical harvesting, and the dumping of unwanted pond or aquarium contents.

Parrotfeather: Propagates only vegetatively. Stem fragments form new roots and shoots. Can tolerate salt concentrations as high as 3000 ppm.

Eurasian watermilfoil: Axillary buds detach readily. In the field, reproduction by seed appears to be insignificant relative to vegetative reproduction. Some populations produce many seeds, but seedlings are rarely observed. Mature nutlets have a hard inner layer (stony endocarp) that must rupture or decompose before germination can occur. Thus, seeds typically have a prolonged dormancy period. However, freshly matured seeds collected in Tennessee germinated readily under laboratory conditions. Seeds germinate at temperatures above ± 10°C. Light increases germination. Seeds can survive at least 7 years under dry conditions. Seeds are consumed by waterfowl and may disperse to great distances with migrating birds.

MANAGEMENT FAVORING OR DISCOURAGING SURVIVAL: Repeated mechanical harvesting can help reduce stem densities, but escaped stem fragments can drift elsewhere and develop into new plants. Removing and destroying stem fragments from recreational equipment, such as boat propellers, docking lines, and fishing gear, can help prevent the spread of non-native watermilfoils. Unlike parrotfeather, Eurasian watermilfoil is more easily controlled by several aquatic herbicides.

SIMILAR SPECIES: Whorled watermilfoil (*Myriophyllum verticillatum* L.) and western watermilfoil (*Myriophyllum hippuroides* Torrey & A. Gray) are native species that are rarely weedy. They both have submerged and emerged leaves but unlike parrotfeather the emerged leaves are bright green and not glaucous. The relationship of Eurasian watermilfoil and northern watermilfoil or Siberian watermilfoil (*Myriophyllum sibiricum* V. Komarov, synonyms: short-spike watermilfoil; *Myriophyllum exalbescens* Fern.; *Myriophyllum spicatum* L. ssp. *exalbescens*) [MYPSE] has been controversial. Past treatments have included the two taxa as subspecies of the same species, but more recent treatments considered the two to be distinct. Northern watermilfoil is a widespread native of North America, including California, and northern areas of Eurasia. Eurasian and northern watermilfoil can be difficult to distinguish. Populations may intergrade in areas where both species occur, and plants with intermediate characteristics occur in California and elsewhere. In North America, Eurasian watermilfoil is typically more common than northern watermilfoil. Keys separating the two species often indicate that North American northern watermilfoil is distinguished by having submersed leaves with 26 lobes (13 pairs) or fewer to 15 mm long, whereas Eurasian watermilfoil has greater than 28 lobes (14 pairs) to 10 mm long. These characteristics are not always consistent and are often unreliable. Northern watermilfoil often develops **turions** in fall and has flower spike stems that **lack or have no more than 2 indistinct, brown or black scales at the inflorescence nodes** and **remain slender** and **erect near the water surface.** In contrast, Eurasian watermilfoil **does not produce turions** and has **flower spike stems that**

Emergent stem of western watermilfoil (*Myriophyllum hippuroides*), a native plant not considered weedy.   J. M. DiTomaso

have 2–3 distinct black scales at the inflorescence nodes and curve to lie parallel to the water surface. Northern watermilfoil occurs in all western states. In California it occurs in the Cascade Range, Klamath Ranges, North Coast, northern Sierra Nevada, Great Basin region, San Francisco Bay region, Central Coast, San Joaquin Valley, and southern Mojave Desert (Mojave River), to 2600 m.

Coontail (*Ceratophyllum demersum* L.) [CEYDE] and fanwort or cabomba (*Cabomba caroliniana* A. Gray) [CABCA] [Washington: B list, California: Q list] are rooted or free-floating submersed aquatic plants that may be confused with the watermilfoils. Coontail is a widespread native annual to perennial that occurs in all western states and is distinguished by having dissected whorled leaves that are evenly forked 2–3 times with conspicuous small teeth along some margins. Fanwort is a perennial with opposite submersed leaves that are palmately dissected and on short stalks. Fanwort occurs in Washington, Oregon, and California in the Sacramento River Delta. It was introduced from the eastern United States. Refer to the Coontail entry (page 78) for more information about coontail and fanwort.

Hydrilla (*Hydrilla verticillata* (L.f.) Royle) [HYLLI]

Brazilian egeria (*Egeria densa* Planch.) [ELDDE]

Common elodea (*Elodea canadensis* L. C. Rich.) [ELDCA]

NOXIOUS WEED LISTS:

Hydrilla: Federal Noxious Weed; California: A list; Oregon: A list; Washington: A list, Wetland & Aquatic Weed Quarantine; Arizona: Prohibited Noxious Weed; CalEPPC: Red Alert

Brazilian egeria: Oregon: B list; Washington: B list, Wetland & Aquatic Weed Quarantine; CalEPPC: A-2

SYNONYMS:

Hydrilla: Florida elodea; waterthyme; *Elodea verticillata* (L.f.) F. Muell.; *Hydrilla lithuanica* (Andrz. ex Besser) Dandy; *Serpicula verticillata* L.f.

Brazilian egeria: egeria; Brazilian elodea; Brazilian waterweed; common waterweed; dense waterweed; leafy elodea; South American waterweed; *Anacharis densa* (Planch.) Victorin; *Elodea densa* (Planch.) Caspary; *Philotria densa* (Planch.) Small & St. John

Common elodea: American elodea; broad waterweed; Canadian pondweed; Canadian waterweed; *Anacharis canadensis* (Michx.) Planch.; *Anacharis canadensis* var. *planchonii* (Caspary) Victorin; *Elodea brandegae* St. John; *Elodea ioensis* Wylie; *Elodea linearis* (Rydb.) St. John; *Elodea planchonii* Caspary; *Philotria canadensis* (Michx.) Britt.; *Philotria linearis* Rydb.

GENERAL INFORMATION: Submerged aquatic perennials. Plants are genetically variable and highly plastic depending on environmental conditions. Stems typically grow rooted in the substrate but fragment easily into free-floating pieces that root at nodes. Fragments can start new colonies when carried elsewhere. Brazilian egeria and hydrilla can aggressively invade new aquatic environments, displace native aquatic vegetation by forming dense stands or large subsurface mats, and alter the dynamics of aquatic ecosystems. Other detrimental and economic impacts from heavy infestations can include water flow impediment in waterways, increased flooding, clogged pumps and boat propellers, and reduced use of lakes and waterways for fishing and other recreational activities.

Hydrilla: Noxious. Many biotypes exist, including monoecious and dioecious types. Both monoecious and female dioecious populations occur in California. Hydrilla occurs in tropical to temperate regions on all continents except Antarctica. Plants develop overwintering tubers in the soil substrate, and stem shoots form specialized perennating buds enclosed by tough leaf scales (**turions**). Native to the warmer regions of Asia and possibly central Africa. Introduced to the west coast of Florida in 1958.

Brazilian egeria: Dioecious. Populations in the United States consist only of male plants. Brazilian egeria is more common than hydrilla in California, but is less

threatening from a management perspective. This is because a very active eradication program was initiated in 1976 to prevent the widespread distribution of
hydrilla. Brazilian egeria is commonly sold as aquarium décor under the name
egeria or anacharis. Plants can naturalize in warm-temperate to cool subtropical
regions when unwanted aquarium contents are released into lakes, ponds, or
waterways. Introduced from eastern South America.

Common elodea: Dioecious. Common elodea is native to North America, where
it is an important component of natural aquatic ecosystems. Populations are
rarely troublesome in natural habitats, but plants can become dominant in
altered or created aquatic systems, especially when bicarbonate, reduced iron,
and phosphorus are plentiful. It is widely distributed throughout the world and
considered a serious weed in Europe and Australia.

SEEDLING: Seldom encountered.

Hydrilla: Stalk below cotyledon (hypocotyl) lacking. Rootlets whorled.
Cotyledon sheath 2–5 mm long, glabrous, often whitish green with purplish
dots. Cotyledon blade lanceolate, 6–8 mm long, 1–2 mm wide, pinched in just
above the base (attenuate), margins smooth. Taproot and first leaves develop
simultaneously. First leaves compound. Leaflets 3–8, linear, 5–8 mm long,
0.5–1 mm wide, sessile, tips acute, margins minutely toothed.

MATURE PLANT: Leaves sessile, whorled, linear to lanceolate, often scalelike and
opposite on lower stems. The number of leaves per node is unreliable for species
identification of hydrilla and Brazilian egeria. Margins minutely toothed, visible
with low magnification.

Hydrilla: Leaves (3)4–8(12)-whorled. Middle and upper leaves often
5–8-whorled, **6–20 mm long**, 1–4 mm wide. Leaves below growing tips straight
or curved. **Toothed margins usually visible without magnification.** Lower

Hydrilla (*Hydrilla verticillata*) stem section with developing tubers.   J. K. CLARK

surface midveins smooth or minutely sharp-toothed. **Leaf axils have pairs of minute scales** (squamulae intravaginales) **up to 0.5 mm long, fringed with fingerlike orange-brown hairs,** usually visible with magnification on some mature leaves and branch points. Dioecious plants sometimes appear more robust than monoecious plants. Monoecious plants often branch freely near the substrate, producing many stolons and a forest of vertical shoots. Dioecious plants usually branch freely near the water surface, forming large submerged mats.

Brazilian egeria: Plants typically look larger and leafier than hydrilla or common elodea. Leaves 3–6(8)-whorled. Middle and upper leaves **15–40 mm long,** 2–5 mm wide. Leaves below growing tips often curved downward. Lower surface midvein smooth or minutely toothed.

Close-up of hydrilla (*Hydrilla verticillata*) stem segment with turions in the leaf axis.   J. K. CLARK

Cross-section of hydrilla (*Hydrilla verticillata*) stem.   J. K. CLARK

Stem turion of hydrilla (*Hydrilla verticillata*).   J. M. DiTOMASO

Common elodea: Leaves dark green, usually **peppered with large dark cells** (visible with low magnification). Middle and upper leaves typically opposite or 3-whorled, **6–15(20) mm long**, 1–5 mm wide. Leaves below growing tips often slightly curved downward. Lower surface midvein smooth.

ROOTS AND UNDERGROUND STRUCTURES: Roots slender, unbranched, in substrate grow to 20 cm long. Certain nodes on stems and stolons develop adventitious roots. Adventitious roots of hydrilla and common elodea typically develop only at nodes of dormant axillary buds or branches.

Hydrilla: Plants often produce a mat of creeping above- and belowground stolons that develop **subterranean structures at the tips** (referred to as tubers). Tubers are tough, whitish to brown-black, plump, ovoid, 4–15 mm long, typically to

Brazilian egeria (*Egeria densa*) infestation in a pond.   J. M. DiTomaso

Fully developed hydrilla (*Hydrilla verticillata*) tuber.
J. M. DiTomaso

15 cm deep in the substrate, remain attached until parent stolon decomposes. Dioecious tubers are usually larger than monoecious tubers.

Brazilian egeria: Adventitious roots and lateral branches grow only from double nodes (specialized nodes separated by a shortened internode) typically spaced along stems at 6–12 node intervals. Only fragments with a double node develop into new plants.

Common elodea: Roots in substrate are more wiry than those of hydrilla or Brazilian egeria. Nodes with axillary buds usually occur at ± 10 cm intervals.

FLOWERS: June–October. Female flowers extend to the water's surface on a long threadlike flower tube (hypanthium) several centimeters long from an axillary spathe (fused bracts). Petals, sepals, styles 3. Ovary inferior. Pistillate (female) flowers often have staminodes (sterile stamens).

Hydrilla: Sepals and petals translucent, white to reddish, **3–5 mm long,** staminate petals linear. Staminate and pistillate flowers **1 per spathe, found in axils, sessile, deciduous,** detach and float to surface. Stamens 3, explosively release pollen at water surface when mature. Staminodes minute (<1 mm long), clear or lacking. Wind-pollinated.

Brazilian egeria: Flowers commonly. **Flowers extend up to 3 cm above water surface. Nectaries shiny green,** 3-lobed, minute. Petals glossy white, broadly ovate, wrinkled. Sepals green, ± one-half petal length. Staminate flowers **2–5 per spathe, persistent.** Staminate petals mostly **7–12 mm long.** Stamens 9. Pistillate flowers 1 per spathe. Pistillate petals 5–8 mm long. Staminodes 1–3 mm long, yellow to red-orange, papillose. Insect-pollinated.

Common elodea: Flowers infrequently. Pistillate and staminate plants seldom grow in the same area. Some flowers bisexual. Staminate and pistillate flowers

Male flower of Brazilian egeria (*Egeria densa*).   J. M. DiTomaso

Brazilian egeria (*Egeria densa*) stem section.

1 per spathe, persistent. Sepals green, often purple-striated, ± equal to petals. Petals fragile, white, narrower than sepals. Staminate petals **3–6 mm long**. Stamens (7)9(18). Pistillate petals 2–4 mm long. Sterile stamens 1–2 mm long, greenish white to pale violet. Water-pollinated.

FRUITS AND SEEDS: Fruit production and seed set is typically low.

Hydrilla: Fruits lomentlike, narrowly cylindrical, 5–15 mm long, smooth or with few to several short to long irregular spines, do not open to release seeds. Seeds 1–5, ellipsoid, 2–3 mm long, smooth, brown.

Brazilian egeria: Fruits and seeds typically not produced in the western United States. Capsules ellipsoid, 7–15 mm long, 3–6 mm in diameter at widest part, thin-walled, translucent, open irregularly to release seeds. Seeds ellipsoid, 5–8 mm long, 2 mm wide, with a beak 3–4 mm long, covered with elongated papillae.

Common elodea: Capsules ellipsoid to ovoid, 5–7 mm long, 2–3 mm wide, with a beak 5–6 mm long, translucent, thin-walled, open irregularly to release seeds. Seeds ellipsoid, 4–6 mm long, with a short beak less than 1 mm long. Base of beak collared by wartlike cells.

OTHER VEGETATIVE REPRODUCTIVE STRUCTURES:

Hydrilla: Stem turions axillary, sometimes terminal on monoeicous plants under certain conditions, tough, green, conical to ovoid, 3–12 mm long, deciduous.

Brazilian egeria: Does not develop turions.

Common elodea: Stem turions terminal, appear as dense, dark green, leafy growing tips with nodes very close together, usually remain attached to parent stems.

POSTSENESCENCE CHARACTERISTICS: Plants decompose rapidly. Stems of Brazilian egeria and common elodea typically decline when water temperatures climb above 25°C. Hydrilla and Brazilian egeria stems usually die during periods of prolonged near-freezing temperatures. Common elodea may turn blackish and die back during the cold season or survive green and intact under ice in near-freezing conditions.

HABITAT: Slow-flowing or still water in ditches, sloughs, canals, rivers, ponds, lakes, and reservoirs; often in nutrient-rich substrates.

Hydrilla: Inhabits water 0.5–3(12) m deep. Grows at 10°–35°C. Tolerates low light and variable water quality, including brackish, turbid, and polluted water. Turions survive near freezing temperatures.

Brazilian egeria: Inhabits acidic to alkaline waters to 1–2(7) m deep. Highly susceptible to iron deficiency. Grows best under low light (optimal ± 100 lux) at 10°–25°C. Tolerates turbidity and short periods under ice. Does not survive prolonged periods of near freezing temperatures.

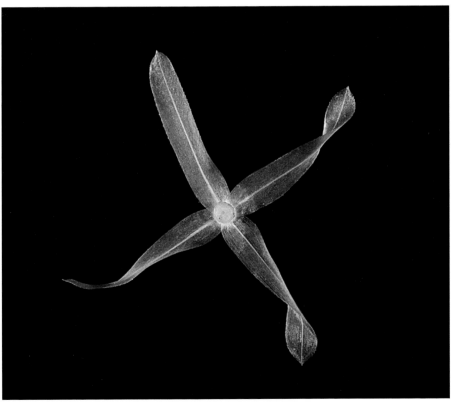

Cross-section of Brazilian egeria (*Egeria densa*) stem.   J. K. CLARK

Common elodea: Sometimes inhabits sheltered areas of fast-flowing streams. Grows best under high light in high-calcium to slightly brackish water, 10°–25°C, to 5 m deep. Tolerates some shade, little turbidity, and near freezing temperatures.

DISTRIBUTION:

Hydrilla: Washington in the Seattle area, Arizona, and California in the eastern North Coast Ranges (Clear Lake area, Lake Co.), Cascade Range (Shasta Lake area, Shasta Co.), north and central Sierra Nevada foothills (northwestern Yuba, central and northwestern Calaveras, southwestern Amador, northeastern San Joaquin, and central and northwestern Tulare Cos.), and Sonoran Desert (Imperial Valley, Imperial Co.), to 200 m. Southern United States and along the east coast as far north as Connecticut. Previous California infestations now eradicated in the Sacramento Valley (northern Sutter Co.), southern North Coast Ranges (central and eastern Sonoma Co.), San Francisco Bay region (northern San Mateo Co.), Central Coast (northwestern Monterey Co.), South Coast (southeastern Santa Barbara, southern Los Angeles, and western San Diego Cos.), and desert regions (west-central San Bernardino and central Riverside Cos.).

Brazilian egeria: Washington west of the Cascade Range, Oregon, Utah, Arizona, New Mexico, and California in the northern and southern Sierra Nevada foothills, San Joaquin Valley, San Francisco Bay region, southeastern Great Basin, and San Jacinto Mountains, to 2200 m. Much of United States, except some northern and midwestern states. Expected to expand range in California and probably elsewhere.

Common elodea: All western states. California in the western North Coast Ranges, high elevations of the Sierra Nevada and Cascade Range, Central Valley, San Francisco Bay region, and central and eastern Transverse Ranges (San Gabriel and San Bernardino Mtns.), to 2600 m. Most of United States.

PROPAGATION AND PHENOLOGY: All reproduce vegetatively. The only known location for seed production is in monoecious hydrilla populations in North Carolina. Vegetative parts disperse with flooding, waterfowl, and human activities, such as fishing and boating.

Hydrilla: Reproduces by stolons, stem fragments, stem turions, and subterranean tubers. Turion and tuber initiation, production, dormancy, and germination are variable, depending on the biotype and environmental conditions. A period of low temperatures often stimulates turion and tuber germination, especially in the monoecious biotype. Stem turions germinate before tubers in spring and have a similar temperature requirement as some native pondweeds. Tubers either remain dormant or germinate in spring when conditions become favorable. Stem turions mostly develop in late summer through fall as day length shortens, but dioecious plants may initiate turions in spring. Stem turions separate from the parent stem in late fall or at maturity. Monoecious plants often produce more turions than dioecious plants. Dense colonies usually develop fewer stem turions. Monoecious turions usually germinate readily and survive up to 4 years under field conditions. Tubers typically develop in midsummer through winter, but in monoecious plants they can form in spring. Monoecious plants often produce 50% or more tubers in a shorter period than dioecious plants, but dioecious tubers are often larger, more likely to remain dormant, and survive for longer periods. Under field conditions monoecious tubers survive for up to 5 years. Tubers can survive from only a few days to weeks under dry conditions. Tubers can survive ingestion and regurgitation by waterfowl and are resistant to most herbicides.

Brazilian egeria: Reproduces **by stolons** and **stem fragments.**

Common elodea: Reproduces **by stolons, stem fragments,** and **terminal stem turions.** Turions typically develop in fall and appear to lack a true dormancy period.

MANAGEMENT FAVORING OR DISCOURAGING SURVIVAL: Removing and destroying stem fragments from recreational equipment such as boat propellers, docking lines, and fishing gear can help prevent the spread of hydrilla and Brazilian egeria. Removing dense canopies of hydrilla by mechanical harvesting or herbicide treatment may stimulate turion germination. Sterile triploid grass carp consume hydrilla and are useful in aquatic systems where total removal of all submerged vegetation is acceptable.

Common elodea (*Elodea canadensis*) stem with flowering stalk.

J. K. CLARK

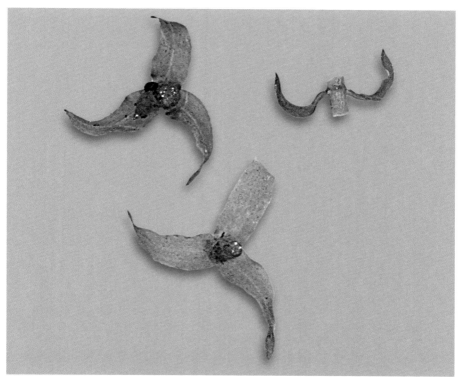

Cross-section of common elodea *(Elodea canadensis)* stem with 2 to 3 leaves per node.

J. M. DiTomaso

SIMILAR SPECIES: Grassy naiad (*Najas graminea* Raff.-Delile) and **southern naiad** (*Najas guadalupensis* (Spreng.) Magnus) are easily distinguished from the above species by having **sessile flowers** and ± whorled linear leaves **0.5–1 mm wide** with **sheathing bases** and that are mostly **crowded on short lateral branches.**

Southern naiad (*Najas guadalupensis* (Spreng.) Magnus) [NAIGU]

Synonyms: southern waternymph; *Caulinia guadalupensis* Spreng.; *Najas flexilis* (Willd.) Rostkov & Schmidt vars. *guadalupensis, curassavica* A.Br. and *fusiformis* Chapm.; *Najas guadalupensis* (Spreng.) Magnus vars. *floridana* Haynes & Wentz, *guadalupensis, olivacea* (Rosendahl & Butters) Haynes, and *muenscheri* (Clausen) Haynes; others

General Information: **Submersed annual** with stems to 0.6 m long and **opposite to subopposite leaves**. Plants grow rooted in the substrate. Detached parts can root in substrate or survive freely suspended in the water. Foliage is highly plastic, depending on environmental conditions. Several species in the genus are weedy and typically thrive in highly disturbed habitats. Populations can become locally dominant, forming dense submersed mats of vegetation. Foliage and seeds are an important food source for wildlife, especially shorebirds and waterfowl. The genus *Najas* is sometimes segregated into the naiad or waternymph family (Najadaceae). Some species are difficult to distinguish. Southern naiad is a common widespread native of North and South America. It is highly variable and appears to consist of ± 4 biotypes that have previously been segregated into varieties or species. The biotype described as *Najas guadalupensis* var. *guadalupensis* occurs throughout the United States. Southern naiad is usually not considered a weed in natural habitats, but it can become troublesome in ditches, human-made ponds, and disturbed or controlled aquatic systems.

Mature Plant: Foliage glabrous. Stems slender, highly branched, root at lower nodes. Leaves sessile, **opposite** to subopposite (appearing whorled), slightly expanded and **sheathing at the base**. Blades linear, flat, lax, 10–25 mm long, 0.5–1 mm wide. **Margins minutely toothed**, usually **visible with 10× magnification**. Leaves ± **evenly spaced along stems**, with straight tips. Sheaths **lack auricles**.

Roots and Underground Structures: Roots fibrous, slender, unbranched, develop at lower nodes. Stolons do not overwinter.

Flowers: July–October. **Male and female flowers develop on the same plant** (monoecious). Flowers inconspicuous, submersed, ± sessile, **solitary to few-clustered in the leaf axils**. Male flowers 2–3 mm long. Male flowers consist of 1 stamen with 2 minute bracts below and a 4-chambered anther. Female flowers 2–3 mm long. Female flowers lack perianth parts (sepals or petals) or have a single membranous sheathing perianth. Ovary 1, with 2–3 stigmas. Water-pollinated.

Fruits and Seeds: Fruits achene- or nutletlike, consist of a delicate wall closely enveloping a single seed. Seeds ± football-shaped (fusiform), 1–3 mm long, 0.5–1 mm wide. Surface dull, **finely reticulate-pitted** when viewed under magnification.

Habitat: Still or slow-moving water in a broad range of substrates. Ponds, lakes, reservoirs, canals, rice fields, and irrigation ditches. Grows at water depths of ± 1–4.5 m. Tolerates polluted water or slightly brackish water.

DISTRIBUTION: Throughout United States, including all western states. California in the western North Coast Ranges, Central Valley, central-western region, South Coast, and desert regions, to 1200 m. South America.

PROPAGATION AND PHENOLOGY: Reproduces **primarily by seed** and to some extent vegetatively from stem fragments.

SIMILAR SPECIES: Grassy naiad (*Najas graminea* Raff.-Delile, synonym: ricefield waternymph) [NAIGR] is a variable, nearly worldwide weed typically associated with rice fields and adjacent irrigation ditches in tropical to warm temperate regions. It is not native to the western United States and was introduced from tropical Asia. Grassy naiad reproduces vegetatively from **stolons** during the growing season. Unlike southern naiad, its leaves are mostly **clustered on short**

Southern naiad (*Najas guadalupensis*) infestation in a rice field irrigation ditch.   J. K. CLARK

Southern naiad (*Najas guadalupensis*) stem section.   J. K. CLARK

107

lateral branches and often appear whorled due to shortened internodes. Mature blades typically **curve backward** (recurved) at tip with **2 conspicuous triangular auricles** (sheath appendages) present at the base. Grassy naiad is uncommon and occurs in California in the Sacramento Valley to 150 m.

Hollyleaf naiad (*Najas marina* L., synonyms: spiny naiad or waternymph; *Najas latifolia* A.Br.; *Najas gracilis* (Morong) Small; *Najas major* All.) [NAIMA] is a variable, nearly worldwide native **annual** that inhabits fresh to brackish water marshes, ponds, lakes, slow-moving streams, canals, and irrigation systems. In some areas it can be an aggressive colonizing species that forms dense submersed mats. Unlike other *Najas* species in North America, hollyleaf naiad has stiff, **conspicuously prickle-toothed leaf blades 1–3 mm wide, stem internodes covered with minute prickles**, **male** and **female flowers on separate plants** (dioecious), and **seeds 1.2–2.2 mm wide**. Hollyleaf naiad occurs in Arizona, Nevada, New Mexico, Utah, and California in the North Coast Ranges, southern Sierra Nevada foothills, Central Coast, South Coast Ranges, South Coast, Peninsular Ranges, San Bernardino Mountains, and desert regions, to ± 1000 m. Plants usually produce abundant hard-coated seeds that persist in the seed bank. Some populations in Europe appear to lack male plants but still produce many seeds, suggesting that seeds may develop apomictically (without pollination).

Widgeongrass (*Ruppia* spp.), **horned pondweed** (*Zannichellia palustris* L.) [ZAIPA], and some pondweeds (*Potamogeton* spp.) may be confused with grassy or southern naiad. Unlike the naiads, widgeongrass has **mostly alternate leaves**

Fruit of southern naiad (*Najas guadalupensis*) in leaf axils.　　　　　　　　J. K. CLARK

Hollyleaf naiad (*Najas marina*) stem section.
J. M. DiTomaso

and **umbel-like fruiting heads on short to long stalks.** Horned pondweed and *Potamogeton* species have leaves with **smooth margins** and **free or sheathing stipules.** Refer to table 8 for a comparison of additional characteristics and to the **Pondweed, Widgeongrass,** and **Horned Pondweed** entries for more information.

Table 8. Submersed aquatic plants with linear leaves

Species	Life cycle	Leaf arrangement	Leaf margins	Leaf bases	Free stipules	Flowers
naiads (*Najas* spp.)	annual	opposite (to subopposite)	minute teeth (may require magnification)	sheathing	none	sessile in leaf axils, unisexual (monoecious, dioecious)
pondweeds (*Potamogeton* spp. and *Stuckenia* spp.)	perennial	alternate (to subopposite)	smooth	sheathing in some spp.	separate from stem or sheathing the stem above leaf base	emergent or floating spikes or heads, bisexual
widgeongrass (*Ruppia* spp.)	perennial	mostly alternate, some opposite	minute teeth (requires magnification)	sheathing	none	± sessile to short-stalked in leaf axils when in flower, umbel-like on a long stalk when in fruit, bisexual
horned pondweed (*Zannichellia palustris*)	perennial (sometimes annual)	mostly opposite, sometimes ± clustered at tips	smooth	not sheathing	sheathing the stem and leaf base	± sessile in leaf axils, unisexual (monoecious)

Yellow pondlily (*Nuphar polysepala* Engelm.) [NUPLP]

SYNONYMS: cow lily; Indian pond lily; Rocky Mountain pond-lily; spatterdock (used for most *Nuphar* spp.); wokas; *Nuphar lutea* (L.) Sm. ssp. *polysepala* (Engelm.) E.O. Beal; *Nuphar luteum* (L.) Sibth. & Sm. ssp. *polysepalum* (Engelm.) E. Beal; *Nymphaea polysepala* (Engelm.) E. Greene; *Nymphozanthus polysepalus* (Engelm.) Fern.

GENERAL INFORMATION: Native aquatic perennial with large ± floating leaves and creeping rhizomes. Yellow pondlily is usually a desirable component of natural aquatic ecosystems. Plants provide habitat and a food source for wildlife and shelter for fish. However, yellow pondlily can develop colonies from creeping rhizomes and become weedy in aquatic systems controlled for water use.

MATURE PLANT: Leaves floating to emersed or slightly submersed, oblong to ovate, 10–45 cm long, tip rounded (obtuse), base deeply heart-shaped. Lobes acute to rounded. Surface glabrous, glossy, pinnate-veined. Leaf stalks round in cross-section, can grow to a few meters long.

ROOTS AND UNDERGROUND STRUCTURES: Rhizomes horizontally creeping, branched, thick (to 5–6 cm), spongy, with numerous alternate buds, often develop an interwoven mat in the upper substrate and can increase the deposition of silt.

Yellow pondlily (*Nuphar polysepala* ssp. *polysepala*) in its native habitat.   J. M. DiTOMASO

FLOWERS: April–September. Flowers mostly emergent, ± spherical, 5–7 cm diameter, with a fragrance reminiscent of fermented fruit, on stalks up to 3 m long, closing at night. Sepals **7–12**, thick, **round to broadly (ob)ovate**, cupped, to 5 cm long. **Inner sepals yellow, petal-like. Outer sepals green. Petals stamenlike, ± equal in length to stamens.** Stamens and petals numerous, yellow to red-tinged. Anther slits open facing inward (introrse). **Ovary superior**, many-chambered, expanded at the apex into a **broad disk** with **15–25 dark slitlike stigmas radiating outward from the center.** Insect-pollinated.

FRUITS AND SEEDS: Fruits berrylike, yellow to greenish, spongy, ovoid to spherical, flattened at the apex, 3–4 cm in diameter, usually mature above the water surface. Sepals persist on fruits until decomposing. Seeds obovoid, 3–5 mm long, smooth, to 30 or more per fruit.

HABITAT: Freshwater ponds and slow-moving streams and canals. Usually grows in water 1–3 m deep. Tolerates some shade.

DISTRIBUTION: All western states. California in the northwestern region, central-western region, Modoc Plateau, north and central Sierra Nevada, to 2500 m.

PROPAGATION AND PHENOLOGY: Reproduces vegetatively from creeping rhizomes and **by seed.** Fruits disperse with water and animals. Foliage dies down in fall/winter and regrows from rhizomes in spring.

SIMILAR SPECIES: Watershield (*Brasenia schreberi* J.F. Gmelin) [BRASC] is a **native aquatic perennial** with **rhizomes** and **oval floating leaves** that somewhat resemble those of yellow pondlily and waterlilies (*Nymphaea* spp.). Unlike yellow pondlily and waterlilies, watershield has floating leaves that **lack basal lobes** and

Yellow pondlily (*Nuphar polysepala* ssp. *polysepala*) plant.   J. M. DiTomaso

are **joined to the stalk at the center** (peltate leaves). In addition, watershield has **maroon to purplish flowers** with **4–18 separate pistils** and anther slits open facing outward (extrorse). Submersed parts are covered with a thick layer of mucilage. Watershield occurs in Oregon, Washington, Idaho, Montana, and California in the northwestern region, Modoc Plateau, Sierra Nevada, and Sacramento Valley, to 2200 m. It is also found throughout the eastern half of the United States. Watershield is a dicot that was previously included within the waterlily family (Nymphaeaceae). However, most taxonomists now segregate it into the watershield family (Cabombaceae) based on floral characteristics.

Mexican waterlily (*Nymphaea mexicana* Zucc.) also has **yellow flowers** but is distinguishable from yellow pondlily by having **numerous lanceolate to elliptic petals that are larger than the stamens, 4 greenish sepals**, and a **partly inferior ovary** with **several curved, fingerlike stigmas at the apex**. Mexican waterlily leaves are **nearly round** to ovate. Refer to the **Mexican Waterlily** entry (page 114) for more information.

Yellow pondlily (*Nuphar polysepala* ssp. *polysepala*) flower.   J. M. DiTomaso

Watershield *(Brasenia schreberi)* in a pond.   G. SAINTY

Mexican waterlily (*Nymphaea mexicana* Zucc.) [NYMME]

NOXIOUS WEED LISTS: California: B

SYNONYMS: banana waterlily; yellow waterlily; *Castalia flava* (Leit.) Greene

GENERAL INFORMATION: Noxious aquatic perennial with **creeping stolons, horseshoe-shaped floating leaves**, and **showy yellow flowers**. Plants can rapidly colonize shallow waters. Heavy infestations can occur in still-water lakes, reservoirs, and ponds or very slow moving channels. Infestations can restrict water movement, contribute to siltation, increase water loss through high evapotranspiration rates, and hinder recreation activities. Introduced from southeastern United States and Mexico as an aquatic ornamental.

SEEDLING: **New plants develop from stolons before seedlings mature**. Early leaves are submerged. Cotyledons remain within seed coat. First leaf linear. Subsequent leaves narrowly arrowhead-shaped, 2–5 cm long. First floating leaves 2–3 cm long with similar shape as mature leaves.

MATURE PLANT: Leaves **floating** to emergent when crowded, **nearly round to horseshoe-shaped**, flat to cupped, narrowly cleft at the base with edges often overlapping, 10–25 cm wide. Leaf margins irregularly blunt-toothed. Upper surfaces glabrous, glossy bright green, often brown-blotched. Lower surfaces often deep red to purplish brown and black-spotted. Leaves usually die during winter. New spring leaves are submerged, narrowly arrowhead-shaped, ± 2–7 cm long.

ROOTS AND UNDERGROUND STRUCTURES: Dormant in the cool season. **Tubers vertical**, 2–30 cm long, 1.5–6 cm in diameter, covered with long light-colored hairs and persistent wartlike petiole bases, anchored by many fibrous roots. **Stolons creeping, white, ± 1 cm** in diameter, grow from the upper portions of tubers. Stolon tips have a few shoot buds and a cluster of **banana-shaped storage roots** 2–3 cm long that overwinter buried in 20 cm or more of mud. In spring, shoot buds elongate into stolons that produce new plants. Tubers seldom survive drying conditions.

FLOWERS: Spring–fall. Flowers musty-scented, **bright yellow**, 6–12 cm in diameter, typically **emergent** to 10 cm above the water surface. Sepals **4, lanceolate to elliptic**. The numerous petals transition inward into smaller, petal-like stamens. Ovary **partially inferior**, with **curved finger-shaped** stigmas. The insect-pollinated flowers open near noon and close in late afternoon for 2 consecutive days. The stigmas are receptive on the first day and anthers disperse pollen the second, thus promoting cross-pollination. Fertilized flowers close and submerge following this 2-day cycle.

FRUITS AND SEEDS: Berries submerged, green, ovoid, ± 2.5 cm long, burst to release 4–60 seeds with buoyant arils. Seeds spherical, ± 0.5 cm in diameter, dull greenish black, covered with fine hairs.

POSTSENESCENCE CHARACTERISTICS: Mature leaves decay rapidly during the cool season.

Mexican waterlily (*Nymphaea mexicana*) in a pond.   G. SAINTY

Fragrant waterlily (*Nymphaea odorata*) in a pond.   J. M. DiTOMASO

Fragrant waterlily (*Nymphaea odorata*) cream-colored flower form.   J. M. DiTOMASO

HABITAT: Still or **slow moving** shallow waters in lakes, ponds, streams, canals, and ditches.

DISTRIBUTION: Arizona and California in the San Joaquin Valley, to 100 m. Southern United States, Mexico, South America. Both Mexican and fragrant waterlily are often sold in nurseries as pond ornamentals.

Fragrant waterlily (*Nymphaea odorata*) pink flower form.   J. M. DiTomaso

Yellow floatingheart (*Nymphoides peltata*) in an irrigation ditch.   R. Breckenridge

PROPAGATION AND PHENOLOGY: Reproduces vegetatively from stolons and by seed. New plants arise 15–60 cm from the parent plant by horizontal stolons. Seeds disperse by floating with the aid of the aril. The aril slowly absorbs water and after about 4 weeks bursts or tears to release the seeds, which sink to the bottom of the water column. Seeds do not survive drying and must be submerged to germinate. Most germination occurs at 19°–23°C.

SIMILAR SPECIES: Fragrant waterlily (*Nymphaea odorata* Aiton.; synonym: large white waterlily) [NYMOR] is also a **noxious aquatic perennial** of quiet shallow waters. It is more common than Mexican waterlily but is not a California state-listed noxious weed. Unlike Mexican waterlily, fragrant waterlily has **sweet-scented white, cream-colored, or pink to reddish flowers** and long, **branched, creeping rhizomes 2–3 cm in diameter** that are densely covered with short black hairs. Fragrant waterlily grows in acidic to alkaline waters and has rhizomes that can tolerate some desiccation. Seed germination in fragrant waterlily requires light and the presence of ethylene, a gas whose production is stimulated when seeds are crowded together. Germination is enhanced by cold stratification for several months. This species is widely dispersed and expected to expand its range. It occurs in all western states except Wyoming. In California, it is found in the Sierra Nevada (especially Lake Tahoe), Sacramento Valley (especially Butte Co.), and San Bernardino Mountains, to 2700 m. Fragrant waterlily is introduced from the eastern United States.

Yellow pondlily (*Nuphar polysepala* Engelm.) has ± **spherical yellow flowers** and is distinguishable by having numerous stamenlike petals, a **superior ovary that is disklike at the apex** with **several dark slit-like stigmas radiating from the center**, and **7–12 broadly ovate ± cupped sepals, the inner sepals yellow** and outer green. In addition, yellow pondlily leaves are **oblong** to ovate and more **heart-shaped**. Refer to the **Yellow Pondlily** entry (page 110) for more information.

Yellow floatingheart (*Nymphoides peltata* (J.G. Gmel.) Kuntze, synonyms: water fringe; *Limnanthemum peltatum* Gmel.; *Nymphoides nymphaeoides* (L.) Britt.) [NYPPE] is a **submersed perennial with creeping rhizomes and stolons,** and **floating rounded heart-shaped leaves 5–12 cm diameter** that may be confused with those of the waterlilies. Yellow floatingheart is readily distinguished when in bloom. The **flowering stems have opposite leaves and simple umbels of showy yellow flowers with 5 ciliate-margined petals** emergent above the water surface. Plants flower from May through October, depending on the water temperature. Yellow floatingheart is cultivated as a pond ornamental but has been released into certain natural lakes where it has become a nuisance weed. Yellow floatingheart often develops dense matlike patches that displace desirable vegetation and create stagnant low-oxygen conditions in the water below. Viable fragments of noxious species such as hydrilla (*Hydrilla verticillata* (L.f.) Royle) may cling to commercial yellow floatingheart and be inadvertently introduced along with the ornamental. Yellow floatingheart occurs in Washington in the Spokane region, Arizona, and California in the northern Sierra Nevada (El Dorado Co., Trout Lake), to ± 1100 m. Yellow floatingheart **reproduces by seed** and **vegetatively from rhizomes, stolons, rhizome and stolon fragments,** and **separated leaves.** Plants can survive exposure on wet mud. It was introduced from Eurasia and the Mediterranean region. Yellow floatingheart is here included within the buckbean family (Menyanthaceae), although some references include it as a member of the gentian family (Gentianaceae).

Pondweeds (*Potamogeton* spp. and *Stuckenia* spp.)

SPECIES AND SYNONYMS: The genus *Potamogeton* is comprised of many widespread, highly variable species that are often difficult to distinguish, resulting in much taxonomic confusion. A complete list of synonyms for each species is beyond the scope of this publication.

Curlyleaf pondweed (*Potamogeton crispus* L.) [PTMCR]: crispate-leaved pondweed; curled-leaved pondweed; crisped pondweed

Leafy pondweed (*Potamogeton foliosus* Raf. var. *foliosus*) [PTMFO]: closed-leaved pondweed

Illinois pondweed (*Potamogeton illinoensis* Morong) [PTMIL]: shining pondweed; ziz's pondweed; *Potamogeton angustifolius* Bercht. & K.; *Potamogeton lucens* L.; *Potamogeton zizii* Koch ex Roth

Floatingleaf pondweed (*Potamogeton natans* L.) [PTMNA]: common floating pondweed; broad-leafed pondweed

American pondweed (*Potamogeton nodosus* Poir.) [PTMNO]: longleaf pondweed; long-leaved pondweed; *Potamogeton americanus* Cham. & Schlecht; *Potamogeton lonchites* Tuckerm.

Sago pondweed (*Stuckenia pectinatus* (L.) Börner) [PTMPE]: fennel-leaf pondweed; *Potamogeton pectinatus* L.; *Coleogeton pectinatus* (L.) D.H. Les & Haynes

Small pondweed (*Potamogeton pusillus* L.) [PTMPU]: Small-leafed pondweed; *Potamogeton panormitanus* Biv.

GENERAL INFORMATION: Aquatic perennials, most with **rhizomes**. Depending on the species, leaves are **floating and/or submersed**. Refer to tables 9–10 for a comparison of distinguishing vegetative characteristics. Pondweeds are highly plastic, changing their appearance according to environmental conditions, and widely distributed, particularly in temperate regions. Most species in the United States are widespread **natives** of North America and elsewhere. In western states, only **curlyleaf pondweed** is introduced from Eurasia. Pondweeds provide habitat for and are an important food source for wildlife. In natural areas, most pondweeds are a desirable component of the aquatic community. However, colonies can be troublesome in drainage canals, irrigation ditches, and other controlled aquatic systems. Most species hybridize with one or more other species. Like fertile plants, sterile hybrids reproduce vegetatively and can persist in colonies.

SEEDLING: Cotyledons lacking. Seed coat (pericarp or testa) usually remains attached to seedlings. Seldom encountered.

MATURE PLANT: Foliage glabrous. Leaves **alternate**, sometimes nearly opposite. Submersed leaves cylindrical, linear, elliptic or ovate to lanceolate. Stipules vary depending on species. Floating leaves (when present) elliptic to ovate, stalked, leathery. Leaves of most species have a prominent midvein. **Sago pondweed** leaves have a small midvein with a larger parallel air channel on each side.

ROOTS AND UNDERGROUND STRUCTURES: Roots typically unbranched. Rhizomes ± creeping, usually whitish, slender in most species, thick in **Illinois pondweed**, typically matted in **leafy** and **sago pondweed**, often reddish spotted in **floating-leaf pondweed**. **Sago pondweed** rhizomes develop numerous **small tubers** on lateral branches that resemble small potatoes ± 1 cm long. **Small pondweed** lacks rhizomes.

FLOWERS: May–September (October). Spikes cylindrical, sometimes headlike, emergent in most species, floating in **sago pondweed**. Flowers greenish, inconspicuous. Perianth parts (petals or sepals) 4, sometimes narrowed at the base (clawed). Anthers 4, sessile, attached to the base of each perianth part. Carpels 4, separate, sessile, 1-chambered. Wind- and water-pollinated.

Curlyleaf pondweed (*Potamogeton crispus*) infestation in a reservoir.   R. BRECKENRIDGE

Curlyleaf pondweed (*Potamogeton crispus*) stems.   W. J. MCHENRY

119

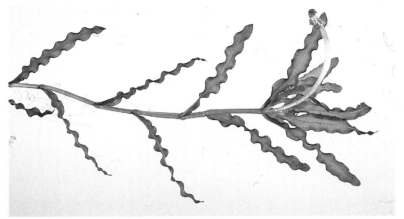

Curlyleaf pondweed (*Potamogeton crispus*) stem section with flowers.   J. K. CLARK

Leafy pondweed (*Potamogeton foliosus*) stem section with flowers.   J. K. CLARK

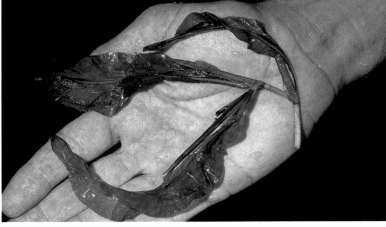

Largeleaf pondweed (*Potamogeton amplifolius*) stem section with leaves.
J. M. DiTomaso

FRUITS AND SEEDS: Fruits achene- or nutletlike, sessile, ± obovate, often 1–3-keeled, usually with a beak at or near the apex. Fruit characteristics can be helpful with species identification. Length given includes beak.

Curlyleaf pondweed: (3)4–6 mm long, back 3-keeled, with a small spur at the base of the central keel. Beak 2–3 mm long, erect to curved.

Illinois pondweed *(Potamogeton illinoensis)* stem section.   L. ANDERSON

Floatingleaf pondweed *(Potamogeton natans)* in a pond with *Lemna* sp.   J. M. DITOMASO

Leafy pondweed: 2–3 mm long, back 3-keeled, central keel winged and ± toothed, sides rounded or slightly concave. Beak less than 1 mm long.

Illinois pondweed: 2.5–4 mm long, back ± keeled. Beak less than 1 mm long.

Floatingleaf pondweed: 3.5–5 mm long, rounded or barely keeled, sides con-

Floatingleaf pondweed *(Potamogeton natans)* inflorescence.   J. M. DiTomaso

Floatingleaf pondweed *(Potamogeton natans)* with floating (broad) and linear (submerged) leaves.

J. M. DiTomaso

cave, back rounded. Beak less than 1 mm long, straight or curved.

American pondweed: 3–5 mm long, 3-keeled, back rounded, sides flat. Beak less than 1 mm long, straight or curved.

Sago pondweed: 2.5–4(5) mm long, obliquely obovoid, barely 2-keeled, back rounded. Beak curved, less than 1 mm long.

Small pondweed: 2–3 mm long, inconspicuously keeled, back rounded, sides concave. Beak less than 1 mm long.

OTHER REPRODUCTIVE STRUCTURES: Curlyleaf and **small pondweed** develop **turions** (specialized stem buds that survive unfavorable conditions) in the leaf axils and/or at the tips of short axillary branches before dormancy. Turions are composed of few to several reduced, overlapping leaves. **Curlyleaf pondweed**

American pondweed (*Potamogeton nodosus*) in an irrigation canal.   J. K. CLARK

American pondweed (*Potamogeton nodosus*) with emerged inflorescences.   J. M. DITOMASO

turions resemble brown pinecones 7–25(50) mm long, with reduced leaves that are broad and hardened at the bases. **Small pondweed** turions are narrowly cylindrical, 1–2 cm long, 0.5–1 mm wide, with 1–3 erect, overlapping to recurved, with separate leaves.

POSTSENESCENCE CHARACTERISTICS: Foliage of most species dies and decays rapidly

American pondweed (*Potamogeton nodosus*) stem section.   J. K. CLARK

American pondweed (*Potamogeton nodosus*) rhizomes.   J. K. CLARK

Sago pondweed (*Stuckenia pectinatus*) infestation with inflorescences in a pond.   J. M. DiTOMASO

as plants become dormant in winter, but rhizomes, tubers, and turions survive. **American pondweed** foliage sometimes survives and remains green through winter. **Curlyleaf pondweed** is adapted to growing under cold conditions. Foliage dies as plants become dormant in summer, but turions remain on the sediment.

HABITAT: All species inhabit ponds, lakes, streams, rivers, reservoirs, irrigation ditches, and marshy areas. Most species commonly grow in shallow water but can grow to depths of ± 6 m or more in clear water. **Floatingleaf, leafy,** and **sago pondweeds** also grow in brackish water. **Small pondweed** can inhabit vernal pools.

DISTRIBUTION: All species occur throughout much of North America, including all western states. The following is more detailed distribution of the most common species in California.

Curlyleaf pondweed: North Coast Ranges, Central Valley, Central Coast, San Francisco Bay region, central and eastern Transverse Ranges, South Coast, Channel Islands, and Mojave Desert, to 2100 m. Nearly worldwide.

Leafy pondweed: Northwestern region, Cascade Range, foothills and northern Sierra Nevada, Great Basin, central-western and southwestern regions, and desert regions, to 2300 m.

Illinois pondweed: North Coast Ranges, Cascade Range, Sierra Nevada, Great Basin, San Francisco Bay region, Central Coast, South Coast, central and eastern Transverse Ranges, and Peninsular Ranges, typically at 400–2350 m.

Floatingleaf pondweed: North Coast, western North Coast Ranges, Cascade Range, Sierra Nevada, Modoc Plateau, San Francisco Bay region, San Joaquin Valley, eastern Transverse Ranges, Peninsular Ranges. To 2700 m.

American pondweed: North Coast Ranges, northern Sierra Nevada, southern Sierra Nevada foothills, Great Basin, Central Valley, San Francisco Bay region, Central Coast, South Coast, eastern Transverse Ranges, Peninsular Ranges, and Mojave Desert, usually at 100–2750 m. Nearly worldwide.

Sago pondweed: Common throughout California to 2400 m. Nearly worldwide.

Small pondweed: North Coast, Klamath Ranges, Sierra Nevada and northern foothills, Great Basin, Central Valley, San Francisco Bay region, South Coast Ranges, southwestern region, and Mojave Desert, to 2700 m.

PROPAGATION AND PHENOLOGY: Most species **reproduce vegetatively from rhizomes** and **stem fragments** and **by seed. Curlyleaf** and **small pondweed** also **reproduce by turions. Sago pondweed reproduces vegetatively by tubers,** rather than the rhizomes they develop on. Tuber production in **sago pondweed** is often high. **Sago pondweed** tubers germinate in early spring and can survive in a drawn-down lake bed or de-watered canal for 3–5 months. **Curlyleaf pondweed** turions germinate in late summer or fall. **Small pondweed** turions germinate in spring. Seed production is often poor in turion-producing species. For all species, seeds float and disperse with water, ingestion by wildlife, and by clinging to the feet, fur, or feathers of animals. Seeds are hard-coated and typically require scarification to germinate. Seeds surviving ingestion by birds germinate readily. **Illinois pondweed** seeds may survive up to 5 years under moist conditions. **Sago pondweed** seeds survive up to ± 1.5 years under dry conditions. Seed longevity of other species is poorly documented.

SIMILAR SPECIES: Widgeongrass (*Ruppia* spp.), **horned pondweed** (*Zannichellia* *palustris* L.) [ZAIPA], and some naiads (*Najas* spp.) may be confused with linear-leaved pondweeds. Unlike pondweeds, widgeongrass and naiad species have **minutely toothed leaf margins** (may require magnification to see) and **sheathing leaf bases without a separate or tubular ligule above the junction of the leaf base and sheath**. In addition, naiads have mostly **opposite leaves**. Horned

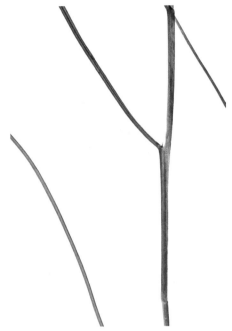

Sago pondweed (*Stuckenia pectinatus*) stem section with inflorescence.   J. K. CLARK

Leaf base and sheath of sago pondweed (*Stuckenia pectinatus*).   J. K. CLARK

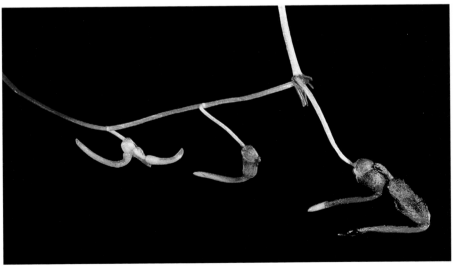

Developing tubers of sago pondweed (*Stuckenia pectinatus*).   J. K. CLARK

pondweed is distinguished by having **mostly opposite sessile leaves** with a **sheathing stipule that surrounds the leaf base and stem**, and ± sessile flowers **or fruits in the leaf axils**. Refer to tables 8–10 (pages 109, 130–131) for a comparison of additional characteristics. There are several native pondweeds that are uncommon to rare in California but sometimes considered weeds elsewhere. The following species typically grow in natural areas where they are a desirable component of the aquatic vegetation in many western states: **largeleaf pondweed** (*Potamogeton amplifolius* Tuckerman), **waterthread pondweed** (*Potamogeton diversifolius* Raf.), **ribbonleaf pondweed** (*Potamogeton epihydrus* Raf. ssp. *nuttallii* (Cham. & Schldl.) Calder & Taylor.), **threadleaf pondweed** (*Stuckenia filiformis* (Pers.) Börner; synonym: *Potamogeton filiformis* Pers.), **variable pondweed** (*Potamogeton gramineus* L.; symonym: grassy pondweed), **whitestem pondweed** (*Potamogeton praelongus* Wulfen), **Richardson's pondweed** (*Potamogeton richardsonii* (A. Bennett) Rydb.; synonym: *Potamogeton perfoliatus* L. ssp. *richardsonii*; (A. Bennett) Hultén), and **flatstem pondweed** (*Potamogeton zosteriformis* Fern.; synonym: eel-grass pondweed). See key on page 37 for separation of *Potamogeton*, *Stuckenia*, and *Ruppia* species.

Potamogeton and *Stuckenia* stipules

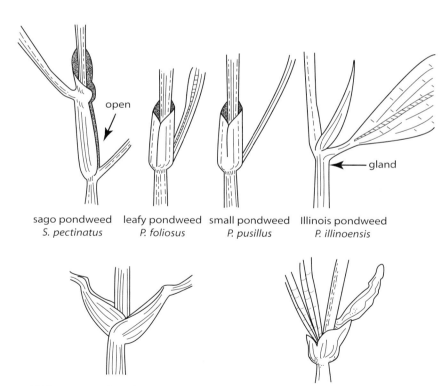

open

gland

| sago pondweed | leafy pondweed | small pondweed | Illinois pondweed |
| *S. pectinatus* | *P. foliosus* | *P. pusillus* | *P. illinoensis* |

Widgeongrass *(Ruppia maritima)*
sheathing leaf bases

Horned pondweed *(Zannichellia palustris)* stipule

Widgeongrass (*Ruppia maritima* L.) [RUPMA]

Synonyms: beaked tasselweed; ditch-grass; *Ruppia pectinata* Rydb.

General Information: **Submersed aquatic perennial**, often in brackish water, with linear leaves and **rhizomes**. Widgeongrass is a widespread native with a nearly worldwide distribution. It is a valuable food and habitat plant for wildlife and is not considered a weed in most natural areas. However, it can be weedy in ditches, irrigation channels, and other controlled aquatic systems. Some taxonomic treatments segregate the genus *Ruppia* into the family Ruppiaceae.

Seedling: Cotyledon lacking. Seed coat (pericarp or testa) usually remains attached to seedlings. First and subsequent leaves resemble reduced mature leaves.

Mature Plant: Foliage glabrous. Stems branched, to 1 m long, slender, rooting at lower nodes, with internodes 2–8 cm long. Leaves sessile, bright green, **mostly alternate**, **some opposite**, **linear**, to 100 mm long and **0.5 mm wide**, elliptical in cross-section, tip ± broadly acute. Margins **minutely serrate**, especially near tip. Leaf bases ± **expanded** and **sheathing stem** for up to 2 cm. Midveins bordered on each side by a longitudinal air channel.

Roots and Underground Structures: Rhizomes slender, whitish or brown. Roots few, shallow, unbranched.

Flowers: April–August. Inflorescences submerged, consist of 2 minute flowers 1–2 mm apart on a **straight stalk** 2–25 mm long. Flowers **lack sepals or petals.** Stamens 2, sessile. Carpels typically 3–5, separate, initially close together and nearly sessile. Carpel stalks elongate as fruits develop. Typically self-pollinated underwater. Pollen is transported on the surface of clinging bubbles.

Fruits and Seeds: Fruiting heads **umbel-like**, with each fruit on a long stalk (to 3.5 cm). Fruits achene- or nutletlike, ovoid, oblique, 2–3 mm long (including beak), dark brown, peppered with minute, slightly raised bumps, tapered at the apex into a straight beak usually less than half the length of the fruit body.

Postsenescence Characteristics: Foliage may die and decay under cold conditions, but rhizomes survive.

Habitat: Marshes, ponds, sloughs, tidal estuaries, ditches, and canals. Typically inhabits brackish, alkaline, or saline water and waters to several meters deep.

Distribution: Oregon, Washington, Idaho, Colorado, New Mexico, and California in the North Coast, central-western region, South Coast, and Channel Islands, to 100 m. Eastern and southern United States, scattered in the central United States. Nearly worldwide.

Propagation and Phenology: **Reproduces vegetatively from rhizomes** and **stem fragments** and **by seed**. Seed production can be high. Seeds disperse with water, mud, and by clinging to the feet, fur, or feathers of animals. Seeds lack a hard coat and germinate in spring. Exposure to cold temperatures during winter stimulates germination. A period of drying conditions can kill plants, but seeds often survive.

Similar Species: **Spiral ditchgrass** (*Ruppia cirrhosa* (Petagna) Grande) is very similar to *Ruppia maritima* and is often considered to be indistinct. The two species are separated in keys by the presence of a long fruit peduncle in *R. cirrhosa* (30–300 mm long) contrasting with a short one in *R. maritima* (2–25 mm long). However, this character may be more variable than previously believed. Linear-leaved pondweeds (*Potamogeton* spp.), **horned pondweed** (*Zannichellia palustris* L.) [ZAIPA], and some naiads (*Najas* spp.) may be confused with widgeongrass. Unlike widgeongrass, pondweeds have leaves with **smooth margins** and **ligule-like stipules** that are **separate** or **sheathing to tubular** with **free tips above the junction** of the **leaf base** and **sheath**. **Horned pondweed** differs by having mostly **opposite leaves** with **smooth margins** and **sheathing stipules** that **surround the leaf base and stem**. Naiads are distinguished by having **mostly opposite leaves** and **sessile fruits in the leaf axils**. Refer to tables 8–10 (page 109, 130–131) for a comparison of additional characteristics. See key on page 37 for separation of *Potamogeton, Stuckenia,* and *Ruppia* species.

Spiral ditchgrass (*Ruppia cirrhosa*) stem section with fruit.   J. K. CLARK

Spiral ditchgrass (*Ruppia cirrhosa*) stem section with male inflorescence.   J. K. CLARK

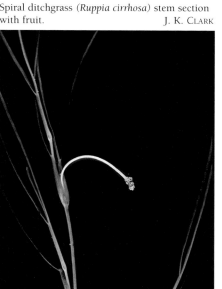

Spiral ditchgrass (*Ruppia cirrhosa*) male inflorescence.   J. K. CLARK

Table 9. Pondweeds (*Potamogeton* spp. and *Stuckenia* spp.) and widgeongrass (*Ruppia* spp.): All leaves submersed and sessile

Species	Leaf L × W (mm)	Leaf margins	Young stipules	Other
Leaves less than 6 mm wide, threadlike to ribbonlike				
waterthread pondweed (*P. diversifolius*)	25–100 × 0.5–2	smooth	fused to leaf base, tubular below for $\frac{1}{2}$–$\frac{1}{3}$ of length (± 0.5 cm), tip free	sometimes has small elliptic floating leaves (see table 10, page 131)
leafy pondweed (*P. foliosus* var. *foliosus*)	30–100 × 0.3–3	smooth	free from leaf base, sheathing and open above leaf (<2 cm), finely veined, later free or decayed	var. *fibrillosus*, with stipules to 12 cm long, coarsely veined and ciliate, later fibrous, rare in CA (CNPS* List 2)
small pondweed (*P. pusillus*)	20–70 × 0.5–3	smooth	free from leaf base, tubular above leaf for less than $\frac{1}{2}$ of length (< 0.75 cm) to free, later fibrous	leaf bases have a pair of tiny raised glands
flatstem pondweed (*P. zosteriformis*)	50–200 × 2–5	smooth	free from leaf base, 2–6 cm long, later torn	stems clearly flattened and ± winged; rare in CA (CNPS* List 2)
widgeongrass (*Ruppia* spp.)	30–120 × 0.2–1	minutely toothed at tip and ± below	completely fused to leaf base, ± enlarged and sheathing below, lack a free tip, margins mostly open	some leaves ± opposite, flowers lack petals or sepals, stamens 2, fruiting inflorescences umbel-like and submersed
threadleaf pondweed (*S. filiformis*)	50–120 × 0.2–2	smooth	fused to leaf base, tubular below for most of length (1–3 cm), tip free	underground tubers, leaf tips often blunt, rare in CA (CNPS* List 2)
sago pondweed (*S. pectinatus*)	30–200 × 0.2–1	smooth	fused to leaf base, sheathing below for most of length (1–7 cm), tip free, margins open, overlapping	underground tubers
Leaves mostly more than 6 mm wide, narrowly oblong to lanceolate				
curlyleaf pondweed (*P. crispus*)	20–80 × 5–12	narrowly oblong	wavy and finely serrate	free most of length, slightly fused to leaf base, <1 cm long, later fibrous
Richardson's pondweed (*P. richardsonii*)	30–120 × 10–20	lanceolate	± wavy, often near tip	
whitestem pondweed (*P. praelongus*)	50–300 × 10–30	narrowly elliptic to lanceolate	± wavy	free, 3–10 cm long, persistent
Illinois pondweed (*P. illinoensis*)	60–200 × 15–50	elliptic to oblanceolate	finely serrate near tip	free, 2.5–7 cm long, persistent

Note: *California Native Plant Society list of rare plants.

Table 10. Pondweeds (*Potamogeton* spp.): At least some leaves floating, stalked, and ovate to elliptic

Species	Submerged leaf shape and width	Submerged leaf attachment	Floating leaves	Young stipules	Other
floatingleaf pondweed (*P. natans*)	cylindrical and stalklike, leathery, to 2 mm	sessile	elliptic to oblong, base slightly lobed, veins 23–37	free, 6–8 cm long, persistent	hybridizes with variable and American pondweed
ribbonleaf pondweed (*P. epihydrus* ssp. *nuttallii*)	ribbonlike with a narrow band of fine netlike veins along midrib, 2–10 mm	sessile	elliptic to oblong, base tapered, often opposite, veins 19–41	free, 2–4.5 cm long	rare in CA (CNPS* list 2); hybridizes with American pondweed
variable pondweed (*P. gramineus*)	ribbonlike to narrowly elliptic or oblanceolate, 2–12 mm	sessile	elliptic to ovate, base tapered, veins 13–17	free, <3 cm long, persistent	hybridizes with Illinois, Richardson's, American, and floatingleaf pondweed
American pondweed (*P. nodosus*)	narrowly elliptic to lanceolate, 10–40 mm	stalks 2–15 cm long	oblong, base tapered, veins 13–21	free, 3–9 cm long, quickly ragged or torn	hybridizes with variable, floatingleaf, ribbonleaf, Illinois, and Richardson's pondweed
Illinois pondweed (*P. illinoensis*)	elliptic to oblanceolate, finely serrate near tip, 15–50 mm	stalks <1 cm long to ± sessile	elliptic to oblong, base wedge-shaped or rounded, veins 13–21	free, 2.5–7 cm long, persistent	sometimes lacks floating leaves; hybridizes with American, variable, and Richardson's pondweed (see table 9)
largeleaf pondweed (*P. amplifolius*)	ovate to lanceolate, folded at midrib and sicklelike, 20–70 mm	stalks ± 1–6 cm long	elliptic to ovate, base wedge-shaped or rounded, veins 29–51	free, 3–10 cm long, later fibrous	hybridizes with Illinois, Richardson's, and whitestem pondweed

Horned pondweed (*Zannichellia palustris* L.) [ZAIPA]

SYNONYMS: Z-grass; *Zannichellia major* (Hartman) Boenn. ex Reichenb.; *Zannichellia palustris* L. ssp. *repens* (Boenn.) Rothm.; *Zannichellia palustris* L. vars. *major* (Hartman) W.D.J., *stenophylla* Aschers. & Graebn.; *Zannichellia repens* Boenn.; others

GENERAL INFORMATION: **Submersed perennial** with **creeping rhizomes**, **linear leaves**, and stems to 0.5 m long. Plants are annual where standing water is seasonal. Horned pondweed is a widespread native throughout most temperate to tropical regions of the world. In natural areas it is a desirable component of the aquatic community. Foliage and fruits provide a valuable food source for wildlife, especially water birds. However, horned pondweed is sometimes a minor weed in irrigation channels. The number of species in the genus *Zannichellia* remains controversial. Some botanists believe there is only one variable species, *Zannichellia palustris*, consisting of ± 6 biotypes. Others give the biotypes species or subspecies distinction. Some references include horned pondweed in the pondweed family (Potamogetonaceae).

SEEDLING: Cotyledon lacking. Seed coat (pericarp or testa) usually remains attached to seedling. First and subsequent leaves 1–4 cm long, resemble reduced mature leaves.

MATURE PLANT: Stems very slender, weak, sparsely branched. Leaves **mostly opposite**, some alternate. Upper leaves often appear clustered or whorled. Leaves sessile, **narrowly linear, flat**, 2–10 cm long, **less than 1 mm wide**, single-veined, tips acute. **Margins smooth.** Stipules separate from leaf base, **fused**, membranous, and **sheathing leaf base** and **stem**.

ROOTS AND UNDERGROUND STRUCTURES: Rhizomes slender, creeping, often dense. Roots shallow, unbranched.

FLOWERS: March–November. Flowers unisexual, with male and female flowers on the same plant (monoecious). Male and female flowers **solitary to few-clustered in leaf axils**. Male flowers sessile, consist of a single stamen with a slender filament and 2-chambered anther. Female flowers develop on a very short stalk above male flowers. Female flowers consist of a cuplike bract (spathe) or perianth (petals or sepals) and 2–6 separate pistils. Each pistil has a short style attached near the center of a shield-shaped (peltate) stigma. Stamens usually mature before or after pistils become receptive. Water-pollinated. Outcrossing and self-compatible.

FRUITS AND SEEDS: Fruits achene- or nutlet-like, grayish, **± oblong, flattened, curved, 2–4 mm long**, with a **slender beak 1–1.5 mm long at the apex**, a **stalk ± 1 mm long at the base**, and **1 or more longitudinal rows of teeth or projections on the back**. Fruits do not open to release the single seed.

HABITAT: Still or slow-moving fresh or brackish water. Estuaries, streams, rivers, ponds, lakes, ditches, and irrigation channels. Grows in soft water or clear water with a high calcium content (calcareous) to nutrient-rich (eutrophic) water. Can grow in water less than 0.5 m deep or among other aquatic species in deeper water.

Horned pondweed (*Zannichellia palustris*) population in a stream.   J. M. DiTomaso

Horned pondweed (*Zannichellia palustris*) stem section.   J. K. Clark

DISTRIBUTION: All western states. Throughout California to 2200 m. Nearly world-wide.

PROPAGATION AND PHENOLOGY: Reproduces by seed and vegetatively from rhizomes. Fruits disperse with water, animals, and in mud. Germination requirements are regionally variable. Seeds of some populations are dormant at maturity and require a cool stratification period before germination can occur. Seeds can survive dry conditions for at least 3 months. Seedlings usually do not emerge from substrate depths greater than ± 1 cm. Immature plants often do not survive burial by sediment. Increasing accumulation of sediment has been implicated with population declines.

SIMILAR SPECIES: Unlike horned pondweed, **widgeongrass** (*Ruppia* spp.) and the naiads (*Najas* spp.) have leaves with **minutely toothed margins** (may require magnification to see) and **sheathing leaf bases**. Linear-leaved *Potamogeton* and *Stuckenia* species differ by having **alternate leaves** (some may be subopposite) and **emergent flower spikes**. Refer to table 8 (page 109) for a comparison of additional characteristics.

Horned pondweed (*Zannichellia palustris*) fruits in leaf axil.   J. M. DITOMASO

Emerged Aquatic Plants

Monocots, Dicots, and Spore Producers

Common waterplantain (*Alisma plantago-aquatica* L.) [ALSPA]

Synonyms: American waterplantain; northern waterplantain; *Alisma brevipes* Greene; *Alisma plantago-aquatica* L. var. *americanum* J.A. Schultes; *Alisma plantago-aquatica* L. var. *brevipes* (Greene) Victorin; *Alisma subcordatum* Raf.; *Alisma triviale* Pursh

General Information: **Tufted emersed perennial**, with leaves to 0.5 m tall, flowering stems to **1.2 m tall**. Waterplantain is a widespread native of North America, Eurasia, mountainous East Africa, and possibly Australia. It is beneficial to wildlife and is usually considered a weed only in rice fields and controlled aquatic systems. In California rice and wild rice fields, waterplantain typically grows as an **annual**. Some taxonomists refer to native California waterplantain as *Alisma triviale* and utilize *Alisma plantago-aquatica* to refer to the European variety.

Seedling: Cotyledon elliptic to lanceolate, long-stalked, typically floating. Stalk often red-tinged. Immature leaves lack blades or blades much reduced. Sometimes occur in swards in shallow water.

Mature Plant: Leaves basal, highly variable, mostly emergent, sometimes floating, lanceolate to ovate, with long petioles that sheath a short, bulbous stem

Waterplantain (*Alisma plantago-aquatica*) in a rice field.　　　J. K. Clark

Waterplantain (*Alisma plantago-aquatica*) leaf.　　　J. M. DiTomaso base. Leaf bases **truncate to nearly cordate**. Blades **5–20 cm long, 1–10 cm wide**. Main veins parallel, with tiny transverse veinlets.

ROOTS AND UNDERGROUND STRUCTURES: Roots fibrous. Stem base **cormlike**, with a terminal bud. Stem bases sometimes produce cormlike side shoots.

FLOWERS: June–July. **Flowering stems taller than leaves**. Panicles whorled, with each branching node subtended by 2–3 papery, leaflike bracts. Petals 3, separate, deciduous, **white, rarely pink**, ovate to rhombic, with **rounded tips**. Margins smooth or minutely toothed (erose). Sepals 3, green, persistent, ovate. **Stamens 6**, arranged in pairs opposite petals. **Carpels numerous, separate, arranged in a ring on a flattened receptacle**. Insect- and wind-pollinated. Self-compatible. Flowers often open after noon.

FRUITS AND SEEDS: Fruiting heads consist of a **ring of achenes** (1-seeded fruits) 3–5 mm diameter. Achenes sectorlike, strongly compressed, 2–3 mm long, **longer than wide**, each with a short ventral beak and rounded back. Lateral walls typically **thick, opaque**.

POSTSENESCENCE CHARACTERISTICS: Foliage usually dies in winter and regrows from the terminal bud in spring. Senesced foliage decays rapidly in water.

HABITAT: Inhabits shallow water or exposed mud in and around ponds, rice and wild rice fields, ditches, wetlands, and streams. Grows best on nutrient-rich mud

Waterplantain (*Alisma plantago-aquatica*) inflorescence.
J. M. DiTomaso

in moderately high nutrient (eutrophic) water. Often colonizes newly cleared or open sites.

DISTRIBUTION: All western states; to Canada, southeastern United States. Throughout California, except Great Basin region and Mojave and Sonoran deserts. To 1600 m. Eurasia, Australia, and most of Africa.

Waterplantain (*Alisma plantago-aquatica*) seedling.   J. M. DiTomaso

0   1mm

Waterplantain (*Alisma plantago-aquatica*) achenes.   J. K. CLARK

Lanceleaved waterplantain *(Alisma lanceolatum)* in a rice field.   J. M. DiTomaso

Lanceleaved waterplantain *(Alisma lanceolatum)* leaf.   J. M. DiTomaso

PROPAGATION AND PHENOLOGY: Reproduces by seed. Seeds disperse by floating on water and clinging to the feet, fur, and feathers of animals. Seeds can float on water for up to 2 months. Germination is usually erratic because of mechanical dormancy imposed by the hard seed coat. Some seeds germinate after the first winter or dry season, others can remain dormant for 4–5 years. Seeds can survive ingestion by birds, and drying can induce rupture of seed coat. Scarified seeds

Lanceleaved waterplantain (*Alisma lanceolatum*) flower and fruit.   J. M. DiTomaso

Lanceleaved waterplantain (*Alisma lanceolatum*) seedling.   J. M. DiTomaso

germinate readily. Seeds germinate on land and in shallow water. Seeds survive frozen water or mud for several weeks. Plants developing from seed reach optimal size in shallow water (± 7 cm) and decrease linearly in size as water depth increases to 40 cm. To a limited extent, plants may reproduce vegetatively from cormlike side shoots. Side shoots may break away and disperse with flooding. Plants from side shoots reach optimal size in deeper water (20–40 cm).

MANAGEMENT FAVORING OR DISCOURAGING SURVIVAL: Removing dense infestations by hand or machinery is often difficult or damaging to the site and seldom gives effective control.

SIMILAR SPECIES: Lanceleaved waterplantain (*Alisma lanceolatum* With.) [ALSLA] is a **perennial** introduced from Eurasia and North Africa. Unlike waterplantain, lanceleaved waterplantain has **leaves with tapered bases, pink to purplish petals that taper to a point** (acuminate), and achenes ± **1–2 mm long** with **thin, translucent lateral walls. Lanceleaved waterplantain** occurs in Oregon and California in the northwestern region, northern Sierra Nevada foothills, and Sacramento Valley, to 500 m. Arrowheads (*Sagittaria* spp.) are distinguished by having leaves with **long, pointed basal lobes** (sagittate). Refer to the **California Arrowhead** entry (page 147) and table 11 for more information.

Upright burhead (*Echinodorus berteroi* (Spreng.) Fassett) has **burlike fruiting heads** and **angled stems and leaf stalks**. Burhead is primarily a rice weed.

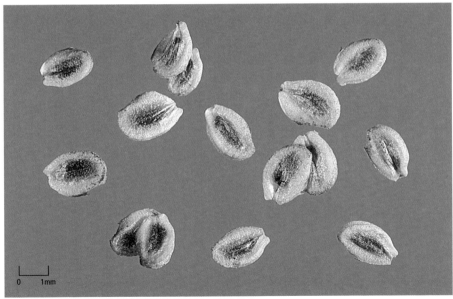

Lanceleaved waterplantain (*Alisma lanceolatum*) achenes.   J. K. CLARK

Table 11. Waterplantain (*Alisma* spp.), upright burhead *(Echinodorus berteroi)*, and arrowhead (*Sagittaria* spp.) commonly found as rice weeds

Species	Life cycle	Tubers, corms	Emergent leaves in shallow water	Petal color and shape	Stamens
lanceleaved waterplantain (*Alisma lanceolatum*)	perennial, bisexual	stem base cormlike		pink to purplish pink, ovate, tip tapered to a point and slightly pinched in	6
common waterplantain (*Alisma plantago-aquatica*)	perennial, bisexual	stem base cormlike		white, rarely pink, ovate-rhombic, tip rounded	6
upright burhead (*Echinodorus berteroi*)	annual to short-lived perennial	fibrous roots only		white, ovate	numerous, anthers attached in middle
Gregg arrowhead (*Sagittaria longiloba*)	perennial, monoecious	tubers tan, spheric; short-lived rhizomes		white, ovate	numerous, filaments slender and glabrous
California arrowhead (*Sagittaria montevidensis* ssp. *calycina*)	annual, monoecious	fibrous roots only		white with a greenish yellow spot at the base, ovate	numerous, filaments stout and papillate-hairy

Upright burhead (*Echinodorus berteroi* (Spreng.) Fassett) [ECOCO]

SYNONYMS: burhead; creeping burhead; *Alisma berteroi* Spreng.; *Alisma rostratum* Nutt.; *Echinodorus berteroi* (Spreng.) Fassett var. *lanceolatus* (Engelm. ex S. Wats. & Coult.) Fassett; *Echinodorus cordifolius* (L.) Griseb. of California references; *Echinodorus rostratus* (Nutt.) Engelm. ex Gray; *Echinodorus rostratus* (Nutt.) Engelm. ex Gray var. *lanceolatus* Engelm ex S.Wats. & Coult.; others

GENERAL INFORMATION: Submersed, floating, emergent, or terrestrial **annual to short-lived perennial**, with **burlike fruiting heads** on emergent stems to 0.6 m tall. Upright burhead is a highly variable widespread native of wetlands throughout much of the United States. In California and probably other western states, upright burhead is often annual. Plants are a desirable component of natural communities but are occasionally weedy in rice fields and ditches. Upright burhead is sometimes cultured as an aquarium or pond ornamental and was consumed by the native peoples of the southwestern United States and South America.

SEEDLING: Juvenile plants are usually submersed and have sessile, narrow to broad ribbonlike leaves with wavy margins.

MATURE PLANT: Leaves basal, highly variable, 8–30 cm long, including stalks. Submerged leaves often ribbonlike, ± sessile, with wavy margins. Floating and

Burhead (*Echinodorus berteroi*) in a rice field.
J. M. DiTOMASO

Burhead (*Echinodorus berteroi*) flower.
J. K. CLARK

Burhead (*Echinodorus berteroi*) fruiting inflorescence.   J. K. CLARK

Burhead (*Echinodorus berteroi*) fruit head.
                                               J. K. CLARK

emergent leaves elliptic to cordate on long stalks. Blades longitudinally coarse-
veined, 6–14 cm long, 3–15 cm wide, often with wavy margins. Stalks ± **angled**,
enlarged and spongy at the base.

ROOTS AND UNDERGROUND STRUCTURES: Roots fibrous. Flowering stems typically
bend over and sometimes develop new plantlets by rooting at the lower nodes.

FLOWERS: Summer–fall. Flowering stems initially erect, typically taller than
leaves, angled below flowers, later arching over. Infloresences panicle- to raceme-
like, with 3–12 flowers per node. Flowers **bisexual**, 12–20 mm diameter. Sepals
3, boat-shaped, ± 5 mm long, persistent, with ridges of minute papillae. Petals 3,
white, 6–9 mm long. Stamens 9–20, with anthers attached in the middle (vers-
atile). Pistils numerous, each with a persistent beaklike style. Receptacle elongated. Insect-pollinated.

FRUITS AND SEEDS: Fruiting heads dense, **burlike**, ovoid, 4–10 mm diameter,
densely covered with achenelike fruits. Fruit body oblong, slightly compressed,
1.5–3 mm long, conspicuously ribbed to narrowly winged, with 2–4 elongated
glands on each side and a beak to 2 mm long at the apex. Each fruit contains 1
seed. Seeds oblong, 1–2 mm long, appear folded in half, glossy, reddish brown,
minutely reticulate-pitted in even rows.

HABITAT: Pond and stream margins, ditches, and rice fields. Grows in shallow
water or on mud.

DISTRIBUTION: Nevada, Arizona, New Mexico, Utah, and California in the eastern
North Coast Ranges, Central Valley, central-western region, and southwestern
region, to 300 m. Southeastern United States, South America.

PROPAGATION AND PHENOLOGY: Reproduces by seed and sometimes vegetatively from stolonlike flowering stems. Fruits float for long periods and disperse with water, in mud, and by clinging to the fur, feet, or feathers of animals.

SIMILAR SPECIES: Unlike upright burhead, **waterplantains** (*Alisma* spp.) and **arrowheads** (*Sagittaria* spp.) have **smooth leaf and flower stalks that are round in cross-section** and **lack burlike fruiting heads**. In addition, arrowhead has **unisexual flowers**, with female flowers at the lowest node and male flowers above (monoecious).

Burhead (*Echinodorus berteroi*) seedling after leaves emerge.　　　　J. K. CLARK

Burhead (*Echinodorus berteroi*) fruits.　　　　J. K. CLARK

California arrowhead (*Sagittaria montevidensis* Cham. & Schlecht. ssp. *calycina* (Engelm.) C.Bogin) [SAGMO]

SYNONYMS: giant arrowhead; hooded arrowhead; *Lophotocarpus californicus* J.G. Sm.; *Lophotocarpus calycinus* (Engelm) J. G. Sm.; *Lophotocarpus depauperatus* J.G. Sm.; *Sagittaria calycina* Engelm. var. *calycina*; *Sagittaria pugioniformis* L. var. *montevidensis* (Cham. & Schlecht.) Kuntze

GENERAL INFORMATION: **Tufted submerged to emergent annual**, with leaves and flowering stems to 0.5 m tall and milky juice. Leaves are highly variable, but most mature leaves are emergent and have **bases with short to long, pointed lobes** (sagittate). The first inflorescence may appear before the first sagittate leaf. California arrowhead is a **native** species that is a common weed in rice and wild rice fields and irrigation canals, but it is beneficial to wildlife in natural ecosystems. The fruits and leaves are an important food source for waterfowl.

SEEDLING: Grows on wet mud or submerged in shallow water. Cotyledons and immature leaves basal, linear, translucent, lack stalks. Juvenile leaves variable in size, stalked, often floating, oblong, ovate, or cordate. Veins parallel and transverse, forming a rectangular pattern.

MATURE PLANT: **Emergent leaves basal, sagittate**, 5–20 cm long, to **20 cm wide**. **Basal lobes nearly equal in length to the blade apex.** Petioles erect to spreading, occasionally reflexed, to 60 cm long, thick, spongy, and sheathing a short stem base. Outer leaves sometimes linear to lanceolate or appear to lack distinct blades. Leaf blades of plants in deep water (>20 cm) are often narrower, with longer basal lobes, or ovate to lanceolate and lacking basal lobes. Mature plant size is highly variable.

California arrowhead (*Sagittaria montevidensis*) in a rice field.   J. K. CLARK

ROOTS AND UNDERGROUND STRUCTURES: Roots fibrous. Stolons or tubers are lacking.

FLOWERS: June–September. **Monoecious** (male and female flowers on the same plant). **Flowering stems are less than or equal to height of leaves**. Panicles simple, whorled, with 3 male (staminate) flowers at all nodes except the lowest. **Lowest node has 2** (rarely 3) **bisexual flowers**. Flower stalks (pedicels)

California arrowhead *(Sagittaria montevidensis)* flower.   J. K. CLARK

California arrowhead *(Sagittaria montevidensis)* leaves.

J. K. CLARK

ascending to spreading, to 3.5 cm long. Sepals 3, ovate, **erect or appressed, persistent**, 1–1.5 cm long in fruit. Petals 3, deciduous, about 1.5 cm long, **white with a green-yellow spot at base**, margins smooth. Stamens **numerous**. Filaments **thick**, covered with **papillate hairs**. Carpels **numerous** (500–2000 per head), **separate, forming a spherical head**. Insect-pollinated. Self-fertilization is possible but uncommon since staminate flowers mature later than bisexual flowers. Anthers and female structures of bisexual flowers mature at the same time.

FRUITS AND SEEDS: Fruiting heads **spherical**, 1.5–3 cm diameter, on **thickened pedicels** that become **reflexed** with maturity. Sepals cover most of fruit. Achenes obovate to wedge-shaped, 2–3 mm long, about 1.3 mm wide, with narrowly

California arrowhead (*Sagittaria montevidensis*) seedling.   J. K. CLARK

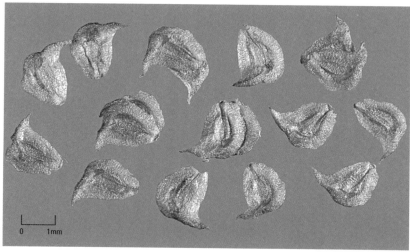

California arrowhead (*Sagittaria montevidensis*) achenes.   J. K. CLARK

winged margins and a horizontal to oblique beak at the top to 1.5 mm long. Each face has a resin duct. Most achenes mature submerged.

POSTSENESCENCE CHARACTERISTICS: Senesced foliage decays rapidly in water.

HABITAT: Rice fields, ponds, ditches, sloughs, streams, and wetland margins. Colonizes open sites on wet mud and in still or slow-flowing shallow water.

DISTRIBUTION: Oregon, Arizona, Colorado, New Mexico to 1220 m, and California in the Central Valley, San Francisco Bay region, central South Coast (Los Angeles Co.), to 300 m. Eastern United States, northern Mexico. Yearly populations are variable and erratic.

PROPAGATION AND PHENOLOGY: Reproduces by seed. Most seeds germinate the following spring (± May), but some seeds may germinate soon after dispersal. Seedlings mature rapidly, and 2 to 3 generations of plants can be produced in a season. Germination is inhibited under dry conditions or in water more than 20 cm deep. Plants compete poorly with perennials. Under optimal conditions, plants produce many seeds. Flowers seldom develop on plants growing in deep water.

SIMILAR SPECIES: Gregg arrowhead (*Sagittaria longiloba* Engelm. ex J.G. Sm., synonyms: longbarb arrowhead; *Sagittaria greggii* J.G.Sm.) [SAGLO] is a native **perennial** that resembles California arrowhead and is frequently weedy in rice fields and irrigation ditches. Unlike California arrowhead, Gregg arrowhead has emergent leaves with **narrow basal lobes** about **twice the length of the terminal lobe** and lowest inflorescence nodes with **3 pistillate flowers**. In fruit, sepals are **reflexed** and pedicels are **straight** and slender. Gregg arrowhead occurs in

Gregg arrowhead (*Sagittaria longiloba*) in a rice field.   J. K. CLARK

Gregg arrowhead (*Sagittaria longiloba*) plant.
                                    J. K. CLARK

Colorado, New Mexico, southern Arizona to 1525 m, and California in the Central Valley to 300 m. Other native *Sagittaria* spp. also occur less commonly throughout the western states. These, however, are rarely weedy in rice fields or managed aquatic systems. Waterplantains (*Alisma* spp.) **lack sagittate leaves**. Refer to table 11 (page 143) for a comparison of other important differences.

Upright burhead (*Echinodorus berteroi* (Spreng.) Fassett) has **burlike fruiting heads** and **angled stems** and **leaf stalks**. It is primarily a weed of rice fields.

Comparison of foliage of Gregg arrowhead (*Sagittaria longiloba*) (top) and California arrowhead (*S. montevidensis*) (bottom).   J. K. CLARK

Gregg arrowhead (*Sagittaria longiloba*) seedling.
J. K. CLARK

Gregg arrowhead (*Sagittaria longiloba*) achenes.   J. K. CLARK

Alligatorweed (*Alternanthera philoxeroides* (C. Martius) Griseb.) [ALRPH]

Noxious Weed Lists: California: A list

General Information: Noxious herbaceous **aquatic to terrestrial perennial** with horizontal to ascending stems to 1 m long. Aquatic form has **hollow, floating,** emergent and submerged stems. Terrestrial form has solid stems. Typically, plants grow rooted in soil in shallow water and form dense, interwoven floating mats that extend over the surface of deeper water. Mats can become dense enough to support the weight of a person. **Floating mats can break away and colonize new sites.** Mats disrupt the natural ecology of a site by reducing light penetration and crowding out native species. Serious infestations can create anoxic, disease-, and mosquito-breeding conditions. Probably introduced from South America. The alligatorweed flea beetle (*Agasicles hygrophila*), stem borer moth (*Arcola malloi* = *Vogtia malloi*), and alligatorweed thrips (*Amynothrips andersoni*) have been released as biocontrol agents in the southeastern United States. These insects can effectively control infestations of alligatorweed. However, none are yet established in California.

Seedling: Seedlings seldom encountered because viable seeds are rarely produced.

Mature Plant: Stems simple or branched and lacking hairs or with 2 opposing lengthwise rows of hairs. Leaves **opposite**, more or less equal at a node, sessile or with narrowly winged petioles (to 1 cm long) that clasp the stem. Leaf blades mostly 4–11 cm long, 1–3 cm wide, narrowly lanceolate (to obovate), with entire margins and a smooth waxy surface.

Roots and Underground Structures: Stolons root at the nodes. Floating plants have shorter, finer roots than plants rooted in soil. Stolon fragments with a node often develop into new plants.

Flowers: June–October. Pleasantly fragrant. **Spikes headlike**, 12–18 mm in diameter, on terminal or axillary **stalks 4–9 cm long**. Flowers and bracts **pearly white, glabrous**. Flowers lack petals. Sepals 5, separate, 5–7 mm long. Stamens 5, opposite sepals, alternate with 5 longer sterile stamens (staminodia). Ovary superior, with a single chamber containing 1 ovule.

Fruits and Seeds: In most of North America, plant produces few, if any, viable seeds. When seeds are produced the utricles are membranous but do not open to release the single seed. Seeds smooth, disc-shaped to flattened wedge–shaped.

Postsenescence Characteristics: Dead stems fall over and contribute to formation of the mat. Mild frost kills leaves but not stems. Severe frosts kill emergent stems but not submerged or buried parts.

Habitat: Shallow water or wet soils, ditches, marshes, and edges of ponds and slow-moving watercourses. Occasionally on dry sites. Tolerates saline conditions (to 100,000 ppm). Requires a warm summer growing season. Tolerates cold winters but cannot survive prolonged freezing temperatures.

Distribution: California in the San Joaquin Valley (Tulare and Kings Cos.) and southwestern region (Los Angeles, San Bernardino and Riverside Cos.) to 200 m. Southeastern United States, Central America.

Alligatorweed (*Alternanthera philoxeroides*) habit in a canal.
CDFA IPC Program

Alligatorweed (*Alternanthera philoxeroides*) is occasionally found on dry areas.　　　D. O. Clark

PROPAGATION AND PHENOLOGY: Reproduces vegetatively from stolons. Each node or fragment with a node is capable of producing a new plant. Plants are highly competitive and have rapid growth rates. Plants rarely grow in water deeper than 2 m. **Seeds rarely develop**, and those that do are seldom viable.

MANAGEMENT FAVORING OR DISCOURAGING SURVIVAL: Plants grow best under high-nutrient (eutrophic) conditions. Mechanical harvesting without careful removal

Stem segment of alligatorweed (*Alternanthera philoxeroides*) with adventitious roots.
CDFA IPC PROGRAM

Alligatorweed (*Alternanthera philoxeroides*) seedlings surrounded by mosquitofern (*Azolla* sp.).
CDFA IPC PROGRAM

of all plant parts can facilitate spread. Stolons can regenerate from burial to ±30 cm deep.

SIMILAR SPECIES: Swamp smartweed (*Polygonum amphibium* L. var. *emersum* Michx.) and other smartweeds are **aquatic perennials with rhizomes** that may be confused with alligatorweed. Swamp smartweed is distinguished by having **alternate leaves** with **fused, sheathing stipules** (ocrea) and **pink flowers**. Refer to the **Swamp smartweed** entry (page 314) for more information. Uruguay waterprimrose (*Ludwigia hexapetala* Hook. & Arn.) Zandini et al.) can have a similar growth form but has alternate leaves and bright yellow flowers.

Node and flower cluster of alligatorweed (*Alternanthera philoxeroides*).

CDFA IPC PROGRAM

Giant hogweed (*Heracleum mantegazzianum* Sommier & Levier)

NOXIOUS WEED LISTS: Federal Noxious Weed; Washington: A; Oregon: A

GENERAL INFORMATION: Robust **biennial or perennial to 5 m tall** with **large 3-part compound leaves**. Once cultivated as an unusual garden ornamental, giant hogweed has escaped cultivation and is a noxious weed in Washington, adjacent Canada, and parts of the northeastern United States. In western North America, giant hogweed often grows in riparian areas, where it can develop a dense canopy and crowd out native riparian species. Unlike other emergent aquatic plants, giant hogweed cannot tolerate prolonged root submergence in water. The loss of understory vegetation increases stream bank erosion. Skin contact with the sap can cause severe photosensitizing dermatitis on most people and some animals. Cattle and pigs consume giant hogweed without any apparent problem. Infestations are nearly always associated with garden escapes. Introduced from southwestern Asia.

SEEDLING: Cotyledons ± 3 cm long, first leaves palmate, not deeply incised. Seedlings grow rapidly.

MATURE PLANT: Stems and leaf stalks typically **purple-blotched**, covered with coarse pustule-based white hairs. Leaves alternate, pinnate-compound with 3 leaflets, **to 3 m long, to 2.6 m wide**. Leaflets deeply bipinnate-lobed and toothed. Leaf stalks inflated, sheathing stem.

ROOTS AND UNDERGROUND STRUCTURES: Rootstocks ± tuberous, often develop additional crowns with buds that overwinter (perennating buds).

Giant hogweed (*Heracleum mantegazzianum*) leaves.   KING COUNTY NOXIOUS WEED PROGRAM

FLOWERS: Umbels compound, to 0.5 m diameter. **Main umbel rays usually 50–150, unequal.** Petals white, ± 1 cm long.

FRUITS AND SEEDS: Schizocarps (fruits) elliptic to obovate, 8–12 mm long, strongly flattened front to back (perpendicular to the central axis), covered with short hairs (pubescent), lateral ribs winged. Stalks 1.5–4 cm long.

HABITAT: Riparian areas, disturbed sites, roadsides, and waste places. Often grows in wet places.

DISTRIBUTION: Washington (Thurston, Kitsap, Mason, King, Island, and Clark Cos.) and isolated locations in Oregon. Northeastern United States. Expanding range.

PROPAGATION AND PHENOLOGY: Reproduces by seed and vegetatively by forming new crowns from the tuberous rootstocks. Plants can produce many seeds. Seeds disperse with water, soil movements, by clinging to the feet, feathers, and

Giant hogweed (*Heracleu m mantegazzianum*) plant.
KING COUNTY NOXIOUS WEED PROGRAM

fur of animals, and by human activities. Seeds survive 7 years or more under field conditions. Individual plants appear to flower once and die, but new plants grow from crowns developed from rootstock during the previous year.

SIMILAR SPECIES: Cow parsnip (*Heracleum lanatum* Michx.) is a widespread **native perennial** to 3 m tall that may be confused with giant hogweed. Unlike giant hogweed, cow parsnip stems and leaf stalks generally **lack purple blotches** and **umbels have fewer than 45 primary rays.** Cow parsnip is usually not considered a weed and is an important component of native riparian ecosystems. Like giant hogweed, it can also cause photosensitizing dermatitis.

Giant hogweed (*Heracleum mantegazzianum*) stem.   KING COUNTY NOXIOUS WEED PROGRAM

Cow parsnip (*Heracleum lanatum*) is rarely weedy in its native habitat.   J. M. DITOMASO

Cow parsnip (*Heracleum lanatum*) fruit (schizocarps). Similar in appearance to giant hogweed (*Heracleum mantegazzianum*), although smaller.   J. K. CLARK

Floating pennywort (*Hydrocotyle ranunculoides* L.f.) [HYDRA]

SYNONYMS: floating marshpennywort; *Hydrocotyle batrachioides* DC.; *Hydrocotyle natans* Cirillo; *Hydrocotyle ranunculoides* L.f. vars. *ranunculoides* and *adoensis* Urb.

GENERAL INFORMATION: Floating to terrestrial perennial with branched **creeping stems** that **root at the nodes**. Plants grow in dense low-growing mats in shallow water or on wet soil near water. Occasionally small colonies are free-floating. Floating pennywort is a widespread native of North America. In natural areas, colonies are usually considered a desirable component of aquatic ecosystems. Because of its creeping habit, floating pennywort can be a nuisance in irrigation and drainage ditches and has become a more prevalent problem in the Sacramento–San Joaquin Delta in areas where water hyacinth has been controlled. Plants are sometimes sold as aquatic or pond ornamentals and have escaped cultivation in some regions. In Britain, floating pennywort has become a problematic weed of natural aquatic habitats, and in southern and western Australia it is a government-listed noxious weed.

MATURE PLANT: Foliage **glabrous, fleshy**. Stems root at most nodes, fragment easily. Leaves alternate, **round or kidney-shaped, deeply 3–7-lobed or cleft**, 1–8 cm wide, palmate-veined, sometimes with a reddish central spot at point of stalk (petiole) attachment. Margins smooth to scalloped (crenate). Stalks thick, 5–35 cm long, sometimes reddish. Stipules **papery** at the base, **not sheathing**.

ROOTS AND UNDERGROUND STRUCTURES: Roots grow from most nodes and are shallow in soil substrate.

Floating pennywort (*Hydrocotyle ranunculoides*) in an irrigation canal.   CDFA IPC PROGRAM

FLOWERS: March–August. **Umbels simple**, dense, on stalks (peduncles) usually shorter than leaves, with 5–10 flowers on stalks (pedicels) 1–3 mm long. Calyx (sepals as a unit) lacking or consisting of 5 minute lobes. Petals 5, greenish or yellowish white to purplish. Stamens 5. Ovary inferior, 2-chambered, with 2 separate styles at the apex.

FRUITS AND SEEDS: Fruits (schizocarps) flattened laterally (wall dividing chambers perpendicular to fruit plane), **on stalks** 1–6 cm long, elliptic to round, 1–3 mm long, with thickened inconspicuous ribs, separating into halves (mericarps) at maturity. Each mericarp contains 1 seed.

POSTSENESCENCE CHARACTERISTICS: Foliage sometimes dies back after plants flower.

HABITAT: Pond and lake margins, marshes, low swamps, slow streams, and irrigation and drainage ditches. Can also grow on turf in overwatered or moist sites.

Floating pennywort *(Hydrocotyle ranunculoides)* in a wet meadow.   J. M. DiTomaso

Floating pennywort *(Hydrocotyle ranunculoides)* foliage.   J. M. DiTomaso

Floating pennywort (*Hydrocotyle ranunculoides*) inflorescence.   J. M. DıТоmaso

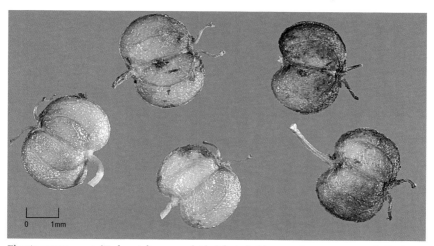

Floating pennywort (*Hydrocotyle ranunculoides*) fruit (schizocarps).   J. K. CLARK

DISTRIBUTION: Oregon, Washington, Arizona, and scattered throughout California, except Great Basin region and deserts, to 1500 m. Many areas in North and South America.

PROPAGATION AND PHENOLOGY: Reproduces by seed and/or vegetatively from creeping stems and stem fragments. Seeds and stem fragments disperse with water, substrate movement, animals, and human activities. In Britain, floating pennywort plants rooted in the substrate produce seeds, while floating colonies primarily reproduce vegetatively. Floating mats sometimes support other vegetation.

SIMILAR SPECIES: Other native *Hydrocotyle* species, including **water pennywort** (*H. umbellata* L.) and **whorled pennywort** (*H. verticillata* Thunb.), also grow in aquatic habitats and have **round leaves** but **with the stalk attached at the center** (peltate). These species are rarely weedy.

Seepwillow (*Baccharis salicifolia* (Ruiz & Pavón) Pers.) [BACGL]

SYNONYMS: mule fat; water-wally; *Baccharis glutinosa* Pers.; *Baccharis viminea* DC.; *Molina salicifolia* Ruiz & Pavón

GENERAL INFORMATION: Native willowlike **shrub** to 4 m tall. Seepwillow is a desirable component of natural ecosystems but is often weedy in irrigation ditches. Two biotypes of seepwillow were previously treated as 2 separate species (*Baccharis glutinosa* Pers. and *Baccharis viminea* DC.) based on phenological and minor morphological differences.

MATURE PLANT: Stems woody, ascending to erect. Twigs longitudinally striated, ± angled. Foliage glabrous. Leaves alternate, **narrowly lanceolate**, 2–15 cm long, 0.5–2.5 cm wide, **3-veined from the base with outer veins near the margin**, ± dotted with sessile resin glands. Bases tapered to a short ± winged stalk. Margins smooth to sharply toothed (serrate).

ROOTS AND UNDERGROUND STRUCTURES: Major roots woody.

FLOWERS: January–October, depending on type and location. **Male and female flowers develop on separate plants** (dioecious). Heads 3–8 mm long, **consist only of disk flowers.** Phyllaries ovate to narrowly lanceolate with ragged papery margins, in **4–5 graduated rows**, sometimes purple-tinged. Corollas (petals as a unit) **cream-colored to pink-tinged or greenish**. Female flowers have an inconspicuous corolla, numerous fine straight white **pappus bristles**, and lack stamens. Male flowers have a conspicuous corolla, barbed wavy **pappus bristles**, and a vestigial ovary with a 2-branched style. **Receptacles lack chaff** (bracts), flat to convex. Insect-pollinated.

Seepwillow (*Baccharis salicifolia*) along a streambed in its native habitat.　　　J. M. DiTomaso

Male flower heads of seepwillow *(Baccharis salicifolia)*.

J. M. DiTomaso

FRUITS AND SEEDS: Achenes cylindrical, ± 1 mm long, 4–5 ribbed, glabrous, with numerous ± even pappus bristles.

HABITAT: Riparian areas, washes, ditches, irrigation canals, and roadsides.

DISTRIBUTION: Utah, Colorado, New Mexico, Arizona, Nevada, and throughout California, except higher regions of the Sierra Nevada and Cascade Range, to 1250 m. Texas, Mexico, South America.

PROPAGATION AND PHENOLOGY: Reproduces by seed. Seeds disperse primarily with wind and water. Female plants can produce many viable seeds. Plants cut above the root crown can resprout.

SIMILAR SPECIES: Seepwillow superficially resembles willow (*Salix*) species. Unlike seepwillow, willow species have **flowers in catkins** and leaves that **lack 3 veins from the base**.

Female flower heads of seepwillow (*Baccharis salicifolia*).   J. M. DiTomaso

Brassbuttons (*Cotula coronopifolia* L.) [CULCO]

Synonyms: common brassbuttons; *Lancisia coronopifolia* (L.) Rydb.

General Information: Emersed to terrestrial perennial to 0.3 m tall, with **yellow buttonlike flower heads**. Foliage is usually mildly aromatic. Introduced from South Africa.

Seedling: Cotyledons oblong, base tapered and ± sheathing, tip rounded, 1–2 mm long, glabrous. First leaves opposite, ± sessile, glabrous, narrowly oblong, base tapered, tip rounded, 4–7 mm long.

Mature Plant: Foliage **glabrous, ± fleshy**, light or yellowish green. Stems spreading, branched. Leaves alternate, sessile, linear to lanceolate or oblong, sheathing stem at the base, 2–7 cm long. Margins smooth to coarsely toothed or lobed.

Roots and Underground Structures: Stems often creep by rooting at the lower nodes.

Flowers: March–December. Heads **yellow, 5–15 mm diameter, solitary on long stalks**, appear to consist only of disk flowers but actually **consist of bisexual disk flowers at the center and pistillate flowers without corollas** (disciform) **around the margin**. Flowers lack a pappus. **Pistillate flowers have a stalk below the ovary** (immature achene) that is as long as the ovary. Phyllaries in 2–3 series. Receptacle flat, lacks chaff.

Fruits and Seeds: Achenes flattened with a ± winged margin, smooth on the outer face, covered with minute papillae on the inner face. Pistillate achenes ovate, 1.5–2 mm long, with a broad membranous wing, **on a stalk ± as long as the achene**. Disk achenes oblanceolate, 1–1.5 mm long, barely winged, nearly sessile.

Brassbuttons (*Cotula coronopifolia*) along a streamside.   J. M. DiTomaso

HABITAT: Freshwater and salt marshes, wetlands, vernal pools, ditches, and seasonally wet places in many plant communities. Does not tolerate significant frost.

DISTRIBUTION: Oregon, Washington, Nevada, Arizona, and California in the North, Central, and South Coast, San Francisco Bay region, Central Valley, and South Coast Ranges, to 300 m.

PROPAGATION AND PHENOLOGY: Reproduces by seed and vegetatively from stems that root at the nodes. Seeds fall near the parent plant or disperse with water and mud. Most seeds germinate after the first fall rains through winter. Seeds survive 1–2 years under field conditions.

Brassbuttons *(Cotula coronopifolia)* stem and flower heads.　　　　　　J. M. DiTOMASO

Brassbuttons (*Cotula coronopifolia*) flower head.

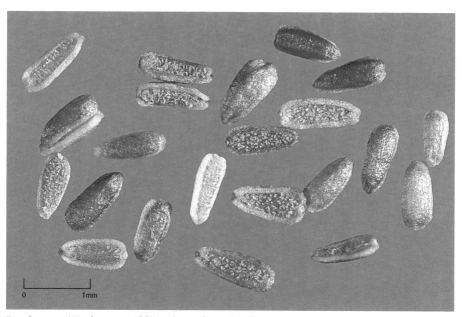

0   1mm

Brassbuttons (*Cotula coronopifolia*) achenes from disk flowers.

Eclipta (*Eclipta prostrata* (L.) L.) [ECLAL]

SYNONYMS: false daisy; yerba de tago; *Eclipta alba* (L.) Hassk.; *Eclipta erecta* L.; *Verbesina alba* L.; *Verbesina prostrata* L.; a few others

GENERAL INFORMATION: Leafy **summer annual** or biennial to 1 m tall, with **opposite leaves** and **small white flower heads**. Eclipta is a widespread native that is weedy in moist crop fields nearly worldwide. It is typically a minor weed of rice fields in California and usually occurs in shallow areas or on levees surrounding fields. Where it occurs in western states, eclipta is designated as a facultative wetland indicator species. It is an important medicinal plant in India and China, is used to treat venomous snakebites in Brazil, and is the source of a dark dye.

SEEDLING: Cotyledons oval, less than 10 mm long, glabrous, taper to a short stalk. First and subsequent leaves opposite, initially ovate, becoming lanceolate to elliptic with age, sparsely covered with short flattened (appressed) hairs, margins entire to weakly irregular-toothed.

MATURE PLANT: Foliage variable, **sparse to moderately covered with short flattened hairs** (strigose). Stems simple to highly branched, prostrate to erect, often reddish, ± succulent. **Leaves opposite, ± sessile, lanceolate to elliptic**, 2–10 cm long, narrow to broad, widest near the middle. **Margins entire to weakly irregular-toothed**.

ROOTS AND UNDERGROUND STRUCTURES: Taproot shallow, with fibrous lateral roots. Lower nodes of stems often develop adventitious roots. Stem fragments may root under favorable conditions.

Eclipta *(Eclipta prostrata)* in a rice field.   J. M. DITOMASO

Eclipta (*Eclipta prostrata*) inflorescence and stem node.   J. M. DiTomaso

Eclipta (*Eclipta prostrata*) seedling.   J. M. DiTomaso

FLOWERS: Year-round. Heads 4–10 mm diameter, hemispherical, single or in small clusters in the leaf axils. **Ray and disk flowers white**. Ray corollas 1.5–3 mm long, narrow. Disk corollas 4-lobed. Phyllaries ovate, separate, usually in **2 ± equal rows**, sometimes in a single row. Receptacle flat, **covered with narrow, flat, bristlelike bracts** (chaff).

FRUITS AND SEEDS: Achenes obovoid to wedge-shaped, flattened, ± 4-sided, **truncate at the apex, blunt at the base**, 1.5–2.5 mm long, smooth to bumpy, **with or without a pappus of minute bristles to 0.2 mm long**.

HABITAT: Moist places, freshwater marshes, pond and stream margins, irrigated agronomic fields, rice fields, levees, irrigation ditches, and seasonally wet sites.

DISTRIBUTION: New Mexico, Arizona, Nevada, and California in the Central Valley, South Coast Ranges, southwestern region, and Sonoran Desert, to 300 m. Central, eastern, and southern United States. Most abundant in the southern states.

PROPAGATION AND PHENOLOGY: Reproduces by seed. Seeds disperse with water, in mud, and with human activities. Seeds germinate midspring through early summer as soil temperatures warm. Germination requires light. One plant can produce several thousand seeds.

MANAGEMENT FAVORING OR DISCOURAGING SURVIVAL: Removing plants before seeds develop can help control infestations. Keeping water level at >10 cm in level rice fields will also prevent establishment.

Eclipta (*Eclipta prostrata*) achenes.   J. K. CLARK

Perennial pepperweed (*Lepidium latifolium* L.) [LEPLA]

NOXIOUS WEED LISTS: Oregon: B list; Washington: B list; California: B list; New Mexico: A list; Colorado: A list; Idaho, Nevada, Utah, Wyoming: Noxious Weed; CalEPPC: A-1

SYNONYMS: broadleaf pepperweed; broadleaved pepperweed; giant white weed; iron weed; perennial peppercress; perennial peppergrass; slender perennial peppercress; tall whitetop; *Cardaria latifolia* (L.) Spach

GENERAL INFORMATION: Erect noxious perennial to 2 m tall, with white flowers and extensively creeping roots. Plants are highly competitive and typically form dense colonies that displace native vegetation and wildlife. Toxicity to grazing livestock is undocumented. Goats appear to tolerate heavy consumption of fresh plants, and cows, under some situations, will also graze the foliage. However, there have been reports of horses becoming ill after being fed contaminated hay, possibly due to the ability of perennial pepperweed to accumulate nitrates. Perennial pepperweed has spread rapidly throughout the western United States since its introduction from Eurasia to California around 1936.

SEEDLING: Cotyledons obovate to oblong, 3–8 mm long, glabrous, tip rounded, base tapered into a short stalk 2–3 mm long. First leaves developmentally alternate but appear opposite, ovate to oblong, 4–12 mm long, glabrous, tip rounded, base wedge-shaped, on a stalk ± 5 mm long. Margins entire to slightly wavy. Subsequent leaves resemble first leaves and are increasingly larger.

Perennial pepperweed (*Lepidium latifolium*) infesting a wetland site.   J. M. DiTomaso

171

MATURE PLANT: Crown and lower stems weakly woody. **Foliage glabrous**, green to gray-green. Leaves alternate, lanceolate to elliptic or oblong. Basal leaves to 30 cm long and 8 cm wide, with serrate margins and on long stalks (3–15 cm long). Stem leaves reduced, ± **sessile, tapered at the base**, margins entire to weakly serrate.

ROOTS AND UNDERGROUND STRUCTURES: Roots long, thick, sometimes curly, minimally branched, vigorously creeping. Most roots occur in the top 60 cm of soil, but some can penetrate to depths of 3 m or more. Experimental evidence suggests that plants extract salts from deep soil and deposit them on the soil surface with leaf litter, inhibiting the germination and growth of other species. Carbohydrate reserves are lowest when flowering stems are elongating (bolting stage).

Perennial pepperweed (*Lepidium latifolium*) plant.   J. M. DiTomaso

Basal rosette of perennial pepperweed (*Lepidium latifolium*).   J. M. DiTomaso

FLOWERS: May–September. Inflorescences ± pyramidal to rounded on top. Petals 4, white, spoon-shaped, ± 1.5 mm long. Sepals oval, less than 1 mm long, often covered with long simple hairs. Stamens 6, 4 long, 2 short. Insect-pollinated.

FRUITS AND SEEDS: Pods (silicles) 2-chambered, **round to slightly ovate, slightly flattened, lacking a notch at the apex,** ± 2 mm long, **covered with long simple hairs. Stigma sessile, persistent.** Stalks much longer than pods, glabrous or sparsely pubescent. Seeds 1 per chamber, ellipsoid, slightly flattened, with a shallow groove on each side, ± 1 mm long, 0.5 mm wide, reddish brown, minutely granular. Seeds fall from pods irregularly through winter and some may remain in pods until the following season.

POSTSENESCENCE CHARACTERISTICS: Aboveground parts typically die in late fall and winter. The pale tan dead stems degrade very slowly and can persist for more than 1 year.

HABITAT: Wetlands, riparian areas, meadows, salt marshes, flood plains, beaches, roadsides, irrigation ditches, agronomic crops (especially alfalfa), orchards, vineyards, irrigated pastures, rangelands, and ornamental plantings. Typically grows on moist or seasonally wet sites. Once established, can also survive on dry sites. Tolerates saline and alkaline conditions.

DISTRIBUTION: All western states. Throughout California, except deserts and northern North Coast and adjacent mountains (Del Norte, Humboldt, and Mendocino Cos.), to 2100 m. Texas, a few central and northeastern states.

PROPAGATION AND PHENOLOGY: **Reproduces vegetatively from creeping roots** and **root fragments** and **by seed.** Roots do not hold soil together very well, allowing erosion of river, stream, or ditch banks. Root fragments and seeds float and disperse with flooding, soil movement, and agricultural and other human activities. Seeds can also cling to tires, shoes, and the feet, fur, and feathers of animals and can contaminate hay or crop and pasture seeds. Large root fragments can survive

Perennial pepperweed (*Lepidium latifolium*) inflorescence.   J. M. DiTomaso

Tapered leaf base of perennial pepperweed (*Lepidium latifolium*).   J. M. DiTomaso

extreme desiccation on the soil surface for extended periods. Fragments as small as 1–2 cm long and 2–8 mm in diameter can develop into new plants. New shoots begin to grow from roots in late winter to early spring. Fluctuating temperatures appear to stimulate seed germination. Plants usually produce many often highly viable seeds, but seedlings are seldom detected in the field. In wet years, seed production is sometimes limited by white rust (*Albugo* sp.) infection. Seedlings emerge midwinter through midspring, depending on the temperature.

MANAGEMENT FAVORING OR DISCOURAGING SURVIVAL: Heavy infestations are difficult to control. Cleaning agricultural or earth-moving machinery after use in infested areas and curtailing movement or use of soil, hay, and crop or pasture seeds contaminated with perennial pepperweed root fragments and/or seeds can help prevent new infestations. Single techniques, such as repeated mowing, hand-digging, cultivation, grazing, and burning, typically do not adequately control perennial pepperweed. In addition, cultivation may increase infestations by dis-

Perennial pepperweed (*Lepidium latifolium*) seedling.   J. M. DiTomaso

Perennial pepperweed (*Lepidium latifolium*) seeds and fruit.   J. K. Clark

Hoary cress (*Cardaria draba*) habit.   J. M. DiTomaso

persing root fragments. Field observations suggest that plants may not tolerate an extended period of flooding during the growing season.

SIMILAR SPECIES: Hoary cress (*Cardaria draba* (L.) Desv.), **lens-podded whitetop** (*Cardaria draba* (L.) Desv. ssp. *chalepensis* (L.) O.E. Schutz, synonym: *Cardaria chalepensis* (L.) Hand.-Mazz.), and **hairy whitetop** (*Cardaria pubescens* (C.A. Meyer) Jarmol.) are **noxious perennials to ± 0.5 m tall**, with **creeping roots**, that are easily confused with perennial pepperweed but are usually found in dry habitats. Unlike perennial pepperweed, *Cardaria* species have **stem leaves with lobed bases that clasp the stems** and **foliage ± covered with short hairs**. In addition, *Cardaria* species typically have **± inflated pods greater than 2 mm long** with **persistent styles 1–2 mm long**. One or more *Cardaria* species occur in all western states.

Clasping leaf base of hoary cress (*Cardaria draba*).   J. M. DiTomaso

Hairy whitetop (*Cardaria pubescens*) fruit.
J. M. DiTomaso

Lens-podded whitetop (*Cardaria draba* ssp. *chalepensis*) flowers and fruit.   J. M. DiTomaso

Smallflower umbrella sedge (*Cyperus difformis* L.) [CYPDI]

Lovegrass sedge (*Cyperus eragrostis* Lam.)

SYNONYMS:

Smallflower umbrella sedge: variable flatsedge; *Cyperus lateriflorus* Torr.

Lovegrass sedge: tall cyperus; tall flatsedge; tall umbrellasedge; umbrellaplant; *Cyperus monandrus* Roth.; *Cyperus serrulatus* Vahl; *Cyperus vegetus* Willd.

GENERAL INFORMATION: Erect grasslike plants with **closed sheaths, 3-sided stems, and clusters of spikelets in compound umbels**.

Smallflower umbrella sedge: Tufted **summer annual** to 0.4 m tall, with inflorescences consisting of small spherical clusters of greenish brown to purplish spikelets at maturity. **Smallflower umbrella sedge** is typically a weed of rice fields in tropical to warm temperate regions nearly worldwide. Some biotypes have developed resistance to certain herbicides. Plants utilize the C3 photosynthetic pathway. Introduced from subtropical regions of Asia and Africa.

Lovegrass sedge: Perennial to 1 m tall, with **rhizomes** and inflorescences consisting of compact clusters of flattened green spikelets that turn tannish with age. **Lovegrass sedge** is a common widespread native and a desirable component of the vegetation in natural areas. However, plants can be weedy in moist agricultural fields, including rice fields, orchards, landscaped areas, and irrigation ditches.

Smallflower umbrella sedge *(Cyperus difformis)* on the edge of a rice field.   J. M. DiTOMASO

SEEDLING:

Smallflower umbrella sedge: Cotyledon elliptic, ± 1 mm long, glabrous, translucent. First leaf blade 4–8 mm long, 0.25–0.5 mm wide, 3-veined, bright green. Sheath 1–2 mm long. Roots sometimes pinkish.

Lovegrass sedge: Resembles **yellow nutsedge**.

MATURE PLANT: Flowering stems (culms) smooth. Basal leaves shorter or ± equal in length to culms.

Smallflower umbrella sedge: Culms sharply triangular in cross-section, sides often concave. Basal leaves typically 2–4 per culm, 1–4 mm wide, slightly rough to touch (scaberulous) on the margins near the tips.

Lovegrass sedge: Flowering stems slightly swollen at the base, **triangular in cross-section, angles smooth** and often **rounded or blunt.** Basal leaves 6–10 per culm, 5–10 mm wide, slightly rough to touch on the margins and lower midvein near the tips.

ROOTS AND UNDERGROUND STRUCTURES:

Smallflower umbrella sedge: All roots fibrous, sometimes reddish.

Lovegrass sedge: Rhizomes short, thick. Fibrous roots coarse.

SPIKELETS AND FRUITS: May–November. **Spikelets persistent,** composed of 2 rows of overlapping **deciduous scales** (tiny bracts) that conceal the achenes. Rachis (stalk to which scales are attached) **straight, lacks narrow wings. Style 3-branched. Achenes 3-sided,** obovoid.

Smallflower umbrella sedge (*Cyperus difformis*) plant.   J. K. CLARK

Smallflower umbrella sedge (*Cyperus difformis*) inflorescence.   J. K. CLARK

Smallflower umbrella sedge: Inflorescence leaves 2–3. Spikelet clusters dense, **spherical**, typically consist of **50–100** spikelets or more, sessile and/or on unequal stalks (rays) to 7 cm long. Spikelets ± oblong, **slightly flattened, 4–8 mm long**. Scales **rounded at the tips**, membranous, **0.5–1 mm long**, green with brown to purplish sides, readily deciduous. Stamens 1–2. Achenes obovoid, 0.5–1 mm long, with a **minute nipplelike tip** (mucronulate), glossy, pale greenish brown. Surface finely cellular under magnification.

Lovegrass sedge: Inflorescence leaves 4–8, 3–50 cm long, slightly rough to touch on the margins and midvein. Spikelet clusters dense, headlike, consist of 20–70

Smallflower umbrella sedge (*Cyperus difformis*) spikelets and achenes.   J. M. DiTomaso

Smallflower umbrella sedge (*Cyperus difformis*) seedling.
J. M. DiTomaso

spikelets, nearly sessile or on stalks to 10 cm long. Spikelets narrowly ovate, **strongly flattened, 10–20 mm long, 3–3.5 mm wide**. Scales ovate, **2–2.3 mm long, tip acute**, keeled on the backs, 3-veined, midvein minutely roughened at the tip, straw-colored, enfold achene, deciduous with achene. Stamens 1. Achenes obovoid, **1–1.5 mm long and half as wide**, with a **short beak at the tip** (mucronate) and **short stalk** (stipitate) **at the base**, black to dark brown. Surface covered with minute sunken dots under magnification.

HABITAT:

Smallflower umbrella sedge: Rice fields, ditches, and pond margins, typically in shallow water or wet soils. Grows best on fertile soils. Does not tolerate deep water.

Lovegrass sedge (*Cyperus eragrostis*) plant.   J. M. DiTomaso

Lovegrass sedge (*Cyperus eragrostis*) inflorescence.   J. M. DiTomaso

Lovegrass sedge (*Cyperus eragrostis*) spikelet clusters.   J. M. DiTomaso

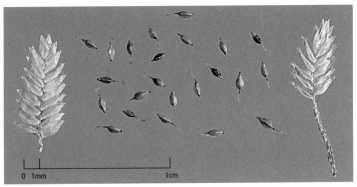

Lovegrass sedge (*Cyperus eragrostis*) achenes and spikelets.   J. K. Clark

Redroot flatsedge (*Cyperus erythrorhizos*) on the bank of an irrigation canal.
                                                                            J. M. DiTomaso

Redroot flatsedge *(Cyperus erythrorhizos)* inflorescence.   J. M. DiTomaso

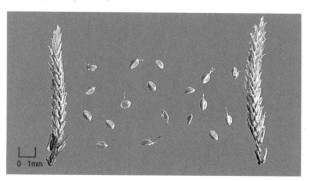

Redroot flatsedge *(Cyperus erythrorhizos)* achenes and spikelets.
J. K. Clark

Whitemargined flatsedge *(Cyperus flavicomus)* inflorescence.   J. M. DiTomaso

Lovegrass sedge: Pond and stream margins, ditches, rice fields, and vernal pools, in shallow water to moist soil.

DISTRIBUTION:

Smallflower umbrella sedge: Arizona, New Mexico, and in the Central Valley and southwestern region of California to 500 m. Southern and eastern United States.

Lovegrass sedge: Oregon, Washington, and throughout California, except Great Basin and desert regions of the state, to 700 m. Southern United States, parts of the northeastern United States.

PROPAGATION AND PHENOLOGY: Seeds disperse with water, soil movement, agricultural activities, and possibly animals.

Smallflower umbrella sedge: Reproduces by seed. Plants typically complete their life cycle (from seed to seed production) in ± 2 months. Seed production is typically high. Germination requires light. Observations suggest that seeds can survive at least 5 years in the field. Deeply buried seeds may survive for many years (50 years in one case).

Lovegrass sedge: Reproduces by seed and **vegetatively from rhizomes.**

SIMILAR SPECIES: Brown flatsedge (*Cyperus fuscus* L.) is an **annual** to 0.3 m tall that resembles **smallflower umbrella sedge.** Unlike smallflower umbrella sedge, brown flatsedge has **open spikelet clusters** consisting of ± **3–15** spikelets. **Brown flatsedge** occurs sporadically in California on wet disturbed sites in the San Joaquin Valley, to 50 m. Introduced from temperate Eurasia.

Redroot flatsedge (*Cyperus erythrorhizos* Muhl., synonym: *Cyperus halei* Torr. ex Britt) [CYPET] is a common widespread **native annual** to 1 m tall, with **reddish**

Whitemargined flatsedge (*Cyperus flavicomus*) spikelet clusters.   J. M. DiTomaso

roots, that resembles **lovegrass sedge**. Redroot flatsedge is distinguished by having more **open** inflorescences with **barely flattened linear spikelets** 3–10 mm long and **1–1.5 mm wide**. In addition, the light brown to light reddish brown scales are **1–1.5 mm long** and **± rounded at the tip with a minute abrupt point** (mucronulate). Achenes are glossy, **light gray to brown**, oblong, **unequally 3-sided**, 0.5–1 mm long, nearly as wide, with a blunt nipplelike tip and finely cellular surface under magnification. Like the other sedges described above, redroot flatsedge flowers have a **3-branched style**. Redroot flatsedge is sometimes weedy in wet agricultural fields and ditches. It occurs in all western states, throughout California to 500 m, and throughout most of the United States.

Whitemargined flatsedge (*Cyperus flavicomus* Michx.; synonym: *Cyperus albomarginatus* (Mart. & Schrad. ex Nees) Steud.) is an **annual** to 1 m tall that looks somewhat like redroot flatsedge. Whitemargined flatsedge is distinguished by having **flowers with a 2-branched style, (ob)ovate flower scales 1.5–2 mm long with a broad translucent-white margin**, and **glossy black lens-shaped achenes (1 mm long) nearly as large as the associated scale**. Whitemargined flatsedge occurs in Arizona, New Mexico, and California but is not included in most current California floras. In California, whitemargined flatsedge is generally associated with rice fields in the northern Sacramento Valley (Butte Co.), to 50 m. It also occurs in the southeastern San Joaquin Valley (Tulare Co.) and may occur elsewhere in California. Introduced from the southern and eastern United States.

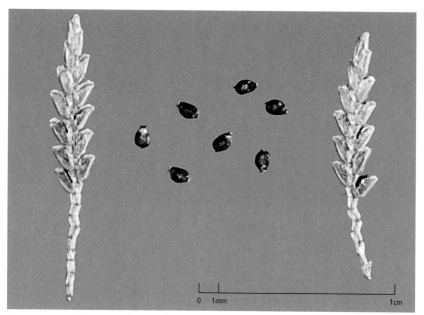

Whitemargined flatsedge (*Cyperus flavicomus*) achenes and spikelets.   J. K. CLARK

Creeping spikerush (*Eleocharis macrostachya* Britt. = *Eleocharis palustris* (L.) Roemer & Schultes in part) [ELOPA]

SYNONYMS: common spikerush; common spikesage; pale spikerush; wiregrass; *Eleocharis mamillata* auct. non Lindb. f.; *Eleocharis perlonga* Fern. & Brack.; *Heliocharis macrostachya* Britt.; *Scirpus palustris* L.; many others

GENERAL INFORMATION: Erect **perennial** to 1 m tall, with **creeping rhizomes** and **bladeless stems** tipped with a single **narrowly conical spikelet.** Creeping spikerush is a widespread native of North America. In natural areas it is not considered a weed, and fruits provide a source of food for wildlife, especially ducks. Creeping spikerush is rarely weedy in rice fields and ditches. *Eleocharis palustris* (sensu lato) consists of a highly variable polyploid complex of species, subspecies, and/or varieties that occur throughout the Northern Hemisphere and which have created much taxonomic confusion. Adding to the confusion, field observations suggest that some variation may be due to differing environmental conditions. *Eleocharis macrostachya* appears to be a regional member of the complex that has been segregated into a species distinct from *Eleocharis palustris*.

SEEDLING: Achenes are important for species identification and typically remain attached to seedlings.

MATURE PLANT: Loosely to densely tufted. Stems slender to stout, **round to oval in cross-section, spongy,** longitudinally ribbed. Leaves are reduced to loose basal

Creeping spikerush (*Eleocharis macrostachya*) in its native habitat along a stream.   J. M. DiTomaso

sheaths; thus, **plants appear leafless**. Leaf sheaths often purplish at the base. Tips obliquely truncate, often with a single tooth.

ROOTS AND UNDERGROUND STRUCTURES: Rhizomes long, creeping, often ± straight, few-branched.

SPIKELETS AND FRUITS: Spikelet **narrowly conical, 5–25 mm long,** slightly wider than stem at the base, consists of **10 or more bisexual flowers**, each hidden by a pale green to brownish or purplish lanceolate scale 1.5–3 mm long. **Style 2-branched.** Achenes **smooth, yellowish brown, obovate lens-shaped (2-sided)** with a yellowish **conical to pyramidal tubercle** at the apex, 1.5–2.5 mm long excluding tubercle. **Tubercle base constricted.**

HABITAT: Shallow water and wet soil of marshes, pond margins, vernal pools, rice fields, ditches, and other wet places or areas subject to flooding. Tolerates some salinity but not shade.

DISTRIBUTION: Throughout most of North America, including all western states. Throughout California to 2500 m.

PROPAGATION AND PHENOLOGY: Reproduces vegetatively from rhizomes and **by seed.** Fruits disperse primarily with water, mud, and animals, especially birds. Seeds typically germinate in standing water midspring through early summer.

SIMILAR SPECIES: Needle spikerush (*Eleocharis acicularis* (L.) Roemer & Schultes var. *acicularis*) [ELOAC], **blunt spikerush** (*Eleocharis obtusa* (Willdenow) Schultes vars. *obtusa* and *engelmanii* (Steudel) Gilly) [ELOOB], and **dwarf spikerush** (*Eleocharis parvula* (Roemer & Schultes) Link ex Buff, Nees & Sauer;

Creeping spikerush (*Eleocharis macrostachya*) flowering stems.　　　　　　J. M. DiTOMASO

Creeping spikerush (*Eleocharis macrostachya*) inflorescence.　　　　　　J. M. DiTOMASO

synonym: *Eleocharis coloradoensis* (Britt.) Filly, *E. parvula* var. *coloradoensis* (Britt.) Beetle) are **widespread native** spikerushes that occasionally inhabit rice fields and/or associated ditches and canals. All of these species are a desirable component of the vegetation in natural areas. Needle spikerush is a major rice weed throughout much of the world but is of only minor importance in California. Experimental evidence suggests that needle spikerush has allelopathic (inhibitory) properties and can displace or inhibit the growth of less desirable aquatic plants, such as **hydrilla** (*Hydrilla verticillata* (L.f.) Royle). With its short stature and allelopathic properties, needle spikerush may actually be a beneficial plant in some canals and ditches. Unlike creeping spikerush, **needle spikerush** is **very short** (to 15 cm tall) and has **3-branched styles** and **weakly 3-sided achenes** with **longitudinal ridges, transverse lines**, and a **small hatlike tubercle**. In addition, plants typically have matted stems, threadlike (filiform) rhizomes (variety *acicularis*), and ± linear spikelets 3–7 mm long. *Eleocharis acicularis* var. *bella* is an annual that lacks rhizomes. Needle spikerush occurs in all western states. In California, it primarily inhabits marshes, vernal pools, wet meadows, and stream banks throughout the state, except deserts and southern Great Basin, to 2500 m.

Blunt spikerush is a **tufted annual** to 0.5 m tall and is distinguished by **lacking rhizomes** and having **± round to ovoid or oblong spikelets** with **rounded tips** and achenes with **deltoid caplike tubercles that lack a constricted base**. Blunt spikerush occurs in California, Oregon, Washington, Idaho, Wyoming, Colorado, and New Mexico. In California, it mostly inhabits marshes and pond and lake margins in the northwestern region, Sierra Nevada, and Modoc Plateau, to 2600 m. It sometimes grows in irrigation channels associated with rice fields but is seldom weedy in the fields themselves.

Creeping spikerush (*Eleocharis macrostachya*) achenes. J. K. CLARK

Blunt spikerush (*Eleocharis obtusa*) in a rice field. J. M. DiTomaso

Dwarf spikerush is very similar to needle spikerush but has small tubers associated with its rhizomes. It has also been demonstrated to be allelopathic to the growth of undesirable aquatic species. It is an occasional weed of rice and irrigation ditches and is found in wet areas, marshes, and saline flats throughout the western states to 2500 m.

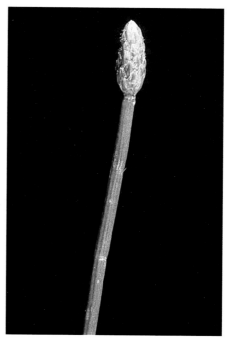

Blunt spikerush (*Eleocharis obtusa*) flowering stems.   J. K. CLARK

Blunt spikerush (*Eleocharis obtusa* var. *engelmanii*) inflorescence.   J. M. DiTOMASO

Blunt spikerush (*Eleocharis obtusa* var. *engelmanii*) achenes.   J. K. CLARK

Needle spikerush *(Eleocharis acicularis* var. *acicularis)* in an irrigation canal.   J. M. DiTomaso

Needle spikerush *(Eleocharis acicularis* var. *acicularis)* shoots and connecting rhizome.   J. M. DiTomaso

Dwarf spikerush *(Eleocharis parvula)* tubers.   J. K. Clark

Hardstem bulrush (*Scirpus acutus* Muhl. ex Bigelow, including var. *occidentalis* (S.Wats.) Beetle) [SCPAC]

SYNONYMS: common tule; great bulrush; tule. *Scirpus acutus* and *Scirpus acutus* var. *occidentalis* are sometimes treated separately. Synonyms for *Scirpus acutus* include *Schoenoplectus acutus* (Muhl. ex Bigelow) A. & D. Love; *Schoenoplectus acutus* (L.) Palla ssp. *acutus* (Muhl. ex Bigelow) A. & D. Love; *Scirpus lacustris* L. in part. Synonyms for *Scirpus acutus* var. *occidentalis* include *Schoenoplectus acutus* (Muhl. ex Bigelow) A. & D. Love var. *occidentalis* (S. Wats.) S.G. Small; *Schoenoplectus rubiginosus* (Beetle) Sojak in part; *Scirpus lacustris* L. var. *occidentalis* S. Wats.; *Scirpus occidentalis* (S. Wats.) Chase; *Scirpus rubiginosus* Beetle in part. Some taxonomists segregate the genus *Scirpus* into *Schoenoplectus*, *Bolboschoenus*, *Isolepis*, and *Trichophorum*.

GENERAL INFORMATION: Erect rushlike perennial to 4(5) m tall, with long creeping rhizomes. Hardstem bulrush is a common widespread native of temperate North America that is sometimes weedy in irrigation and drainage ditches and rice fields. However, plants are an important component of natural wetland communities, as they provide cover, nesting sites, and food for a variety of wildlife. Native Americans utilized the stems to create a variety of items, from small boats to woven mats.

SEEDLING: Achenes typically remain attached to seedlings. Leaves 1–3 cm long, margins inrolled.

Hardstem bulrush (*Scirpus acutus* var. *occidentalis*) in its native habitat at the margin of a pond.

J. M. DiTomaso

Hardstem bulrush *(Scirpus acutus* var. *occidentalis)* infloresence.   J. M. DiTomaso

Hardstem bulrush *(Scirpus acutus* var. *occidentalis)* achenes.   J. K. Clark

River bulrush *(Scirpus fluviatilis)* in a rice field.   J. K. Clark

MATURE PLANT: Stems to 2 cm diameter. **Upper stems round in cross-section** (sometimes slightly rounded-3-angled), spongy. Stem bases thick, hard. Leaves basal, **reduced**. Sheaths conspicuous. Blades 1–2 per stem, typically much shorter than sheaths, to **8 cm long**, flat, glabrous.

ROOTS AND UNDERGROUND STRUCTURES: Rhizomes long, thick, brown.

SPIKELETS AND FRUITS: May–August. Inflorescence bract stiff, erect, mostly 1–5 (10) cm long, looks like an extension of the stem. Inflorescences open with lax branches and umbel-like clusters of spikelets to dense and headlike. Spikelets ovoid, 8–20(24) mm long, 3–5 mm wide. Flower scales (bracts) **ovate**, ± 4 mm long, straw-colored to orangish or dark reddish brown, **often reddish brown spotted**, with a **notched tip** and **short, often bent or wavy awn** (0.5–1 mm long) extending from between the lobes. **Midvein ridgelike. Margins ciliate with wavy hairs**. Styles 2- or 3-branched. Achenes **2–3 mm long, obovate-lens-shaped** (2-sided), sometimes flattened 3-sided in cross-section, **smooth**, grayish brown, with a minute nipplelike beak 0.1–0.3 mm long at the apex and 6 persistent barbed bristles at the base that are shorter than or equal to the achene length.

HABITAT: Salt and freshwater marshes, ponds, lakes, steam margins, ditches, and rice fields.

DISTRIBUTION: Temperate regions of North America, including all western states. Throughout California, except eastern desert regions, to 2500 m.

PROPAGATION AND PHENOLOGY: Reproduces vegetatively from rhizomes and by seed. Seeds disperse primarily with water, mud, and wildlife. Seed germination typically occurs in spring/summer. A cool moist stratification period followed by fluctuating temperatures of 10°–25°C appears to increase germination.

SIMILAR SPECIES: Numerous *Scirpus* species occur in the western states. Some of the following species are **widespread native perennials** that are not considered weeds in natural areas but may sometimes grow where they are not wanted, such as in rice fields and other controlled aquatic systems. Refer to table 12 (page 198) for a comparison of distinguishing characteristics.

California bulrush (*Scirpus californicus* (C.A. Mey.) Steud., synonyms: southern bulrush; *Schoenoplectus californicus* (C.A. Mey.) Palla) [SCPCA] is native to Arizona, New Mexico, and California in the North, Central, and South Coast, San Francisco Bay region, Central Valley, and along the Colorado River in the eastern desert regions, to 200 m.

River bulrush (*Scirpus fluviatilis* (Torrey) A. Gray, synonyms: *Bolboschoenus fluviatilis* (Torr.) Soják; *Schoenoplectus fluviatilis* (Torr.) M.T. Strong) [SCPFV] is native to all western states except Nevada and Wyoming. In California it occurs in the Sacramento Valley, San Francisco Bay region, North Coast Ranges, northern Sierra Nevada, and Modoc Plateau, to 1300 m.

Cosmopolitan bulrush (*Scirpus maritimus* L., synonyms: Pacific coast bulrush; *Bolboschoenus maritimus* (L.) Palla; *Schoenoplectus maritimus* (L.) Lye) is native to all western states. In California, it is in the northwestern, central-western, and southwestern regions, Central Valley, Modoc Plateau, and deserts, to 2500 m. Cosmopolitan and sturdy bulrush sometimes hybridize with one another.

Sturdy bulrush (*Scirpus robustus* Pursh, synonyms: *Bolboschoenus robustus* (Pursh) Soják; *Schoenoplectus robustus* (Pursh) M.T. Strong) is native to California in the Klamath Ranges, San Francisco Bay region, and South Coast, to 800 m.

Hardstem bulrush

River bulrush *(Scirpus fluviatilis)* inflorescence.   J. K. Clark

River bulrush *(Scirpus fluviatilis)* rhizome.   J. K. Clark

Tuberous bulrush (*Scirpus glaucus* Lam., synonyms: *Bolboschoenus glaucus* (Lam.) S.G. Smith; *Scirpus tuberosus* auct. non Desf..) and **ricefield bulrush** (*Scirpus mucronatus* L., synonyms: roughseed bulrush; *Schoenoplectus mucronatus* (L.) Palla) [SCPMU] are **introduced perennials, less than 1 m tall**, from Europe and Eurasia, respectively. **Tuberous bulrush** occurs in Oregon, Idaho, and California, where it inhabits rice fields, marshes, ditches, and other disturbed wet sites in the Central Valley and San Francisco Bay region, to 150 m. Tuberous bulrush is sometimes cultivated to provide food for waterfowl. **Ricefield bulrush** occurs in California and typically inhabits rice fields and other disturbed wet places in the Sacramento Valley, San Francisco Bay region, western North Coast Ranges, and South Coast, to 150 m.

River bulrush (*Scirpus fluviatilis*) achenes.   J. K. Clark

California bulrush (*Scirpus californicus*) in its native habitat.   J. M. DiTomaso

193

Hardstem bulrush

California bulrush *(Scirpus californicus)* inflorescence.   J. M. DiTomaso

California bulrush *(Scirpus californicus)* triangular stem.   J. M. DiTomaso

California bulrush *(Scirpus californicus)* achenes.
J. K. Clark

Cosmopolitan bulrush *(Scirpus maritimus)* flowering stems.   J. M. DiTomaso

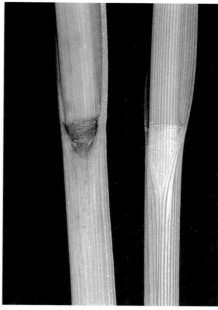

Cosmopolitan bulrush (*Scirpus maritimus*) inflorescence.   J. M. DiTomaso

Cosmopolitan bulrush (*Scirpus maritimus*) leaf sheath with a triangular veinless region.
J. M. DiTomaso

Cosmopolitan bulrush
(*Scirpus maritimus*) achenes.
J. K. Clark

Sturdy bulrush (*Scirpus robustus*) flowering stem.
J. M. DiTomaso

Sturdy bulrush *(Scirpus robustus)* inflorescence.   J. M. DiTOMASO

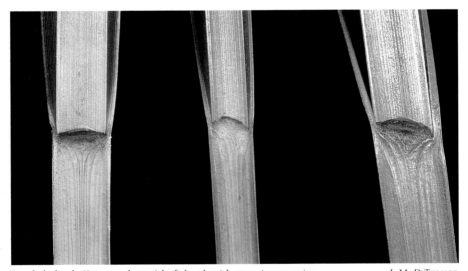

Sturdy bulrush *(Scirpus robustus)* leaf sheath with conspicuous veins.   J. M. DiTOMASO

Sturdy bulrush *(Scirpus robustus)* achenes.
                                 J. K. CLARK

Tuberous bulrush *(Scirpus glaucus)* achenes.
                                 J. K. CLARK

Ricefield bulrush (*Scirpus mucronatus*) flowering stems.   J. M. DiTomaso

Ricefield bulrush (*Scirpus mucronatus*) inflorescences.   J. M. DiTomaso

Ricefield bulrush (*Scirpus mucronatus*) achenes.
J. K. Clark

Ricefield bulrush (*Scirpus mucronatus*) seedling.
J. K. Clark

Table 12. Bulrushes (*Scirpus* spp.)

Species	Max. height (m)	Rhizomes	Stem cross-section	Leaf blades	Flower clusters	Flower cluster bracts	Spikelet length × width (mm)	Achenes (fruits)	Other
hardstem bulrush (*S. acutus*)	4	long	round	± basal, 1–2, shorter than sheaths	head-, umbel-, or panicle-like	single, erect, stem-like	8–20 × 3–5	lens-shaped to flattened, 3-sided, 2–3 mm long	flower scale often red-spotted with a bent or wavy awn; flower bristles 6, slender, barbed
California bulrush (*S. californicus*)	4	long	round to ± triangular	± basal, 0–2, shorter than sheaths	panicle-like	single, erect, stem-like	5–12 × ± 3	lens-shaped, ± 2–3 mm long	flower bristles 2–4, broad, flat, ciliate with soft hairs, often dark red
river bulrush (*S. fluviatilis*)	2	long, with tubers to 3 cm diameter	triangular	distributed on stems, longer than sheaths	head- or umbel-like	2–3, leaflike, spreading, ± 4–18 mm wide	10–30 × 6–10	sharply 3-sided, side ± concave, ± 4 mm long	flower bristles 6, persistent in fruit, ½ achene length or more; achenes pale brown
tuberous bulrush (*S. glaucus*)	0.5	long, with tubers to 2 cm diameter	triangular	distributed on stems, upper much longer than sheaths	head- or panicle-like	2–3, leaflike, spreading, <5 mm wide	10–20 × 4–5	sharp to flattened, 3-sided, 2–3 mm long	triangular patch at sheath top lacks veins; stigmas always 3
cosmopolitan bulrush* (*S. maritimus*)	1.5	long, with tubers to 2 cm diameter	triangular	distributed on stems, upper much longer than sheaths	head- or umbel-like	2–3, leaflike, spreading, ± 2–8 mm wide	10–30 × 5–8	lens-shaped to flattened, 3-sided, ± 3–4 mm long	triangular patch at sheath top clearly lacks veins; stigmas 2–3
ricefield bulrush (*S. mucronatus*)	0.8	short	triangular	± basal, 0–2, much shorter than sheaths	headlike	single, ± horizontal, stemlike	6–12 × 4–5	flattened, 3-sided, transverse-ridged, ± 2–2.5 mm long	tufted habit
sturdy bulrush* (*S. robustus*)	1.5	long, with tubers to 2 cm diameter	triangular	distributed on stems, upper much longer than sheaths	head- or panicle-like	2–3, leaflike, spreading, ± 2–8 mm wide	15–30 × 6–10	sharp to flattened, 3-sided, 3–3.5 mm long	triangular patch at sheath top with veins; stigmas 2–3

Note: * These species hybridize with one another.

Russian olive (*Elaeagnus angustifolia* L.)

NOXIOUS WEED LIST: CalEPPC: A-2

SYNONYMS: narrow-leafed oleaster; oleaster; silverberry; wild olive. The original spelling is changed to *Elaeagnus angustifolius* L. in a few references.

GENERAL INFORMATION: Fast-growing **deciduous tree** to 7 m tall, with **silvery foliage**. Russian olive is cultivated as a hardy landscape ornamental and wind-break tree but has escaped cultivation in many areas of the United States. It is especially invasive in seasonally wet riparian habitats and can replace native willows (*Salix* spp.) and cottonwoods (*Populus* spp.) at some locations, particularly areas of the intermountain west (Vintah and Bighorn Basins) and western plains. Although Russian olive fruits provide food for wildlife, the trees are used to a lesser degree than native vegetation. Russian olive is most problematic in the Southwest, Intermountain West, and Great Plains regions of the United States. Introduced from the temperate regions of Asia.

MATURE PLANT: Small branches dark reddish brown, ± smooth. Twigs and branches sometimes thorny. Leaves **alternate, simple, narrowly lanceolate or elliptic**, mostly **4–8 cm long**. Margins smooth. Upper leaf surfaces **gray-green, covered with silvery star-shaped hairs and scales**. Twigs, lower leaf surfaces, and leaf stalks **silvery gray, densely covered with silvery shield-shaped** (peltate) **scales**.

ROOTS AND UNDERGROUND STRUCTURES: Root system deep, with many well-developed laterals. Cut trees typically resprout from the crown and roots. Depending on location, roots sometimes associate with nitrogen-fixing bacteria (*Frankia* spp.).

Russian olive (*Elaeagnus angustifolia*) tree.   J. M. DiTomaso

FLOWERS: May–June. Flower clusters umbel-like, axillary on current year's growth. Flowers highly **fragrant, bisexual**, consist of a **narrowly bell-shaped calyx** (sepals as a unit) with **4 acute lobes**, 5–10 mm long and wide. Calyx **dark yellow inside, silver-scaly outside. Petals lacking.** Ovary superior but appears inferior. Stamens 4, open by slits. Insect-pollinated.

FRUITS AND SEEDS: Fruits **drupelike** (with a fleshy outer layer covering 1 seed), ovoid, 10–20 mm long, **silvery-yellow when ripe.** Most fruits mature September–November. Seeds oblong to football-shaped with a few longitudinal ridges, slightly smaller than fruits. Some seeds are hard-coated.

POSTSENESCENCE CHARACTERISTICS: Dormant trees without leaves usually retain a few fruits.

HABITAT: Riparian areas, flood plains, grasslands, roadsides, fencerows, seasonally moist pastures, wetland margins, ditches, and other disturbed sites. Often inhabits seasonally moist areas and sites near farmlands. Grows under a wide range of environmental conditions, including clay, sandy, and fairly alkaline or saline soils. Grows best in inland areas with warm summers and cold winters. Tolerates drought, high water tables, and temperatures well below freezing (to –45°C) to as high as 46°C.

DISTRIBUTION: Throughout much of the United States, including all western states but excluding most southeastern states. In California, it occurs in the San Joaquin Valley, San Francisco Bay region, eastern Sierra Nevada, Modoc Plateau, and Mojave Desert, mostly to 1500 m.

PROPAGATION AND PHENOLOGY: **Reproduces by seed.** Most fruits remain on trees until distributed by animals, especially birds. Seeds survive ingestion by animals. Seeds are dormant at maturity and require a cool, moist stratification period of

Russian olive (*Elaeagnus angustifola*) in flower.   J. M. DiTOMASO

2–3 months. Hard-coated seeds may require scarification as well. Seeds germinate in many soil types and over a variable period of time, depending on conditions. Stored seeds survive up to 3 years, but longevity in the field is undocumented. Seedlings grow best under moist, slightly alkaline conditions.

ADDITIONAL ECOLOGICAL ASPECTS: Seeds germinate under a broader range of conditions than native willows and cottonwoods. Russian olive seedlings can survive under a canopy of mature willows and cottonwoods and then grow quickly when the loss of a tree creates an opening in the canopy. Conversely, willow and cottonwood seedlings seldom survive under a canopy of Russian olive trees.

MANAGEMENT FAVORING OR DISCOURAGING SURVIVAL: Manually removing seedlings and saplings with roots before they mature is a more effective method of control than removing mature trees. Cut trees typically resprout from the roots and crown. Cutting trees before fruits mature and immediately painting the stump with a systemic herbicide is more effective than cutting alone. Choosing non-invasive landscape ornamentals to plant at sites near natural areas can help prevent the spread of Russian olive.

SIMILAR SPECIES: Russian olive can resemble some willow (*Salix* spp.) species with light green foliage, particularly **Coyote willow** (*Salix exigua* Nutt.). However, willows have inconspicuous flowers on erect stalks and small windblown seeds.

Russian olive (*Elaeagnus angustifolia*) in fruit.   J. M. DITOMASO

Field horsetail (*Equisetum arvense* L.) [EQUAR]

Scouringrush (*Equisetum hyemale* L. ssp. *affine* (Engelm.) Calder & R.H. Taylor) [EQUHY]

SYNONYMS:

Field horsetail: bottlebrush; common horsetail; foxtail-rush; horsepipes; horse-tail fern; meadow-pine; pinegrass; scouringrush; shavegrass; snake-grass; *Equisetum arvense* L. vars. *alpestre* Wahenb., *boreale* (Bong.) Rupr., *campestre* Wahlenb., and *riparium* Farw.; *Equisetum boreale* Bong.; *Equisetum calderi* Boivin; *Equisetum saxicola* Suksd.

Scouringrush: common scouringrush; western scouringrush; scouringrush horsetail; shavegrass; *Equisetum affine* Engelm.; *Equisetum hiemale* L. var. *californicum* in some older California references; *Equisetum hyemale* L. var. *affine* (Engelm.) A.A. Eat.; *Equisetum praealtum* Raf.; *Equisetum robustum* A. Braun; *Hippochaete hyemalis* (L.) Bruhin.

GENERAL INFORMATION: Primitive, widespread **native perennials** with **rhizomes**, **whorled branches**, and **fused sheathing leaves**. In natural areas, *Equisetum* species are a common and desirable component of the riparian ecosystem. However, dense colonies can be problematic in agricultural fields, pastures, and

Infertile stem and branches of field horsetail (*Equisetum arvense*).   J. NEAL

controlled aquatic systems. Both species contain alkaloids that deactivate thiamine and are **toxic** to livestock, especially horses, when ingested. Stem surfaces accumulate silica, and for this reason, both species were historically utilized for scrubbing purposes.

Field horsetail: Plants produce **2 types of stems: green annual vegetative stems** to 0.6 m tall and **pale tan short-lived fertile stems** to 0.4 m tall. Plants can accumulate heavy metals, such as cadmium, lead, gold, zinc, and copper. Field horsetail is a highly variable widespread native of North America and Eurasia. It is considered a noxious weed in parts of Australia.

Scouringrush: All stems green, perennial, to 2 m tall. Scouringrush is a widespread native of North America.

MATURE PLANT: Main stems longitudinally ribbed, hollow except at the nodes. Branches whorled. Leaves small, united into a node-sheathing tube that is toothed along the upper margin (referred to as leaf sheath).

Field horsetail: Vegetative stems green, slender, **2–5 mm wide, 6–14-ribbed,** with **many slender, evenly whorled, 3–4-angled branches** at most nodes. **Lowest branch internodes are longer than the leaf sheath just below.** Leaf sheaths ± 5 mm long, with **6–14 teeth. Fertile stems unbranched, pale tan to pinkish** (lack chlorophyll), ± succulent, slightly thicker than vegetative stems, with dark leaf sheaths ± 10–20 mm long with **6–10 teeth.**

Scouringrush: All stems **green, ± thick, 5–15 mm wide,** 20–40-ribbed, **unbranched or with a few scattered branches at some nodes.** Leaf sheaths **10–15 mm long and wide,** mostly with **2 dark bands** (top and bottom) and **22–50 deciduous teeth.**

ROOTS AND UNDERGROUND STRUCTURES: Extensive **rhizomes,** creeping, branched, dark, root at the nodes. Rhizomes typically store starch in shortened swollen internodes (tubers). Some tubers readily detach from the parent rhizomes and develop into new plants. The rhizome system can extend to ± 1.5 m deep or more.

SPORE-BEARING STRUCTURES: Mostly March–July. Spikes (strobiles) terminal, consist of numerous small flower-shaped bracts (sporophylls) on short stalks, with spore-bearing structures (sporangia) on lower surfaces.

Field horsetail: Spikes **lanceolate-ovoid,** 20–30 mm long, 3–10 mm wide. **Tip bluntly tapered.**

Scouringrush: Spikes **ovoid,** 10–30 mm long, mostly 10–15 mm wide. **Tip abruptly pointed** (apiculate).

POSTSENESCENCE CHARACTERISTICS: Vegetative stems of field horsetail typically die at the end of the growing season, turn blackish, and usually do not persist into winter.

HABITAT:

Field horsetail: Grows best in moist locations with sandy soil, high water table, and poor drainage. Disturbed sites such as pastures, orchards, nursery crops, agricultural fields, and irrigation ditches. In natural systems, meadows and riparian zones.

Scouringrush: Moist sandy sites, riparian areas, marshy places, and ditches.

DISTRIBUTION:

Field horsetail: Throughout most of the United States, including all western states, Canada. Throughout California, except deserts and region east of the Sierra Nevada, to 3000 m.

Scouringrush: Throughout United States, including all western states, Canada. Throughout California to 3000 m.

PROPAGATION AND PHENOLOGY: Reproduce vegetatively from rhizomes and tubers, and less importantly by spores. Rhizome fragments and tubers can develop into new plants. Fragments and tubers disperse with water, soil movement, and human activities. Plants produce large numbers of spores, but few survive because spores are short-lived and require specific environmental conditions to grow. Fertile stems of field horsetail typically emerge in late winter/early spring and usually wither by the time vegetative stems emerge.

MANAGEMENT FAVORING OR DISCOURAGING SURVIVAL: Colonies are difficult to control because of the extensive rhizome systems. Mowing and burning do not kill rhizomes. Cultivation fragments rhizomes and tubers and can spread horsetail infestations. Mulching field horsetail with leaf compost can reduce the horizontal

Fertile field horsetail (*Equisetum arvense*) stem.
J.NEAL

Scouringrush (*Equisetum hyemale* ssp. *affine*) stem.
J. M. DiTomaso

growth of rhizomes. Mulching with black plastic sheeting for 3–4 years can kill rhizomes in the upper 60 cm of soil. When possible, draining a system and lowering the water table can help reduce populations. Field horsetail tolerates most herbicides used in agriculture.

SIMILAR SPECIES: Giant horsetail (*Equisetum telmateia* Ehrh. ssp. *braunii* (Milde) R.L. Hauke; synonym: *Equisetum braunii* Milde) [EQUTE] is a widespread **native perennial** with extensive rhizomes that is sometimes invasive. Giant horsetail has thick, regularly branched, pale green vegetative stems to 3 m tall and short-lived, unbranched, pale tan fertile stems to 0.6 m tall. Giant horsetail resembles field horsetail but is typically larger in all respects. Unlike field horsetail, giant horsetail has **4–6 angled stem branches** with the **lowest internode shorter than the leaf sheath immediately below**, main stems with **20–40 ribs**, and leaf sheaths 7–20 mm long with **14–28 teeth**. In addition, **fertile stems** have **spikes 4–8 cm long** and leaf sheaths with **20–30 teeth**. Giant horsetail occurs in Washington, Oregon, Idaho, and California, where it inhabits marshes, stream banks, wet ditches, and other disturbed wet places throughout the northwestern, central-western, and southwestern regions to 1000 m.

Smooth scouringrush (*Equisetum laevigatum* A. Braun, synonyms: *Equisetum funstoni* A.A. Eaton; *Equisetum kansanum* J. Schaffner) is a **widespread native**

Giant horsetail (*Equisetum telmateia* ssp. *braunii*) along a creek in its native habitat.
J. M. DiTomaso

Giant horsetail (*Equisetum telmateia* ssp. *braunii*) stems. J. M. DiTomaso

perennial that is seldom weedy but is sometimes confused with scouringrush. Unlike scouringrush, smooth scouringrush has **annual stems**, spikes with **rounded tips**, and leaf sheaths that are **longer than wide with 1 dark band at the tip**. Smooth scouringrush occurs in all western states. It is found primarily in natural communities throughout much of California to 3000 m, including desert mountains but excluding areas east of the Sierra Nevada and low-elevation areas of the deserts.

Fertile smooth scouringrush (*Equisetum laevigatum*) stems.   J. M. DiTomaso

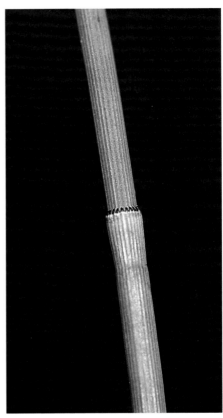

Node of smooth scouringrush (*Equisetum laevigatum*) with one dark band at tip.
J. M. DiTomaso

Rough jointvetch (*Aeschynomene rudis* Benth.)

NOXIOUS WEED LISTS: California: A

SYNONYMS: zigzag jointvetch; *Aeschynomene natans* Hassler

GENERAL INFORMATION: Tropical emergent aquatic or terrestrial perennial, to 2 m tall. Plants are typically annual in California. Infestations are currently restricted to rice fields. Heavy infestations can reduce rice harvest yields, and seeds are difficult to remove from rice grains during the milling process. Introduced from South America as a contaminant in dry bean seeds. Rough jointvetch has often been misidentified as Indian jointvetch (*A. indica* L.) or northern jointvetch (*A. virginica* (L.) B.S.P.) in the southeastern United States.

MATURE PLANT: Stems often woody at the base. Stem tips densely covered with stiff hairs on dark, wartlike bases. Leaves even-pinnate compound, 4–15 cm long. Leaflets 30–60 mostly glabrous, usually 0.9–1 cm long, narrowly oblong, dotted with minute glands, typically with minutely toothed margins. Stipules narrowly triangular, ± shieldlike, with bases extending beyond points of

Rough jointvetch (*Aeschynomene rudis*) at the edge of a rice field.
J. M. DiTomaso

attachment, 0.7–1.5 cm long, 0.2–0.3 cm wide, usually with minutely toothed margins, deciduous.

ROOTS AND UNDERGROUND STRUCTURES: Taprooted, with many long, fine lateral roots. Associated with nitrogen-fixing bacteria.

FLOWERS: July–October. Racemes axillary, with 1–4 pealike flowers. Corolla **whitish, purple-tinged**, 8–15 mm long. Self-fertile.

Stipules at leaf base in rough jointvetch (*Aeschynomene rudis*). R. BRECKENRIDGE

Rough jointvetch (*Aeschynomene rudis*) flower. J. M. DITOMASO

FRUITS AND SEEDS: Pods linear, segmented, constricted between segments along lower margins, 3–5 cm long, 0.4–0.7 cm wide, break apart into 7–12 square, 1-seeded segments at maturity. Stalk 0.3–1 cm long. Immature pods sparsely covered with dark pustulate-based hairs. Seeds kidney-shaped, ± 3 mm long, 2 mm wide, gray-brown to black.

HABITAT: Edges of rice fields and nearby ditches.

DISTRIBUTION: Nearly eradicated in California in the Sacramento Valley (northeastern Colusa Co.), to 20 m. Southeastern United States.

Rough jointvetch (*Aeschynomene rudis*) fruit pod.   J. M. DiTOMASO

Rough jointvetch (*Aeschynomene rudis*) seedling.   J. K. CLARK

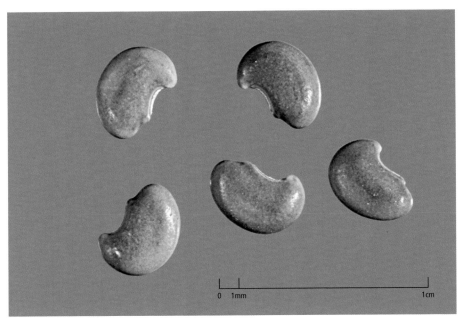

0 1mm   1cm

Rough jointvetch (*Aeschynomene rudis*) seeds.   J. K. CLARK

PROPAGATION AND PHENOLOGY: Reproduces by seed. Like many legumes, seeds are probably long-lived in the field. Field reports indicate that seeds survive at least 10 years in the soil.

SIMILAR SPECIES: Hemp sesbania (*Sesbania exaltata* (Raf..) Cory) is a widespread **native summer annual** that is sometimes weedy in ditches and moist agronomic fields. It is distinguished by having glabrous stem tips, narrowly triangular stipules to 1 cm long that **do not extend below the point of attachment, yellowish orange flowers** often mottled with maroon, and ± 4-sided pods that are typically **15–20 cm long**, ± 0.5 cm wide with **straight margins**. Refer to the **Rattlebush** entry (page 214) for more information.

White sweetclover (*Melilotus albus* Medicus) [MEUAL]

SYNONYMS: honey clover; tree clover; white melilot; *Melilotus alba* Medicus; *Sertula alba* (Medicus) Kuntze

GENERAL INFORMATION: Erect **biennial**, sometimes annual or short-lived perennial to 3 m tall, with **racemes of small white pealike flowers**. White sweetclover is sometimes cultivated for livestock forage and as a cover crop. It is also a useful honey bee plant, and foliage and seeds are consumed by wildlife. However, *Melilotus* species incorporated into hay or silage can enhance the growth of **toxic** molds that cause sweet clover poisoning, a severe hemorrhagic and often fatal disease that primarily affects cattle that have ingested moldy sweetclover. Introduced from Eurasia.

SEEDLING: Cotyledons oblong, 6–8 mm long, 3–4 mm wide, glabrous. First leaf simple, obovate, tip ± squared with a minute nipplelike point (cuspidate), 2–5 mm long and wide, glabrous or sparsely hairy, margin minutely toothed near apex. Subsequent leaves compound with 3 leaflets. Leaflets resemble first leaf. Terminal leaflet short-stalked.

White sweetclover (*Melilotus albus*) along the edge of a pond.   J. M. DiTomaso

Inflorescence and leaf of white sweetclover (*Melilotus albus*).   J. M. DiTomaso

Mature Plant: Foliage glabrous or hairy. Leaves alternate, pinnate compound with 3 leaflets, **terminal leaflet short-stalked**. Leaflets obovate to ± oblong, 1–2.5 cm long, tip weakly squared. Margins smooth to weakly toothed. Stipules ± narrowly triangular, 5–7 mm long.

Roots and Underground Structures: Taproot tough, deep. Roots associated with nitrogen-fixing bacteria.

Flowers: May–November (December). Sweetly fragrant. **Racemes 2–12 cm long**, axillary and terminal. Flowers **white**, mostly **4–6 mm long**. Insect-pollinated. Self-compatible.

Fruits and Seeds: Pods ovoid, 3–5 mm long, glabrous, surface reticulate-veined, on stalks that bend downward (reflexed), contain 1 seed (2 mm long), rarely 2. Pods do not open to release seeds. Seeds ovoid, slightly smaller than pod, smooth, dull yellowish green to orange-tan.

Habitat: Disturbed, usually open places in many plant communities, riparian sites, agronomic fields, pastures, roadsides, and ditches. Often grows where soil moisture is abundant, especially in the southern portion of California. Does not tolerate extended periods of standing water.

White sweetclover (*Melilotus albus*) seedling.   J. K. Clark

DISTRIBUTION: All western states. Throughout California, except deserts, to 1500 m. Much of North America.

PROPAGATION AND PHENOLOGY: Reproduces by seed. Seeds fall near the parent plant and disperse to greater distances with water, mud, as a seed or feed contaminant, and by clinging to the clothing of people or the fur, feathers, and feet of animals. Most mature seeds are hard-coated and can remain viable for up to 20 years or more under field conditions. Seeds typically germinate fall through spring in California. Seedlings compete poorly with perennial species.

MANAGEMENT FAVORING OR DISCOURAGING SURVIVAL: Burning can kill some existing plants but often stimulates seed germination when moisture conditions become favorable. In natural areas, establishing a cover of desirable perennial species can eliminate white sweetclover in ± 2 years.

SIMILAR SPECIES: Other sweetclover species in western states have **yellow flowers** and typically grow in drier places than white sweetclover.

White sweetclover (*Melilotus albus*) seeds and pods.   J. K. CLARK

Rattlebush (*Sesbania punicea* (Cav.) Benth.) [SEBPU]

Noxious Weed Lists: CalEPPC: Red Alert

Synonyms: bladderpod; coffeeweed; purple sesban; rattlebox; scarlet wisteria tree; *Daubentonia punicea* (Cav.) DC.; *Emerus puniceus* (Cav.) Kuntze; *Piscidia ovalifolia* Larrañaga; *Piscidia punicea* Cav.; *Sesbania tripetii* (Poit.) hort ex Hubb.

General Information: Deciduous shrub or small tree to 4 m tall, with **even-pinnate compound leaves** and **red to orange-red pealike flowers**. Rattlebush is grown as an ornamental in many countries but has escaped cultivation and invaded riparian areas and other moist habitats in South Africa, southern United States, particularly Georgia and Florida, and California. In South Africa, where **rattlebush** is especially noxious, three weevil species (*Trichapion lativentre, Rhyssomatus marginatus, Neodiplogrammus quadrivittatus*) that feed specifically on rattlebush were released as biocontrol agents in the 1980s. Recent studies indicate that rattlebush populations there have been significantly reduced where two or three weevil species are well established. Foliage, flowers, and especially immature seeds contain a saponin and are **toxic** to humans and animals when ingested. Introduced from South America (Argentina, Brazil, Paraguay, and Uruguay).

Seedling: Cotyledons oblong, sessile, 1.5–2.5 cm long, ± 1 cm wide, stalk below (hypocotyl) often reddish. First leaf simple, elliptic to oval, tip tapered to rounded, with an abrupt point (mucro), larger than cotyledons, short-stalked. Subsequent 2 leaves even-pinnate compound, slightly larger than first leaf. Leaflets 6, oblong to obovate, smaller than cotyledons, tip rounded to slightly squared, with an abrupt point.

Rattlebush (*Sesbania punicea*) along the bank of the American River, California.   J. M. DiTomaso

MATURE PLANT: Foliage sparsely hairy to glabrous. Leaves alternate, **even-pinnate compound, 8–20 cm long**, typically drooping. Leaflets 10–40, oblong, 1–3 cm long, nearly sessile, tip rounded to slightly truncate with a minute abrupt point (mucro).

ROOTS AND UNDERGROUND STRUCTURES: Main roots woody. Fine roots associated with nitrogen-fixing bacteria.

FLOWERS: Mostly June–September in California. Flowers **showy**, **pealike, red to orange-red, 2–3 cm long**, in ± drooping axillary racemes to 8–25 cm long. Calyx (sepals as a unit) cuplike, weakly lobed, usually tinged dull dark red.

Rattlebush (*Sesbania punicea*) plants in flower.   J. M. DITOMASO

Rattlebush (*Sesbania punicea*) inflorescence.   J. M. DITOMASO

FRUITS AND SEEDS: Pods dark brown, glabrous, **oblong** with a pointed tip, 6–12 cm long, **1.5–2.5 cm wide**, **longitudinally 4-winged**, wings 5–10 mm wide. Seeds 4–10 per pod, separated by partitions, oblong, 5–9 mm long, smooth, dull brown to tan.

HABITAT: Riparian areas, marshes, disturbed moist places, margins of ponds, ditches, and canals.

DISTRIBUTION: California in the southern North Coast Ranges, Sacramento and San Joaquin Valleys, as well as the surrounding foothills and possibly elsewhere

Rattlebush (*Sesbania punicea*) fruit pod.   J. M. DiTOMASO

Rattlebush (*Sesbania punicea*) seedling.   J. M. DiTOMASO

to ± 50 m. Appears to be rapidly expanding its range in California. Southern United States.

PROPAGATION AND PHENOLOGY: Reproduces by seed. Pods open slowly and do not eject seeds. Seeds appear to disperse primarily with water. Seeds are hard-coated and require scarification or decomposition of the seed coat to germinate. After water is imbibed, germination can occur at any time when the temperature is 10°–35°C. Seedlings emerge from soil depths to 12 cm. Plants typically attain reproductive maturity at 2–3 years of age. Individual plants survive for up to 15 years.

Rattlebush (*Sesbania punicea*) seeds.   J. K. CLARK

Hemp sesbania (*Sesbania exaltata*) leaf and flower.   J. M. DITOMASO

SIMILAR SPECIES: Hemp sesbania (*Sesbania exaltata* (Raf.) Cory, synonyms: coffee-weed; indigoweed; *Sesbania herbacea* (P. Mill.) McVaugh; *Sesbania macrocarpa* Muhl.;) [SEBEX] is an erect **native summer annual** to 3 m tall with leaves that resemble those of rattlebush. Unlike rattlebush, hemp sesbania has **yellow to pale orange pealike** flowers 1–1.5 cm long that are **often maroon-speckled on the upper petal** (banner) and **linear pods 15–20 cm long** and **0.3–0.4 cm wide**. Seeds are cylindrical, rounded to slightly truncate at the ends, 3–5 mm long, glossy dark brown to tan with dark spots. Seedlings have glabrous oblong cotyledons 10–25 mm long and 4–10 mm wide. First leaves are pinnate-compound, with ± 15 lanceolate to oblong leaflets 5–10 mm long. Leaflet tips have a small abrupt point (mucro). Hemp sesbania is sometimes cultivated for green manure or as a cover crop and can escape cultivation under favorable conditions. In southeastern states it is a common weed in soybeans, rice, and cotton. Hemp ses-

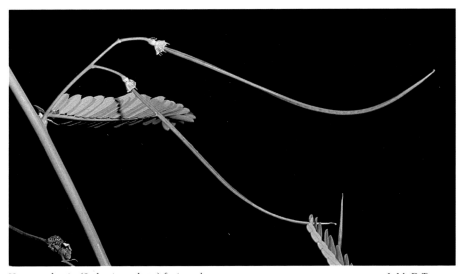

Hemp sesbania *(Sesbania exaltata)* fruit pod. J. M. DiTomaso

0 1mm   1cm

Hemp sesbania *(Sesbania exaltata)* seeds. J. K. Clark

bania grows in riparian areas and is sometimes weedy along irrigation ditches and in moist agronomic fields in Arizona and California in the Sonoran Desert, especially the Imperial Valley, to 500 m. It may occur as an agricultural weed elsewhere in California. Hemp sesbania is not usually considered a weed in natural riparian plant communities within its native range. Like rattlebush, foliage, flowers, and seeds of hemp sesbania are **toxic** to animals and humans when ingested.

Indigobush (*Amorpha fruticosa* L., synonyms: false indigobush; western false indigo; *Amorpha occidentalis* Abrams; many others) [AMHFR] [Washington Noxious Weed: B] is a bushy or openly branched **deciduous shrub** to 4 m tall, with **odd-pinnate compound leaves** composed of 11–25 obovate to oblong

Hemp sesbania (*Sesbania exaltata*) seedling.   J. K. CLARK

Stem and foliage of indigobush (*Amorpha fruticosa* var. *occidentalis*).   J. M. DiTomaso

leaflets, **spikelike racemes of small dark purple to bluish flowers that have only 1 petal**, and oval 1- or 2-seeded pods ± 0.5 cm long that do not open. **Foliage is dotted with nearly flat resinous glands** and has a pungent fragrance when crushed. In addition, the leaf axis lacks pricklelike glands, and leaflets are 1.5–4 cm long and tipped with a minute bristle. Seeds are hard-coated and require scarification or decomposition of the seed coat before germination can occur. Indigobush is a widespread native shrub of the eastern and central United States and parts of the southwestern United States. It is sometimes cultivated as a garden ornamental and has escaped cultivation in Washington, Oregon, Idaho, and Utah. Indigobush is particularly invasive along the riparian corridors of southwestern Idaho, eastern Washington, and adjacent Oregon. Where it is native, indigobush is not considered a weed and is a desirable component of natural ecosystems. Indigobush inhabits riparian areas, canyons, and lake margins and occurs in all western states except Nevada and Montana. It is introduced to Washington, Oregon, Idaho, and Utah and native to Southern California, Arizona, New Mexico, central and eastern Colorado, and eastern Wyoming to the eastern United States and northern Mexico.

Inflorescence of indigobush (*Amorpha fruticosa* var. *occidentalis*).　　　　J. M. DiTomaso

Flowers of indigobush (*Amorpha fruticosa* var. *occidentalis*).　　　　J. M. DiTomaso

Yellowflag iris (*Iris pseudacorus* L.) [IRIPS]

NOXIOUS WEED LISTS: CalEPPC: B

SYNONYMS: paleyellow iris; yellow flag; *Iris acoriformis* Boreau; *Iris bastardi* Boreau; *Iris curtopetala* F. Delaroche ex Redoute; *Iris lutea* Lam.; *Iris paludosa* Pers.

GENERAL INFORMATION: Herbaceous **perennial** to 1.5 m tall with **bright yellow or cream-colored flowers** and thick **rhizomes**. Yellowflag iris is often grown as an ornamental but has escaped cultivation in some areas. It typically develops colonies along river and stream banks, sloughs, pond margins, in irrigation ditches, and other wet places. In natural wetlands and riparian areas, yellowflag iris displaces desirable vegetation. Yellowflag iris is state-listed as an injurious weed in Nevada. *Iris* species can be toxic to livestock when consumed in quantity. Introduced from Europe.

MATURE PLANT: Leaves **swordblade-shaped**, alternate in the same plane (equitant), stiff, to **1.5 m long**, **1–2.5 cm wide**, glabrous, sometimes with a bluish white bloom (glaucous).

ROOTS AND UNDERGROUND STRUCTURES: Rhizomes **3–4 cm diameter**, creeping, brown.

FLOWERS: Spring–early summer. Flower stems **branched, 0.5–1.5 m tall**, slightly compressed in cross-section. Flowers **many per stem, 2–3 per bract pair** (spathe), **bright yellow or cream-colored**, 8–10 cm diameter. Sepals (3 outer petal-like parts) often purple or brown-veined with an orange spot near the base, **lack a patch of dense thick hairs on the upper surface** (not bearded). Petals

Yellowflag iris (*Iris pseudacorus*) habit along the margin of a pond.   J. M. DiTOMASO

Yellowflag iris (*Iris pseudacorus*) flower.　　J. M. DiTomaso

Yellowflag iris (*Iris pseudacorus*) fruit.　　　　　　J. M. DiTomaso

(erect parts) narrow near middle. Stigmas 3, **rounded**. Bract pairs typically opposite, outer bract ± 5 cm long, 0.7–1 cm wide. Insect-pollinated.

FRUITS AND SEEDS: Capsules **5–8 cm long**, elliptic, with an abrupt tiny point at
the apex (apiculate), 3-chambered. Seeds D-shaped to ± round, flattened,
light brown.

HABITAT: Disturbed wet places, irrigation ditches, pond margins, wetlands, and
riparian areas.

DISTRIBUTION: Oregon, Washington, Idaho, Montana, Utah, Nevada, and
California in the San Francisco Bay region, southern San Joaquin Valley, Central
Coast, and South Coast, to 100 m. Throughout most of the eastern half of the
United States.

PROPAGATION AND PHENOLOGY: Reproduces vegetatively from rhizomes and
by seed.

SIMILAR SPECIES: Yellowflag iris is distinctive by having **yellow or cream-colored
flowers** with **sepals that lack a crest or beard** and **several swordlike leaves to
1.5 m long** and **1–2.5 cm wide**. Unlike other native yellow or cream-colored iris
species, it has rhizomes >1 cm in diameter.

Large rhizome of yellowflag iris (*Iris pseudacorus*).   J. M. DiTomaso

Pennyroyal (*Mentha pulegium* L.)

NOXIOUS WEED LISTS: CalEPPC: A-2

SYNONYMS: European pennyroyal; *Mentha daghestanica* Boriss.; *Pulegium dagestanicum* (Boriss.) Holub; *Pulegium vulgare* Mill.

GENERAL INFORMATION: Low-growing aromatic perennial to 0.8 m tall, with **rhizomes** and **stolons**. Pennyroyal is cultivated as a garden ornamental and medicinal plant but has escaped cultivation into pastures, along roadsides, and in other disturbed places in California. Pennyroyal also invades wetland habitats, including sensitive vernal pools in the Central Valley and Santa Rosa Plain. Pennyroyal appears to be rapidly spreading in California. Although it is sometimes used medicinally, it contains an essential oil that can be fatally **toxic** to humans when ingested. Plants or the oil can cause dermatitis in sensitive individuals. Foliage has been used as an insect repellent. Introduced from Europe.

MATURE PLANT: Stems square in cross-section, usually prostrate, decumbent (with upturned tips) to ascending, green to reddish, covered with **short white hairs**. Leaves **opposite**, gray-green, ovate to elliptic or oblong, with a rounded tip, 1–3 cm long, 0.5–2 cm wide, covered with **short white hairs** and **glandular dots**. Margins entire to finely serrate. Lower leaves short-stalked. Upper leaves reduced, nearly sessile.

ROOTS AND UNDERGROUND STRUCTURES: Rhizomes short, with fibrous roots at nodes. Fibrous roots grow up to ± 40 cm deep. Stems typically root at the lower nodes. Stem and rhizome fragments can develop into new plants.

Pennyroyal (*Mentha pulegium*) in a wet meadow.   J. M. DiTomaso

FLOWERS: June–September. Flower clusters **headlike in whorls around stems** (verticils), typically **spaced more than 1 cm apart** on terminal portions of stems. **Each cluster sits just above a pair of down-turned leaves or leaflike bracts less than 1 cm long,** usually with **smooth margins** and ± **rounded tips.** Calyx (sepals as a unit) tubular, radial, hairy, glandular, 2–4 mm long. Calyx teeth dissimilar, lower 2 narrow and ± awl-like. Corolla (petals as a unit) weakly bilateral, lavender to violet, 5–9 mm long. Stamens 4, ± equal, protrude beyond corolla.

FRUITS AND SEEDS: Fruits consist of 4 nutlets enclosed by the calyx. Nutlets ovoid, 3-sided, 0.5–1 mm long, pale brown. Each nutlet contains 1 seed. Nutlets disperse with the enclosing calyx.

POSTSENESCENCE CHARACTERISTICS: Foliage usually dies in fall and regrows from rhizomes in spring. Flowering stems typically dry by late fall and may retain many intact fruits through winter.

HABITAT: Disturbed moist places, ditches, roadsides, pastures, seasonally flooded sites, seeps, vernal pools, edges of marshes, streams, and ponds. Grows best in clay or silty soils where moisture is plentiful. Often grows in the partial shade of other vegetation. Tolerates some alkalinity and seasonal drought.

DISTRIBUTION: Washington, Oregon, and California in the northwestern region, central-western region, Cascade Ranges, Central Valley, Sierra Nevada foothills, and South Coast, to 1000 m. Northeastern United States.

Pennyroyal *(Mentha pulegium)* plant.
J. M. DiTomaso

Pennyroyal *(Mentha pulegium)* inflorescence.
J. M. DiTomaso

PROPAGATION AND PHENOLOGY: Reproduces vegetatively from rhizomes and stolons and by seed. Stem and rhizome fragments can develop into new plants under favorable conditions. Fragments disperse with agricultural and construction activities such as road building. Fruits disperse with water, soil movement, human activities, and by clinging to the fur, feathers, and feet of animals. Seeds may germinate throughout much of the year if moisture and light are available. Seeds can germinate under water, and seedlings continue to grow during an extended period of shallow inundation. In Australia, high seed bank numbers are associated with grazing disturbance. Most growth occurs late spring through early summer.

MANAGEMENT FAVORING OR DISCOURAGING SURVIVAL: Manual removal of individual plants and small patches, including as many rhizomes and stolons as possible, and then hand-pulling seedlings as soon as discovered can control pennyroyal infestations.

SIMILAR SPECIES: Spearmint (*Mentha spicata* L. var. *spicata*) [MENSP] and **apple mint** (*Mentha suaveolens* J.F. Ehrh.) [MENSU] are perennial garden herbs that have escaped cultivation in many areas throughout much of California. Unlike pennyroyal, spearmint and apple mint typically have **inconspicuous internodes less than 6 mm long between whorls of flowers** and a pair of **linear-lanceolate to awl-like bracts below each flower whorl**. Spearmint is usually **nearly glabrous** and has leaves with **slightly rounded to broadly wedge-shaped bases** and **acute tips**. Apple mint has ± **woolly-glandular apple-scented foliage** and

Pennyroyal (*Mentha pulegium*) stem along a stream.

J. M. DiTomaso

leaves with **slightly lobed bases** and **rounded tips**. Spearmint occurs throughout most of the United States, including all western states. It inhabits marshes, lake margins, riparian areas, and moist disturbed places in many plant communities throughout California, except Great Basin and desert regions, to 1650 m. Apple mint occurs in Oregon, Washington, New Mexico, Arizona, and California, where it inhabits ditchbanks and moist places in the northwestern and central-western regions, Sierra Nevada and adjacent eastern region, and South Coast, to 1200 m. It is scattered in the southern and eastern United States. Apple mint is expected to expand its range.

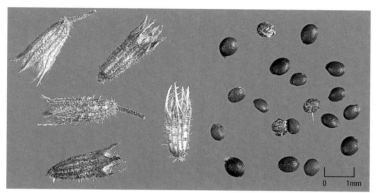

Pennyroyal *(Mentha pulegium)* nutlets and calyx.   J. K. Clark

Spearmint *(Mentha spicata)* flowering stem.
J. M. DiTomaso

Apple mint *(Mentha suaveolens)* flowering stem.
J. M. DiTomaso

Purple ammannia (*Ammannia robusta* Heer & Regel = *Ammannia coccinea* Rottb. in most references prior to 1979) [AMMCO]

Indian toothcup (*Rotala indica* (Willd.) Koehne) [ROTIN]

SYNONYMS:

Purple ammannia: grand redstem; long-leaved ammannia; redberry; *Ammannia coccinea* Rottb. ssp. *robusta* (Heer & Regel) Koehne; *Ammannia sanguinolenta* Sw. ssp. *robusta* (Heer & Regel) Koehne

Indian toothcup: *Ammannia nana* Roxb.; *Ammania peploides* Spreng.; *Peplis indica* Willd.

GENERAL INFORMATION: Erect to prostrate plants of wet sites, with **4-angled stems**, **opposite leaves**, and small **pink to purplish flowers in the leaf axils**.

Purple ammannia: **Terrestrial summer annual**, to 1 m tall. Purple ammannia is a widespread native throughout much of the United States. Although it is usually a desirable component of natural communities, it can be weedy in wet agricultural fields, especially rice fields. There has been some confusion regarding the taxonomy of *Ammannia* species in the United States. Prior to 1979, purple ammannia was mistakenly referred to as *Ammannia coccinea* in many references and publications. However, a different native species that closely resembles purple ammannia is now known as *Ammannia coccinea*. This species, **redstem**

Purple ammannia (*Ammannia robusta*) along the margin of a rice field.   J. M. DiTomaso

(*Ammannia coccinea* Rottb.) [AMMAU], was previously incorrectly referred to as *Ammannia auriculata* Willd. Redstem is an amphidiploid derived from the hybridization of *Ammannia robusta* and *Ammannia auriculata*. It is very difficult to distinguish purple ammannia and redstem using characteristics provided in taxonomic keys. The differences between redstem and purple ammannia are not consistent and the two species may have a wide range of variability. In this treatment, we are using the name purple ammannia, although redstem can also be weedy in rice fields and other wet agronomic crops. In California, resistance to certain herbicides has occurred within the *Ammannia* group.

Indian toothcup: Emergent or terrestrial summer annual to perennial, to 0.3 m tall. Indian toothcup is a widespread weed of rice fields throughout much of Eurasia and tropical Africa. It is sometimes sold as an aquarium or pond ornamental. In rice in California, it is a minor weed and is not as competitive as purple ammannia. Introduced from Southeast Asia.

SEEDLING: Glabrous. First leaves opposite.

Purple ammannia: Cotyledons ovate, dark green, sometimes red-tinged. First leaves ovate.

Purple ammannia (*Ammannia robusta*) flowering stem.
J. M. DiTomaso

Indian toothcup: Cotyledons oblong to elliptic, sessile, 1–2 mm long, ± 0.5 mm wide. First leaves narrowly obovate to elliptic, sessile, 2–4 mm long, ± 1 mm wide, slightly indented at the tip, with a distinct midvein. Stems 4-angled.

MATURE PLANT: Foliage glabrous. **Stems 4-angled.** Leaves opposite, **pairs are perpendicular to one another** (4-ranked or decussate). Stipules lacking.

Purple ammannia: Stems single or branched, often reddish. Leaves linear to narrowly lanceolate, lobed and clasping the stem at the base, 1.5–8 cm long, 0.5–1.5 cm wide.

Indian toothcup: Stems usually branched, **often creeping and rooting at the nodes.** Leaves oblong to obovate, 0.5–2 cm long, with thick margins.

Purple ammannia (*Ammannia robusta*) flowers.   J. K. CLARK

Purple ammannia (*Ammannia robusta*) seedling.   J. K. CLARK

Roots and Underground Structures:

Purple ammannia: Initially taprooted, later ± fibrous. All roots slender, shallow.

Indian toothcup: Fibrous, fine, shallow, densely numerous.

Flowers: Sepals fused into an **urn-shaped tube** (hypanthium), 4-lobed. Petals 4. Insect-pollinated. Self-compatible.

Purple ammannia: May–October. Flowers **sessile**, mostly in **clusters of** (1)2–5 **per leaf axil.** Hypanthium ± 4-ridged, **4-lobed, with toothlike appendages**

Purple ammannia (*Ammannia robusta*) seeds.   J. K. Clark

Indian toothcup (*Rotala indica*) infestation in a rice field.   J. M. DiTomaso

between the lobes. Appendages ± equal to sepal lobes in fruit. Petals usually **red to pale lavender**, mostly 3–5 mm long, but sometimes up to 8 mm long. Stamens 4(5–12), protruding (exserted). **Redstem** is reported to have **deep rose-purple** petals and **lower flowers on stalks are often 3–9 mm long, although these characteristics are variable**.

Indian toothcup: Summer. Flowers **sessile, 1 per leaf axil** or sometimes in short axillary spikes. Hypanthium to 2 mm long, often pinkish, **4-lobed, lobes ± triangular, toothlike appendages lacking**. Petals pink, shorter than sepal lobes. Stamens included within the hypanthium. Anthers red.

FRUITS AND SEEDS: Capsules contain numerous seeds.

Purple ammannia: Capsules round, 3–6 mm in diameter, **open irregularly**. Seeds ovate, angled, 0.5–1 mm long, to 0.4 mm wide, surface minutely pitted.

Indian toothcup: Capsules **oblong, 1–2 mm long, shorter than the hypanthium, open regularly by 2 valves**. Seeds elliptic to oblong, flattened, ± 0.5 mm long, 0.2 mm wide, often curved, amber.

HABITAT: Wet sites, ditches, agronomic fields, especially rice fields; pond, lake, creek margins, and shallow water.

Indian toothcup (*Rotala indica*) flowering stem.
J. M. DiTomaso

Indian toothcup (*Rotala indica*) seedling.
J. K. Clark

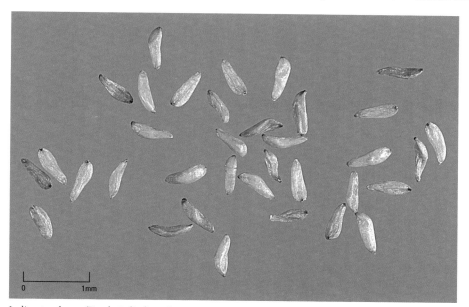

Indian toothcup *(Rotala indica)* seeds.

J. K. Clark

Distribution:

Purple ammannia: Oregon, Washington, Idaho, Montana, Wyoming, Colorado, Utah, Nevada, Arizona, and California in the North Coast Ranges, southern Sierra Nevada foothills, Central Valley, central-western region, South Coast, Catalina Island, and Sonoran Desert, to 500 m. Central and parts of the eastern United States, Mexico. **Redstem** occurs in New Mexico, Arizona, and California in the Cascade Range foothills, central and southern Sierra Nevada foothills, Central Valley, San Francisco Bay region, southwestern region, and Sonoran Desert, to 300 m. Central and eastern United States, Mexico, Central and South America.

Indian toothcup: California in the Sacramento Valley (Butte, Yuba, and Placer Cos.), to 100 m. Louisiana.

Propagation and Phenology: Reproduce primarily by seed. Seed coats become sticky when moistened. Seeds disperse with water, soil movement, and by clinging to agricultural equipment and the feet, feathers, and fur of animals. Indian toothcup stem fragments can root and develop into new plants under optimal conditions.

Similar Species: Toothcup *(Rotala ramosior* (L.) Koehne) [ROTRA] is a widespread native species with leaves and **calyces with toothlike appendages** that resemble those of purple ammannia and capsules that open by valves like fruits of Indian toothcup. Toothcup is distinguished from purple ammannia by having sessile leaves that are **not lobed or clasping at the base**. Unlike Indian toothcup, toothcup has **round to ovoid capsules 2–5 mm long** that **open regularly by 4 valves**. Flowers are white to pink. Toothcup is occasionally weedy in ditches, irrigated fields, and rice fields. It occurs in Oregon, Washington, Idaho, Montana, Colorado, Arizona, and California in the eastern North Coast Ranges, Central

Comparison between flowering stems of Indian toothcup (*Rotala indica*) (left) and toothcup (*Rotala ramosior*) (right).   J. M. DiTomaso

Toothcup (*Rotala ramosior*) flowering stem.

J. M. DiTomaso

Valley, and central and northern Sierra Nevada, to 1900 m. It is also found throughout most of the central, southern, and eastern United States, Mexico, and Central and South America.

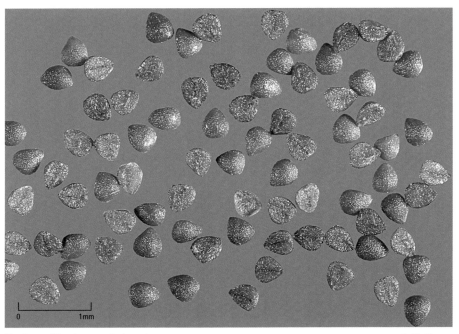

Toothcup *(Rotala ramosior)* seeds.   J. K. CLARK

Purple loosestrife (*Lythrum salicaria* L.) [LYTSA]

Hyssop loosestrife (*Lythrum hyssopifolium* L.) [LYTHY]

Noxious Weed Lists:

Purple loosestrife: California: B; Oregon: B; Washington: B; Montana: 2; Colorado: A; New Mexico: A; Arizona: 3; Idaho, Wyoming, Utah, and Nevada: Noxious Weed; CalEPPC: Red Alert

Synonyms:

Purple loosestrife: bouquet-violet; purple lythrum; *Lythrum salicaria* vars. *gracilior* Turcz., *tomentosum* (P. Mill) DC., and *vulgare* DC.

Hyssop loosestrife: grass poly; hyssop lythrum; *Lythrum adsurgens* Greene. The original spelling *Lythrum hyssopifolia* L. is sometimes used.

General Information:

Purple loosestrife: Erect **perennial** with **showy pinkish purple to red magenta flower spikes**, to 2(3) m tall. A mature plant can develop into a large clump up to 1.5 m in diameter. Aboveground foliage usually dies during the cool season, and new shoots sprout from a broad woody crown in spring. Originally cultivated as an ornamental and medicinal herb, purple loosestrife has escaped cultivation and become a **noxious** weed of wetlands in many regions throughout temperate North America. Plants often form dense colonies that displace native vegetation and wildlife. In the northeastern United States, monotypic stands have perpetuated themselves for at least 20 years. Introduced from Eurasia. In 1992,

Purple loosestrife (*Lythrum salicaria*) along a riverbank.   J. M. DiTomaso

237

Purple loosestrife *(Lythrum salicaria)* inflorescence.   J. M. DiTomaso

Purple loosestrife *(Lythrum salicaria)* flower.
J. M. DiTomaso

Purple loosestrife *(Lythrum salicaria)* inflorescence post-flowering.   J. M. DiTomaso

Purple loosestrife *(Lythrum salicaria)* vegetative stem.   J. M. DiTomaso

the black-margined and golden loosestrife beetles (*Galerucella calmariensis, Galerucella pusilla*), and loosestrife root weevil (*Hylobius transversovittatus*) were released as biocontrol agents in some northern states. By 1994, the beetles were established in Washington, Oregon, Montana, and Idaho, and the root weevil was established in Washington, Oregon, and Colorado. The loosestrife flower-feeding weevil (*Nanophyes marmoratus*) was released in 1994 in Washington, Oregon,

Purple loosestrife (*Lythrum salicaria*) node with whorled leaf arrangement.   J. M. DiTomaso

Purple loosestrife (*Lythrum salicaria*) seeds.   J. K. Clark

Montana, and Colorado, and in 1997 in California. All four species are well established in the northern United States, where their populations are increasing; however, they have established at only a few sites in California.

Hyssop loosestrife: Prostrate to erect **summer annual or biennial** to 0.6 m tall—with **small pale pink to lavender flowers.** Hyssop loosestrife is a common weed of seasonal wetlands and agronomic crops, especially rice fields. Introduced from Europe.

SEEDLING:

Purple loosestrife: Cotyledons ovate, 3–5 mm long, tips rounded, bases wedge-shaped, glabrous, on petioles 1–2 mm long. Stalk below cotyledons (hypocotyl) often purplish dotted. First and subsequent few leaves opposite, 5–8 mm long, resemble cotyledons.

Hyssop loosestrife: Cotyledons ovate, ± fleshy, tips rounded, bases tapered, sessile. First and subsequent few leaves resemble cotyledons.

MATURE PLANT: Stems simple or branched, sometimes ± square or 5-angled. **Leaves sessile, margins smooth.** Stipules lacking.

Purple loosestrife: Stems typically **covered with short hairs.** Leaves **lanceolate, 5–14 cm long, base slightly lobed** (cordate), covered with short hairs or glabrous, **mostly opposite or whorled.** Upper leaves sometimes alternate.

Hyssop loosestrife: Foliage pale green, **glabrous.** Leaves **linear to oblong,** 5–30 mm long, rounded at the tip, typically ascending toward stem tip. **Lower leaves opposite. Upper leaves usually alternate.**

Hyssop loosestrife (*Lythrum hyssopifolium*) near a rice field.   J. M. DiTomaso

ROOTS AND UNDERGROUND STRUCTURES:

Purple loosestrife: Taprooted and/or with locally spreading roots. Spreading roots typically form an expanded crown to 0.5 m in diameter. New shoots grow from the expanded crown in spring. Roots can associate with mycorrhizae.

Hyssop loosestrife: Taproot to 10 cm long, with fine lateral roots to 5 cm long. Lower stems sometimes develop adventitious roots.

FLOWERS: Calyx tube (hypanthium) **cylindrical, 4–6 mm long**, longitudinally 8–12-ribbed, with **4–6 triangular sepal lobes 0.5–1 mm long** at the top and

Hyssop loosestrife (*Lythrum hyssopifolium*) flowering stem.   J. M. DiToMASO

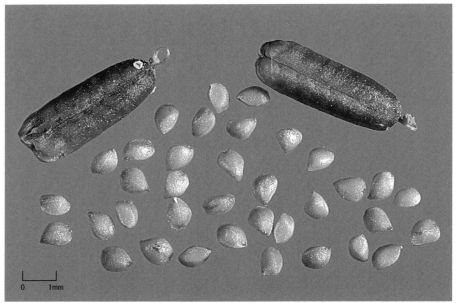

Hyssop loosestrife *(Lythrum hyssopifolium)* seeds and fruit. J. K. CLARK

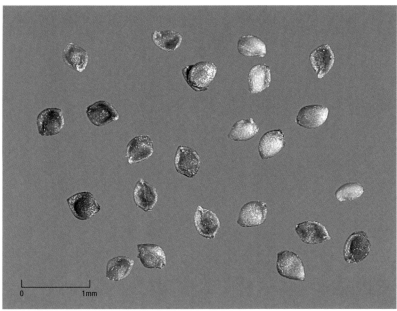

Threebract loosestrife *(Lythrum tribracteatum)* seeds. J. K. CLARK

longer appendages in between. Petals 4–6(7). Ovary superior but appearing inferior, surrounded by and not fused to calyx tube. Insect-pollinated.

Purple loosestrife: June–September. Spikes showy, terminal, ± dense, with 1–2 flowers per bract (reduced leaf) axil. Bracts ovate, slightly pinched-in at tip (acuminate). Petals bright pinkish purple, 8–14 mm long, with ± ruffled margins. Calyx tube appendages linear, 2–3 mm long. Stamens ± 12. Flower types consist of 3 combinations of style and stamen length (heterostyly). Primarily outcrossing.

Hyssop loosestrife: April–October. Flowers solitary in axils. Petals pale pink to lavender, 2–5 mm long. Calyx tube appendages awl-shaped, ± 1 mm long. Stamens 4–6. Self-compatible and outcrossing.

FRUITS AND SEEDS: Capsules oblong-ovoid, surrounded by persistent calyx tube, open into halves at tip. Seeds numerous, flattened, sometimes 3-angled in cross-section, often concave on 1 side, 0.5–1 mm long.

Purple loosestrife: Capsules 3–4 mm long. Seeds narrowly ovoid to triangular, reddish brown.

Hyssop loosestrife: Capsules 4–6 mm long. Seeds ovoid, shiny brown to straw-colored, striated.

POSTSENESCENCE CHARACTERISTICS: Aboveground parts of purple loosestrife typically die in late fall. Senescing foliage often turns red. Dead brown stems can persist through winter, are oppositely branched, and may retain a few capsules.

Spatulaleaf loosestrife (*Lythrum portula*) seeds.   J. K. Clark

HABITAT:

Purple loosestrife: Perennial and seasonal wetlands, including marsh and pond edges, streambanks, canals, and ditches. Especially invasive on disturbed sites. Tolerates some shade and most soil types, including infertile soils. Grows best in slightly acid to neutral soils. Does not tolerate submergence during the growing season.

Hyssop loosestrife: Seasonal wetlands, ditches, and cultivated fields, especially rice fields. Often grows on exposed mud. Tolerates some salinity. Sensitive to heavy frost.

DISTRIBUTION:

Purple loosestrife: Oregon, Washington, Idaho, Montana, Wyoming, Colorado, Utah, Nevada, and California, where it is scattered in the western North Coast

California loosestrife (*Lythrum californicum*) flowering stem, a native nonweedy plant along streamsides.   J. M. DiTOMASO

Ranges, southern North Coast, northwestern Modoc Plateau, northern and southern Sierra Nevada foothills, Central Valley, and San Francisco Bay region, to 1000 m. Much of temperate North America, especially northeastern United States. Rapidly expanding range in Northern California.

Hyssop loosestrife: Washington, Oregon, and throughout California, except deserts and Great Basin region, to 1600 m. Northeastern United States, South America.

PROPAGATION AND PHENOLOGY: Reproduce primarily by seed. Stem fragments can develop roots under favorable conditions. Seeds disperse with water, mud, human activities, and by clinging to feathers, fur, and feet of animals.

Purple loosestrife: A large plant can produce more than 2 million viable seeds in one season. Most seeds sink in water. Seeds typically germinate in midspring through early summer. Upon germination, seedlings float to the surface. Optimal temperature range for germination is from 15°–20°C. Light appears to increase germination. Seeds under cold dry storage remain highly viable for at least 3 years, but longevity under field conditions is unknown. Seedlings can mature and flower within 8–10 weeks.

Hyssop loosestrife: Plants produce an estimated average of 3200 seeds per plant. Seeds lack a dormancy period. Seeds stored in dry soil at room temperature can survive for at least 14 years, but longevity under field conditions is unknown. Most seeds germinate in spring when conditions become favorable. Fall-germinated seedlings may overwinter under mild conditions. Seedlings typically emerge after water levels subside.

MANAGEMENT FAVORING OR DISCOURAGING SURVIVAL:

Purple loosestrife: Monitoring uninfested areas and hand-pulling newly discovered seedlings before seeds are produced can help prevent the spread of purple loosestrife. Flooding can lead to spread of the weed. Mechanical removal before seed maturation will help reduce the spread of the plant. Cut stems can reroot under certain conditions.

SIMILAR SPECIES: Spatulaleaf loosestrife (*Lythrum portula* (L.) D. Webb, synonym: *Peplis portula* L.) and **threebract loosestrife** (*Lythrum tribracteatum* Salzm. ex Spreng.) are wetland plants introduced from Europe that resemble hyssop loosestrife. Spatulaleaf loosestrife is a **creeping summer annual** that **roots at the nodes** and has inconspicuous white to pink flowers ± 2–3 mm long. Unlike hyssop loosestrife, spatulaleaf loosestrife has **bell-shaped calyx tubes 1–2 mm long** and **fleshy spoon-shaped leaves that gradually tapered to a narrow base**. Spatulaleaf loosestrife occurs in Washington, Oregon, and California in the northern Sierra Nevada, to 2200 m. Threebract loosestrife is a **summer annual** to short-lived perennial with ± **obovate leaves**. Unlike hyssop loosestrife, threebract loosestrife has **triangular calyx tube appendages that resemble the sepal lobes** and are covered with red glands. Threebract loosestrife occurs in Utah, Idaho, and California in the Central Valley, San Francisco Bay region, and northern Modoc Plateau, to 1500 m.

Garden loosestrife *(Lysimachia vulgaris)* in flower.   J. M. DiTomaso

Garden loosestrife (*Lysimachia vulgaris*) flowers.   J. M. DiTomaso

California loosestrife (*Lythrum californicum* Torrey & A. Gray) is a **native perennial** that may be mistaken for purple loosestrife. However, California loosestrife is not generally considered a weed. Unlike purple loosestrife, California loosestrife has **glabrous stems, petals mostly 4–8 mm long**, and **linear inflorescence bracts** with **acute or rounded tips**. California loosestrife inhabits wetland sites in Utah, New Mexico, Arizona, Nevada, and California in the southeastern North Coast Ranges, Sierra Nevada foothills and high regions of the southern Sierra Nevada, Central Valley, central and southwestern regions, and deserts, to 2200 m.

European wand loosestrife (*Lythrum virgatum* L.) is thus far not naturalized in any western state. However, this species is a B-listed noxious weed in Washington because it closely resembles purple loosestrife. Many ornamental selections sold as cultivars of European wand loosestrife are actually purple loosestrife cultivars.

Lysimachia species are also referred to as loosestrife but belong to the primrose family (Primulaceae). **Garden loosestrife** (*Lysimachia vulgaris* L.) [LYSVU] [Washington Noxious Weed: B] is an erect **pubescent perennial** to 1 m tall, with **creeping rhizomes** and **showy yellow flowers**. Leaves are **opposite or whorled**, nearly sessile, lanceolate, 7–12 cm long, and **dotted with minute, ± sunken, black or orange glands** (punctate). Flowers have 5 glabrous **yellow** petals that are fused at base, have lobes 8–12 mm long, and **lack reddish or black streaks and dots**. Garden loosestrife is sometimes cultivated as an ornamental, but it has escaped cultivation in Washington, Montana, and Colorado and is expanding range in some areas. Garden loosestrife is particularly invasive in riparian and wetland sites, where dense colonies can develop. **Dotted loosestrife** (*Lysimachia punctata* L., synonym: large yellow loosestrife) [LYSPU] is an erect **pubescent perennial** to 1 m tall with slender rhizomes. It has escaped cultivation in some wet places in Oregon and the northeastern United States. Dotted loosestrife is distinguished by having **lower flowers in whorled clusters of 2–5 in the leaf axils** and upper flowers ± solitary in the leaf axils. Introduced from Eurasia. Unlike garden loosestrife and dotted loosestrife, native *Lysimachia* species of many western states are **glabrous** and have at least one of the following characteristics: flowers solitary in the leaf axils, flowers in short dense racemes in the leaf axils, flowers in loose terminal racemes, or petals with reddish or black streaks or dots.

Garden loosestrife (*Lysimachia vulgaris*) young vegetative growth.

J. M. DiTomaso

Creeping waterprimrose (*Ludwigia peploides* (Kunth) Raven) [LUDPE]

SYNONYMS: California waterprimrose; creeping primrose-willow; floating primrose-willow; yellow water-weed; *Jussiaea californica* (L.) Jeps.; *Jussiaea patibilcensis* Kunth; *Jussiaea peploides* Kunth; *Jussiaea polygonoides* Kunth; *Jussiaea repens* L. vars. *peploides* (Kunth) Griseb. and *californica* Wats.; others

GENERAL INFORMATION: Floating to emergent perennial with stems to 3 m long. Plants sometimes develop a tangled mat of stems that can reduce water flow in irrigation channels and drainage ditches. Creeping waterprimrose is a widespread species that consists of 3 subspecies in the United States. Subspecies *peploides* is native to California, Arizona, New Mexico, Texas, and Louisiana, and subspecies *glabrescens* (Kuntze) Raven is native to the central and eastern United States. Subspecies *montevidensis* (Spreng.) Raven is introduced in California and Louisiana from southern South America. Creeping waterprimrose is sometimes sold as an aquarium or pond ornamental. Seeds can be consumed by water birds but are not considered a valuable food source.

SEEDLING: Rarely encountered.

MATURE PLANT: Variable. Stems simple or branched, **creeping**, lower portions ± prostrate (decumbent) and rooting at nodes, upper portions often matted, typically **floating to ascending**. Stems and leaf veins often reddish. Leaves **alternate**, usually clustered and **oblong or obovate**, sometimes lanceolate or elliptic, tapered at the base into a stalk, **1–4 cm long** not including stalk. Margins smooth. Foliage of ssp. *peploides* is glabrous. Foliage of ssp. *montevidensis* is covered with soft spreading and glandular hairs, especially near stem tips, and leaf tips are glandular.

Creeping waterprimrose (*Ludwigia peploides* ssp. *montevidensis*) along an irrigation canal.

J. M. DiTomaso

ROOTS AND UNDERGROUND STRUCTURES: Stems typically develop a dense clump of roots covered with numerous fine root hairs at lower to middle nodes.

FLOWERS: May–October. Flowering stems are usually **creeping** and **floating** to ascending. Flowers solitary in upper leaf axils, trumpet-shaped with a long slender tube (inferior ovary), on a stalk 1–6 cm long. Petals 5(6), usually yellow, sometimes white, separate, **7–25 mm long**. Sepals 5(6), mostly **3–12 mm long**, persistent on flowers. Stamens 10–12, in 2 unequal whorls. Near the base of the flower tube is a pair of small **triangular** (deltate) **to ovate** bractlets.

Creeping waterprimrose (*Ludwigia peploides* ssp. *montevidensis*) in flower.   J. M. DiTomaso

Creeping waterprimrose (*Ludwigia peploides* ssp. *montevidensis*) flowering stem.   J. M. DiTomaso

FRUITS AND SEEDS: Capsules hard, narrowly cylindrical, 4–5-chambered, 20–40 mm long, 2–4 mm in diameter, ± 5-sided, on a stalk to 9 cm long that is typically bent downward (fruits reflexed). Capsules of ssp. *peploides* are **10–25 mm long**, and those of ssp. *montevidensis* are usually **25–40 mm long**. Seeds ovoid, truncate at the ends, ± triangular in cross-section, 1–1.5 mm long, several in a single row per chamber and embedded in inner wall of capsule. Seeds do not individually disperse from capsule.

Floating leaves of creeping waterprimrose (*Ludwigia peploides* ssp. *montevidensis*).
J. M. DiTomaso

Dense stand of Uruguay waterprimrose (*Ludwigia hexapetala*) in an irrigation canal.
J. M. DiTomaso

HABITAT: Ditches, irrigation channels, streambanks, ponds, and lake margins.

DISTRIBUTION:

Subspecies *peploides*: New Mexico, Arizona, and California at the North Coast, western North Coast Ranges, Sierra Nevada foothills, Central Valley, Central Coast, San Francisco Bay region, South Coast, western Transverse Ranges, and southwestern Mojave Desert, to 900 m. Texas, Louisiana, South America.

Subspecies *montevidensis*: California at the southern North Coast, northern and central Sierra Nevada foothills, Central Valley, and South Coast, to 500 m. Louisiana, Europe, Australia.

Uruguay waterprimrose (*Ludwigia hexapetala*) in flower.   J. M. DiTomaso

Uruguay waterprimrose (*Ludwigia hexapetala*) flowering stem.   J. M. DiTomaso

PROPAGATION AND PHENOLOGY: Reproduces by seed and vegetatively from creeping stems and stem fragments. The biology of this species is poorly understood. Seeds and stem fragments disperse with water and soil movement and probably by clinging to the fur, feathers, feet, and beaks of animals.

SIMILAR SPECIES: Uruguay waterprimrose (*Ludwigia hexapetala* (Hook. & Arn.) Zardini, Gu & Raven; synonyms: *Jussiaea grandiflora* (M. Michelli) Greuter & Burdet; *Jussiaea repens* L. var. *grandiflora* M. Michelli; *Jussiaea uruguayensis* Camb.; *Ludwigia uruguayensis* (Camb.) Hara var. *major* (Hassler) Munz) [LUDUR] is a widely distributed glabrous to hairy **native perennial** that closely resembles creeping waterprimrose. Uruguay waterprimrose typically has slightly larger leaves and flowers and is distinguished by usually having **erect flowering stems** (sometimes floating), mostly lanceolate to elliptic leaves **5–11 cm long**, sepals mostly **13–19 mm long**, petals mostly **20–30 mm long**, and ovate to obovate bractlets near the base of the flower tube. Uruguay waterprimrose inhabits marshes, lake margins, irrigation canals, and other wet sites in Oregon, Washington in the southwestern region and Seattle area, and California in the North Coast, southwestern North Coast Ranges, Central Coast, San Francisco Bay region, and South Coast, to 300 m. It is also found in the southern and eastern United States and southern South America. Uruguay waterprimrose is a polyploid species with a chromosome count of $2n = 80$. Creeping waterprimrose has a chromosome count of $2n = 16$. Both species are often found growing together.

Waterpurslane (*Ludwigia palustris* (L.) Elliot) [LUDPA] is a highly variable, nearly **worldwide native perennial** that is sometimes weedy. Waterpurslane is distinguished by having **opposite leaves** less than 5 cm long, flowers with **4 sepals** 1–2 mm long, **0 petals**, an **ovary with 4 green stripes**, and fruits **2–5 mm long**. Waterpurslane occurs in Washington, Oregon, Idaho, New Mexico, Arizona, and California in the western northwestern region, northern and central Sierra Nevada, San Francisco Bay region, Central Coast, San Joaquin Valley, and South Coast, to 1000 m. It also occurs in the eastern half of the United States, northern South America, western Asia, northern Africa, and much of Europe. It is a weedy introduction to South Africa, New Zealand, and Hawaii.

Waterpurslane (*Ludwigia palustris*) in its native habitat in a pond.   J. M. DITOMASO

Giant reed (*Arundo donax* L.)

Noxious Weed Lists: California: C; CalEPPC: A-1

Synonyms: bamboo reed; donax reed; elephant grass; reed cane; reed grass; Spanish reed; wild cane; *Arundo glauca* Bubani; *Arundo latifolia* Salisb.; *Arundo sativa* Lam.; *Cynodon donax* (L.) Raspail; *Donax arundinaceus* P. Beauv.; *Scolochloa arundinacea* (P. Beav.) Mert. & Koch; *Scolochloa donax* (L.) Gaudin. A cultivated variety with variegated leaves is often called *Arundo donax* L. var. *versicolor* (P. Mill.) Stokes, synonym: *Arundo versicolor* P. Mill.

General Information: **Bamboolike perennial** to 8 m tall, with **well developed rhizomes**. Plants are typically terrestrial but tolerate periodic flooding. In California in the late 1700s to early 1800s, giant reed was often planted for erosion control in flood channels and as windbreaks. In recent years, **giant reed** has become problematic in riparian corridors throughout many areas of California and other western states. Dense monocultures typically develop, displacing native vegetation, diminishing wildlife habitat, and increasing flooding and siltation. In addition, giant reed is adapted to a periodic fire regime. It is readily flammable throughout much of the year, increasing the susceptibility of riparian corridors to fire. Large stands can significantly increase water loss from underground aquifers in semiarid regions due to a high evapotranspiration rate, which is many times greater than that of native riparian vegetation. It was historically used for erosion control and as building material. Giant reed is occasionally cultivated as an ornamental in the United States. In other areas of the world it is grown for industrial cellulose and to produce reeds for woodwind instruments. It is an alternate host for beet western yellows virus, sugarcane mosaic virus, and maize dwarf mosaic virus. Introduced from the Mediterranean region and tropical Asia.

Giant reed (*Arundo donax*) adjacent to a riparian area.   J. M. DiTomaso

Seedling: Generally not encountered in North America.

Mature Plant: Mostly glabrous. Canes erect, **semiwoody, inflexible, 1–4 cm thick**, with long, hollow internodes. First-year green canes have unbranched stems the same diameter as older canes but are more pliable. Older canes are often branched, sometimes with leaves only on the branches. Leaves alternate in the same plane (2-ranked), ± evenly spaced along the stem length. Blades flat, less than 1 m long, 2–8 cm wide, middle and base ± equal in width, margins rough to touch (scabrous). Blade bases (region of auricles) **broadly round-lobed to ± truncate, clasping stem**, often with long wavy hairs along the margins.

Giant reed (*Arundo donax*) within a stream.   J. M. DiTomaso

Giant reed (*Arundo donax*) along a roadside.   J. M. DiTomaso

Giant reed (*Arundo donax*) inflorescence. No viable seeds are produced.   J. M. DiTomaso

Second-year branching pattern of giant reed (*Arundo donax*).   J. M. DiTomaso

Giant reed (*Arundo donax*) collar and sheath region.   J. M. DiTomaso

Auricle and collar region pale yellowish green. Ligules consist of a short, even, minutely fringed membrane 1–2 mm long. Sheaths open, tightly enveloping stem.

ROOTS AND UNDERGROUND STRUCTURES: Rhizomes creeping, thick, scaly, often forming a dense network, firm and knotty at the stem bases. Rhizome and stem fragments with a node can develop into a new plant under suitable moist conditions.

SPIKELETS AND FLORETS: Mostly March–November but can occur at any time and nearly year-round in some areas. Panicles terminal, dense, plumelike, 30–60 cm long, silvery cream-colored to purplish or brown, open with ascending branches

Giant reed (*Arundo donax*) vegetatively reproducing from stem fragment.   J. M. DiTomaso

Giant reed (*Arundo donax*) spikelets.
J. K. Clark

0 1mm   1cm

or contracted with ± erect branches. Spikelets 10–15 mm long, 4–5-flowered (florets), detach from above the glumes and between florets. **Floret stalks** (rachilla) **glabrous**. Glumes 3–5-veined, membranous. Lemma tips short-awned from between 2 teeth. **Lemma base covered with long silky hairs**. North American populations are not known to produce viable seeds.

POSTSENESCENCE CHARACTERISTICS: Dead canes lose their leaves, turn grayish, and become brittle and splintery. They eventually fall over and typically remain on-site until the next flooding or fire event.

Common reed *(Phragmites australis)* in native habitat along a stream.   J. M. DiTomaso

Common reed *(Phragmites australis)* inflorescence.   J. M. DiTomaso

HABITAT: Riparian areas, floodplains, and ditches, typically on sites with a low slope. Occurs in a wide range of soil types but grows best in well-drained moist soils. Tolerates some salinity and extended periods of drought. Does not survive in areas with prolonged or regular periods of freezing temperatures.

DISTRIBUTION: Arizona, Nevada, Utah, New Mexico, and California in the North Coast, southern North Coast Ranges, central-western region, southwestern region, deserts, central Sierra Nevada foothills, and Central Valley, to 500 m. Southern United States, Mexico. Nearly worldwide in tropical to warm temperate regions.

PROPAGATION AND PHENOLOGY: Reproduces vegetatively from rhizomes and rhizome and stem fragments. Fragments disperse with water, mud, and human activities. Under optimal conditions, plants grow and spread rapidly during the warm season. Intact rhizomes buried under 1–3 m of silt can develop new shoots. Under experimental conditions, rhizome fragments readily develop new shoots from a depth of 25 cm, whereas stem fragments mostly resprout from less than 10 cm. Viable seeds have not been observed in North America. Some Asian populations produce viable seeds.

MANAGEMENT FAVORING OR DISCOURAGING SURVIVAL: Rhizomes must be removed or killed to eradicate infestations. Hand-removing small populations can prevent the development of large problematic infestations. Prescribed burning removes canes but does not kill rhizomes. Mechanical removal can fragment rhizomes and stems, which may develop into new plants if not removed from the site. Systemic herbicide applications either through foliar or cut stump treatment of mature

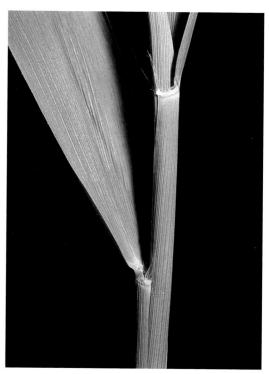

Common reed (*Phragmites australis*)
collar and sheath region.

J. M. DiTomaso

plants are most effective in late summer to early fall after the flowering period (July–October). Treatment of re-growth is most effective from March through July. Cutting the stems of mature plants and treating the stumps with systemic herbicide is effective from March to October.

SIMILAR SPECIES: Common reed (*Phragmites australis* (Cav.) Trin. ex Steud.; synonym: *Phragmites communis* Trin.) [PHRCO] is a smaller, widespread **native perennial** to 4 m tall, with long stolons and/or **rhizomes** that may be mistaken for **giant reed**. Unlike giant reed, common reed has **blade bases that are**

Common reed (*Phragmites australis*) spikelets.   J. K. CLARK

Ravennagrass (*Saccharum ravennae*) habit in riparian site.   J. M. DiTOMASO

Ravennagrass (*Saccharum ravennae*) inflorescence.   J. M. DiTOMASO

gradually narrowed (not round-lobed, truncate, or clasping stem), glabrous lemmas long-tapered to a point, and floret stalks covered with long silky hairs. In addition, stems are typically less than 1 cm in diameter with ligules consisting of a very short membranous section at the base (usually less than 1 mm long) and ciliate hairs ± 1 mm long at the top. Common reed is usually considered a desirable component of natural aquatic ecosystems where it is native. However, it can occasionally be weedy in drainage areas and other controlled aquatic systems in the western states, especially in Southern California. It has also become an invasive problem in marsh areas of Humboldt County, California, where it is not native. It is a common roadside weed in the eastern United States. Common reed usually produces viable seeds. Most seeds typically germinate mid to late spring. Submersed seeds do not germinate until water recedes. Seeds are short-lived under field conditions; thus, persistent seed banks do not accumulate. Common reed is less tolerant than giant reed of high or low water tables. Common reed occurs nearly worldwide and throughout much of North America, including all western states. It is scattered in freshwater and salt marshes, pond and lake margins, and riparian areas throughout California to 1600 m.

Ravennagrass (*Saccharum ravennae* (L.) L. (also listed as *S. ravennae* (L.) Murray, synonyms: hardy pampasgrass; *Erianthus ravennae* (L.) P. Beauv.) is a **large tufted perennial** with flowering stems to 4 m tall that have leaves distributed to the

Young bunchgrass of ravennagrass (*Saccharum ravennae*).   J. M. DiTomaso

Ravennagrass (*Saccharum ravennae*) collar and sheath.   J. M. DiTomaso

base of the inflorescence. Unlike giant reed and common reed, ravennagrass has unlobed **blade bases that are very densely covered with long fuzzy tawny hairs that typically hide the ligule and upper blade base surface.** Ravennagrass inhabits moist places such as ditches, marshes, and riparian areas in the southern Sonoran Desert (Imperial Co., CA), Sacramento Valley (Cache Creek, Yolo Co.), and possibly elsewhere, to 300 m. Introduced from Eurasia as an ornamental.

Ravennagrass (*Saccharum ravennae*) spikelets.   J. K. CLARK

Junglerice (*Echinochloa colona* (L.) Link.) [ECHCO]

Barnyardgrass (*Echinochloa crus-galli* (L.) P. Beauv.) [ECHCG]

Synonyms: Complete synonymy for these species is extensive and beyond the scope of this publication.

Junglerice: fingergrass; small barnyardgrass; watergrass; *Echinochloa colonum* (L.) Link; *Echinochloa crus-gallis* (L.) P. Beauv. ssp. *colonum* Honda; *Echinochloa zonalis* Parl.; *Milium colonum* Moench; *Oplismenus colonum* H.B.K.; *Panicum colonum* L.; *Panicum incertum* Bosc ex Steud.; *Panicum prorepens* Steud.; *Panicum zonale* Guss.; many others

Barnyardgrass: cocksfoot panicum; cockspur grass; summergrass; watergrass; *Milium crusgalli* Moench; *Panicum grossum* Salisb.; *Pennisetum crusgalli* Baumg.; *Oplismenus crusgalli* Dum.; *Orthopogon crusgalli* Spreng.; *Panicum crusgalli* L.; many others

General Information: Tufted **summer annuals** with **flattened sheaths**, blades that **lack ligules**, and panicles of **short, densely flowered racemes**. Both species occur in temperate to tropical regions nearly worldwide and are often associated with agricultural lands, including rice fields in much of the world. The genus *Echinochloa* consists of numerous similar yet highly variable species. Some closely related species or complexes have been treated as varieties, subspecies, and distinct species by different taxonomists, resulting in much taxonomic confusion. Some taxonomic problems in the genus remain unresolved.

Junglerice (*Echinochloa colona*) in an agricultural area.   C. Elmore

Junglerice: Stems erect to prostrate with erect tips (decumbent), to 1 m tall, but usually shorter. Junglerice is most troublesome in tropical to subtropical regions. Introduced from tropical regions worldwide.

Barnyardgrass: Stems erect to 1.5 m tall. Plants are extremely variable. Introduced from Eurasia.

SEEDLING: Vegetative characteristics resemble those of mature plants.

MATURE PLANT: Highly variable. Blades flat, rolled in bud, upper surfaces usually glabrous. Sheaths open, ± flattened, glabrous. **Ligules and auricles lacking**.

Junglerice: Stems hairy at the nodes, otherwise glabrous. Blades 3–22 cm long, 0.3–0.8 cm wide, often with **purplish transverse bands**. Sheaths 4–9 cm long. Collar and auricle regions glabrous.

Barnyardgrass: Blades 0.5–30 cm long, 0.5–2 cm wide. Collar region glabrous. Margins of auricle region sometimes with many long hairs. Sheaths 3–7 cm long.

ROOTS AND UNDERGROUND STRUCTURES: Roots fibrous, shallow. Adventitious roots often develop at the base of tillers in contact with soil.

SPIKELETS AND FLORETS: June–October. Spikelets crowded, nearly sessile, **detach as a unit**, often purple-tinged. Upper glume 3–5-veined, larger than lower glume, ±

Junglerice (*Echinochloa colona*) inflorescence.
J. M. DiTomaso

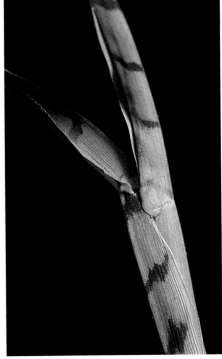

Junglerice (*Echinochloa colona*) collar and sheath with purple stripes. J. M. DiTomaso

covered with short stiff hairs, especially veins. Florets 2 per spikelet, appearing as 1, the upper fertile, the lower sterile. **Fertile lemma and palea firm, tightly enclose the grain** (caryopsis). Sterile floret consists of a glumelike lemma and membranous palea.

Junglerice: Panicles 3–15 cm long. Branches **simple, 1–3 cm long**, ascending to erect (appressed), **well-spaced along the central axis**, glabrous. Spikelets ovate to elliptic, **2–3 mm long, 1–1.5 mm wide, lack awns**, arranged in 4 regular rows on one side of the branch.

Barnyardgrass: Panicles 6–25 cm long, erect to drooping, sometimes purplish. Primary branches stiff, mostly **erect to ascending, 3–7 cm long**, glabrous or hairy. Lower primary branches typically have 2 secondary branches. Spikelets elliptic to lanceolate, **3–4(5) mm long** excluding awns when present, **1.5–2 mm wide**. Sterile floret lemma pinched-in and pointed (acuminate) or awned to 50 mm long. Awn length often varies greatly on the same plant. **Fertile lemma abruptly pointed, tip withered or different color or texture than lemma body.** Self-compatible.

Junglerice (*Echinochloa colona*) collar and sheath lacking obvious purple stripes.   J. M. DiTomaso

HABITAT: Disturbed moist places, fields, roadsides, ditches, summer-irrigated crops, margins of ponds and rice fields, pastures, orchards, vineyards, and landscaped areas.

DISTRIBUTION:

Junglerice: Washington, Oregon, New Mexico, Arizona, and California in the Central Valley, San Francisco Bay region, western South Coast Ranges, southern

Junglerice (*Echinochloa colona*) seedling.   J. M. DITOMASO

Junglerice (*Echinochloa colona*) florets (shiny structures) and spikelets.   J. K. CLARK

Sierra Nevada foothills, southwestern region, and Sonoran Desert, to 100 m. Southern and eastern United States. Expanding range.

Barnyardgrass: Throughout most of North America, including all western states. Throughout California to 1500 m.

PROPAGATION AND PHENOLOGY: Reproduce by seed. Plants can produce large quantities of seeds. Seeds disperse with water, animals, agricultural activities, soil movement, and as a seed or feed contaminant. Seeds germinate after soil temperatures warm in spring through summer.

Junglerice: Increased exposure to light and the presence of nitrogen stimulate germination.

Barnyardgrass: A large proportion of seeds can float on water for up to 5 days. Fresh seeds are hard-coated and variably dormant. A cool moist period can enhance germination. Seeds germinate over a wide temperature range. Some seeds buried at shallow depths (to 20 cm) can survive up to 12 years under field conditions. Most seedlings emerge from a depth of 1–2 cm.

MANAGEMENT FAVORING OR DISCOURAGING SURVIVAL: Junglerice and barnyardgrass do not establish in rice fields that remain continuously flooded. Once established in moist soil or very shallow water, they tolerate continuously flooded fields. Regularly removing plants before seeds develop can eventually control infestations. In contrast, watergrasses (see **SIMILAR SPECIES,** below) are the worst weeds

Barnyardgrass (*Echinochloa crus-galli*) in a rice field.   J. K. CLARK

Barnyardgrass (*Echinochloa crus-galli*) inflorescence.   J. M. DiTomaso

Barnyardgrass (*Echinochloa crus-galli*) spikelets on inflorescence branch.   J. M. DiTomaso

Barnyardgrass (*Echinochloa crus-galli*) collar and sheath (ligule lacking).   J. M. DiTomaso

of California rice. These species are aquatic and have adapted to the wet-seeded, continuously flooded rice system of California. Thus they are more difficult to control with flooding than barnyardgrass, which used to be the prevalent weed of rice in the past. Many of the currently available herbicides for watergrass control are becoming inefficient due to selection for resistance biotypes.

SIMILAR SPECIES: Refer to table 13 (page 275) for a comparison of distinguishing characteristics of *Echinochloa* species.

Comparison of barnyardgrass (*Echinochloa crus-galli*) collar (left) with rice (*Oryza sativa*)(right).

J. K. CLARK

0 1mm   1cm

Barnyardgrass (*Echinochloa crus-galli*) florets (shiny structures)and spikelets.

J. K. CLARK

Gulf cockspur (*Echinochloa crus-pavonis* (Kunth) Schultes) [ECHCV] and **rough barnyardgrass** (*Echinochloa muricata* (Beauv.) Fern.) are **summer annuals** that resemble barnyardgrass and grow in the same types of habitats. Gulf cockspur occurs in Oregon, Utah, Colorado, New Mexico, Arizona, and California in the Central Valley and South Coast to 300 m. Gulf cockspur is also found in many southern states. It is expected to expand its range. Introduced from Eurasia and Africa. Rough barnyardgrass occurs throughout the United States, including all western states. In California, it is found at elevations up to 1000 m. Evidence suggests that rough barnyardgrass is sometimes unable to produce a quantity of mature seeds before soil moisture is depleted in summer, making it less efficient at colonizing open wet sites compared to barnyardgrass. Introduced from Eurasia.

Late watergrass (*Echinochloa oryzicola* (Vasing.) Vasing., synonyms: rice barnyardgrass; *Echinochloa crus-galli* (L.) P. Beauv. var. *oryzicola* (Vasing.) Ohwi;

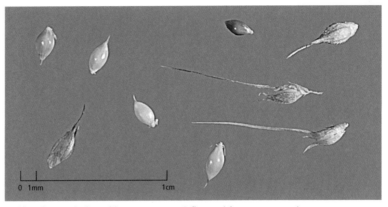

Gulf cockspur (*Echinochloa crus-pavonis*) florets (shiny structures) and spikelets.   J. K. Clark

Rough barnyardgrass (*Echinochloa muricata*) inflorescence.   J. M. DiTomaso

Echinochloa phyllopogon (Stapf) Koss. [ECHPH]) [ECHOR] is a **summer annual** that is generally restricted to rice fields. The taxonomy and correct scientific names of late watergrass and **early watergrass** (*Echinochloa oryzoides* (Ard.) Fritsch) [ECHOR] are controversial. Some taxonomists believe that *Echinochloa oryzicola* and *Echinochloa oryzoides* are names applied to the same species, but

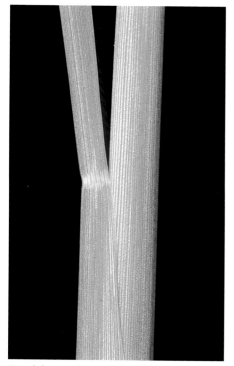

Rough barnyardgrass (*Echinochloa muricata*) collar and sheath.   J. M. DiTomaso

Rough barnyardgrass (*Echinochloa muricata*) seedling.   J. M. DiTomaso

Rough barnyardgrass (*Echinochloa muricata*) florets (shiny structures) and spikelets.   J. K. Clark

current treatments indicate they are distinct species. Late watergrass germinates underwater and develops flowers and seeds at the same time as rice, ± 90 days after planting. Late watergrass inhabits rice fields in the Central Valley of

Inflorescences of barnyardgrass *(Echinochloa crus-galli)* (left), late watergrass *(E. oryzicola)* (center), and early watergrass *(E. oryzoides)* (right).   J. M. DiTomaso

Late watergrass *(Echinochloa oryzicola)* inflorescence.   J. M. DiTomaso

Late watergrass *(Echinochloa oryzicola)* spikelets on inflorescence branch.   J. M. DiTomaso

Late watergrass (*Echinochloa oryzicola*) collar and sheath (ligule lacking).   J. M. DiTomaso

Late watergrass (*Echinochloa oryzicola*) florets (shiny structures) and spikelets.   J. K. Clark

Early watergrass (*Echinochloa oryzoides*) inflorescence.   J. M. DiTomaso

273

California, to 100 m. It also occurs in Florida. Introduced from Eurasia with rice seeds. Early watergrass is also a **summer annual** that occurs in rice fields of the Central Valley, California. Early watergrass germinates underwater and matures before rice, ± 40 days after flooding. Introduced from Eurasia.

Early watergrass (*Echinochloa oryzoides*) spikelets on inflorescence branch.

J. M. DiTomaso

Early watergrass (*Echinochloa oryzoides*) collar and sheath (ligule lacking).   J. M. DiTomaso

Early watergrass (*Echinochloa oryzoides*) seedling.   J. M. DiTomaso

Early watergrass (*Echinochloa oryzoides*) florets (shiny structures) and spikelets.

J. K. CLARK

Table 13. Barnyardgrass and related *Echinochloa* species

Species	Mature panicle	Panicle branch length (cm)	Spikelet length excluding awns (mm)	Spikelet width (mm)	Awns	Other
junglerice (*E. colona*)	erect	1–2(3), simple	2–3	1–1.5	none	spikelets in 4 regular rows on one side of branch; blades sometimes transversely purple-banded
barnyardgrass (*E. crus-galli*)	erect to drooping at tip	3–7	3–4(5)	1.5–2	none to 50 mm long, ± variable on same plant	spikelets often purple-tinged; fertile lemma abruptly pointed, point withered or of a different color and texture than lemma body; 2n = 54
gulf cockspur (*E. crus-pavonis*)	strongly drooping	3–7	2.5–3.5	1–1.5	none to 15 mm long, fine, ± uniform on same plant	spikelets usually green; fertile lemma abruptly pointed, point withered or of a different color and texture than lemma body; 2n = 36
rough barnyardgrass (*E. muricata*)	erect to slightly drooping	3–6	3–4	1.5–2	none to ± 40 mm long, ± uniform on same plant	fertile lemma long-tapered to a firm point of same color and texture of lemma body; 2n = 36
late watergrass (*E. oryzicola,* synonym: *E. phyllopogon*)	erect	3–6	4–6	2–2.5	none	foliage dark green; matures ± 90 days after flooding
early watergrass (*E. oryzoides*)	strongly drooping	3–6	4–6	2–2.5	± 5–50 mm long, ± uniform on same plant	foliage light (yellowish) green; matures ± 40 days after flooding

Bearded sprangletop (*Leptochloa fascicularis* (Lam.) A. Gray) [LEFFA]

Mexican sprangletop (*Leptochloa uninervia* (C. Presl) A. Hitchc. & Chase) [LEFUN]

SYNONYMS: Complete synonymy for these species is extensive and beyond the scope of this publication.

Bearded sprangletop: loose-flowered sprangletop; raygrass; scale grass; spreading millet; *Festuca fascicularis* Lam.; *Festuca polystachya* Michx.; *Festuca texana* Steud.; *Diplachne fascicularis* (Lam.) Beauv.; *Leptochloa fusca* (L.) Kunth ssp. *fascicularis* (Lam.) N. Snow (often used outside of California); *Leptochloa polystachya* Kunth; *Leptochloa tracyi* (Vasey) Beal; *Uralepis composita* Buckley (orthographic variant, *Uralepsis composita* Buckley)

Mexican sprangletop: clustered saltgrass; sprangletop; spreading millet; *Diplachne verticillata* Nees & Mey.; *Leptochloa fusca* (L.) Kunth ssp. *uninervia* (J. Presl) N. Snow (often used outside of California); *Leptochloa imbricata* Thurb.; *Megastachya uninervia* J. Presl; *Poa uninervia* Kunth; *Uralepis verticillata* (Nees & Meyen) Steud. (orthographic variant, *Uralepsis verticillata* (Nees & Meyen) Steud.); *Rabdochloa imbricata* Kuntze

GENERAL INFORMATION: Widespread **native summer annuals** to 1 m tall, with panicles consisting of **well-spaced spikelike branches**. Both species inhabit summer moist soils. Bearded sprangletop is often associated with rice fields. It is typically more problematic in fields where the water is maintained at a low level during the early growth stages of rice, but some ecotypes can emerge through 20 cm of water. Bearded sprangletop seeds are smaller than rice grains and are readily separated from the rice during the cleaning process.

SEEDLING: Foliage characteristics resemble those of mature plants.

MATURE PLANT: Loosely tufted, stems erect to spreading. Blades (rolled in bud), flat to loosely rolled, 10–50 cm long, 1–5 mm wide, mostly glabrous, rough to touch (scabrous). Blade midvein often pale (more distinct in Mexican sprangletop). Sheaths open, keeled, loose, glabrous to scabrous. Ligules membranous, delicate, often ragged at the apex, 2–7 mm long. Auricles lacking.

ROOTS AND UNDERGROUND STRUCTURES: Roots fibrous, ± shallow.

SPIKELETS AND FLORETS: Panicle branches ascending to spreading, **spikelike**, with **1 sessile spikelet per node**. Spikelets ± **cylindrical**, detach above glumes and between florets. Lemmas lanceolate, 3-veined, backs rounded. Glumes 1(3)-veined, upper glume larger than lower.

Bearded sprangletop: May–November. Panicles **gray-green**. Spikelets **6–12 mm long**, consist mostly of 6–12 florets. **Lemmas 3.5–5 mm long**, hairy on veins below middle, with an **awn 1–3(5) mm long at the tip** from between 2 minute teeth. Glumes 2–4 mm long. Usually self-pollinating.

Mexican sprangletop: March–December. Panicles **dark gray-green to lead-colored**, sometimes tinged purplish or reddish. Spikelets **5–7 mm long**, consist mostly of 6–9 florets. **Lemmas 2–3 mm long**, margins hairy near base. **Lemma**

Bearded sprangletop (*Leptochloa fascicularis*) in a rice field. J. K. CLARK

Bearded sprangletop (*Leptochloa fascicularis*) inflorescence. J. M. DiTOMASO

Bearded sprangletop (*Leptochloa fascicularis*) spikelets on inflorescence branch.

J. M. DiTOMASO

Bearded sprangletop (*Leptochloa fascicularis*) collar and sheath. J. K. CLARK

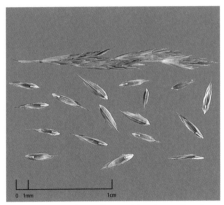

Bearded sprangletop (*Leptochloa fascicularis*)
seedling. J. K. CLARK

Bearded sprangletop (*Leptochloa fascicularis*)
florets and spikelets. J. K. CLARK

Mexican sprangletop (*Leptochloa uninervia*)
plant. J. M. DiTOMASO

Mexican sprangletop (*Leptochloa uninervia*)
inflorescence. J. M. DiTOMASO

tips ± rounded to truncate with an abrupt short point. Awn lacking. Glumes 1–2 mm long.

POSTSENESCENCE CHARACTERISTICS: Plants senesce late summer through fall. Old panicles are straw-colored, and branches retain the empty glumes.

HABITAT: Marshes, wetlands, moist disturbed places, summer irrigated crops, rice field margins, irrigation and drainage ditches, orchards, vineyards, moist pastures, pond margins, and wet places in waste areas, landscaped sites, and on roadsides. Can inhabit moist alkaline or acid soils.

DISTRIBUTION:

Bearded sprangletop: Throughout most of the United States, including all western states. California in the Central Valley, Great Basin region, and deserts, to 1200 m. Mexico, South America.

Mexican sprangletop: Oregon, Utah, Colorado, New Mexico, Arizona, Nevada, and California in the San Joaquin Valley, Great Basin region, southern Sierra Nevada foothills, southwestern region, and deserts, to 1000 m. Southern United States, parts of the northeastern United States. Mexico, South America.

Mexican sprangletop (*Leptochloa uninervia*) spikelets on inflorescence branch.
J. M. DiTOMASO

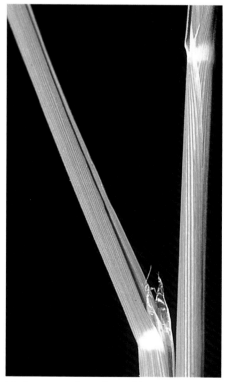

Mexican sprangletop (*Leptochloa uninervia*) collar and sheath.
J. M. DiTOMASO

PROPAGATION AND PHENOLOGY: Reproduce by seed. Florets disperse with water, mud, human activities, and by clinging to feet, fur, and feathers of animals. Seeds germinate as the weather warms in spring.

MANAGEMENT FAVORING OR DISCOURAGING SURVIVAL: Manually removing plants before seeds develop can control infestations. In rice fields, maintaining higher water levels during the early growth stages of rice can help control problematic infestations.

SIMILAR SPECIES: Bearded and Mexican sprangletop are unlikely to be confused with other weedy grasses of wet places.

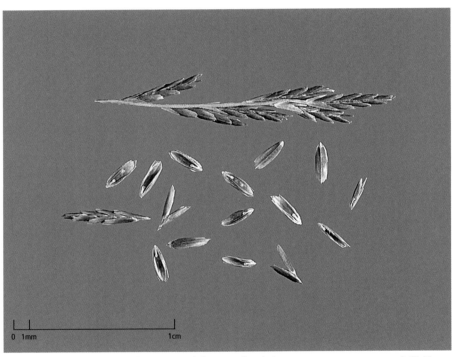

Mexican sprangletop (*Leptochloa uninervia*) florets and spikelets.   J. K. CLARK

Dallisgrass (*Paspalum dilatatum* Poir.) [PASDI]

Knotgrass (*Paspalum distichum* L.) [PASDS]

SYNONYMS:

Dallisgrass: dallis grass; paspalum; water grass; *Digitaria dilatata* (Poir.) Coste; *Panicum platense* (Spreng.) Kuntze; *Paspalum eriophorum* Schult.; *Paspalum lanatum* Spreng.; *Paspalum ovatum* Nees ex Trin.; *Paspalum pedunculare* J. Presl; *Paspalum platense* Spreng.; a few others

Knotgrass: ditchgrass; jointgrass; mercer grass; water couch; wiregrass; *Digitaria disticha* (L.) Fiori & Paol.; *Digitaria paspalodes* Michx.; *Digitaria paspaloides* Michx.; *Dimorphostachys oaxacensis* (Steud.) E. Fourn. ex Hemsl.; *Paspalum digitaria* Poir.; *Milium distichum* (L.) Muhl.; *Panicum digitarioides* Raspail ex Kunth; *Paspalum paspalodes* Scribner; *Paspalum paspaloides* (Michx.) Scribner; many others

GENERAL INFORMATION: Warm-season perennials that consist of numerous regional biotypes. Both species are weeds of crops and turf in many regions of the world.

Dallisgrass: **Tufted perennial** to 1.5 m tall, with **short rhizomes**. Dallisgrass is cultivated for pasture in many places but is less commonly utilized as forage in the western United States because of its weedy character. It is susceptible to an ergot fungus (*Claviceps paspali*) that is **toxic** to cattle when ingested. Infected seed heads have a dark sticky or slimy substance on them. Introduced from South America.

Knotgrass: **Mat-forming perennial** to 0.6 m tall, with **creeping rhizomes** and **stolons**. Knotgrass is a widespread native of the Americas and elsewhere. It is a

Dallisgrass (*Paspalum dilatatum*) habit. A common weed of wet and dry areas. J. M. DiTomaso

good forage grass and is useful for controlling erosion in ditches and canal banks. However, extensive mats can clog small ditches and waterways. In natural areas, knotgrass is usually considered a desirable component of the ecosystem. Foliage and seeds are consumed by numerous mammal and bird species.

SEEDLING: Foliage characteristics resemble those of mature plants.

MATURE PLANT: Stems prostrate with upturned tips (decumbent) to erect. Blades rolled in bud. Ligules membranous, ± truncate. Sheaths open, ± compressed, glabrous or hairy. Auricles lacking.

Dallisgrass: Nodes glabrous. Blades mostly 9–35 cm long, 0.4–1 cm wide, flat, 2-ranked (alternate in one plane), upper surface glabrous, except often for a few long hairs at the base. **Ligules 2–8 mm long.**

Knotgrass: Nodes pubescent. Blades mostly 2–22 cm long, 0.2–0.7 cm wide, upper surface glabrous except for a few long hairs at the collar margins. **Ligules 1–2 mm long.**

ROOTS AND UNDERGROUND STRUCTURES:

Dallisgrass: Rhizomes short, root at the nodes to gradually enlarge tufts.

Knotgrass: Rhizomes and stolons creeping, extensively branched, typically form large mats. Most rhizomes grow in the top 15 cm of soil.

Dallisgrass (*Paspalum dilatatum*) inflorescence branches.   J. K. CLARK

Dallisgrass (*Paspalum dilatatum*) inflorescence.   J. M. DiTOMASO

SPIKELETS AND FLORETS: Inflorescence branches **spikelike**, spreading to ascending, with **nearly sessile spikelets in 2 rows on the lower side of each branch.** Spikelets compressed, 2.5–4 mm long, detach as units. Fertile florets 1 per spikelet, hard, milletlike, lemma convex, palea flat. Sterile floret 1 per spikelet, consists of an empty lemma that resembles the upper glume, often mistaken for the lower glume. Lower glume reduced or lacking.

Dallisgrass: May–November. Main axis 3–20 cm long, with **3–6 branches 4–13 cm long.** Spikelets elliptic to ovate, 2–2.5 mm wide, pale green to purplish. Upper glume and empty lemma 2.5–4 mm long, **margins ciliate with long white silky hairs.** Empty lemma 5–9-veined. Lower glume lacking.

Knotgrass: June–October. Main axis to ± 15 cm long, with **2(–3) branches 1–6 cm long.** Spikelets elliptic to obovate, ± 1.5 mm wide, usually pale green. Upper glume and empty lemma 2.5–4 mm long, **margins glabrous. Upper glume back covered with very short hairs** (puberulent). Empty lemma 3–5-veined. Lower glume to 2.5 mm long, 1-veined.

HABITAT: Irrigation and drainage ditches, canals, pond and reservoir margins, stream banks, moist waste places, roadsides, turf, rice fields, irrigated pasture and alfalfa, orchards, and vineyards. **Knotgrass** also inhabits marshes, riparian areas, and moist grassland, and often grows in standing water to ± 0.5 m deep or seasonally wet places.

DISTRIBUTION: Both species occur throughout much of world, except some northern regions.

Dallisgrass: Oregon, Colorado, New Mexico, Arizona, and throughout California, except the Great Basin region and Sonoran Desert, to 400 m. Primarily the southern half of United States. Mexico, South America.

Knotgrass: Oregon, Washington, Idaho, Utah, New Mexico, Arizona, Nevada, and throughout California, except southern Mojave and Sonoran deserts, to

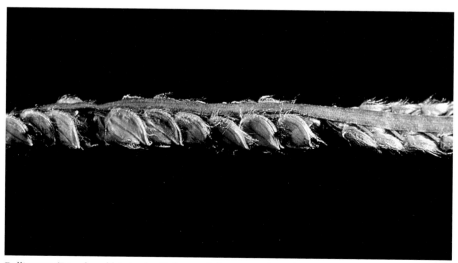

Dallisgrass (*Paspalum dilatatum*) spikelets on inflorescence branch.   C. ELMORE

1650 m. Southern and eastern United States, except northernmost states. Mexico, South America.

PROPAGATION AND PHENOLOGY: Dallisgrass **reproduces primarily by seed**. Knotgrass **reproduces vegetatively from stolons and/or rhizomes** and **by seed**. Stolon and rhizome fragments and seeds disperse with water, especially flooding, soil disturbance, agricultural operations, and other human activities. Seeds may also disperse with animals. Seeds are hard-coated, and scarification and/or exposure to light stimulates germination. Most seeds appear to germinate in mid-spring through early summer. Viable seed production is sometimes low. Some dallisgrass biotypes develop seeds without fertilization (apomixis). Both species utilized the C4 photosynthetic pathway.

MANAGEMENT FAVORING OR DISCOURAGING SURVIVAL: In rice fields, ploughing to a depth of 15 cm followed by ploughing or harrowing once or twice in a period of 1–2 months during the summer can control knotgrass.

SIMILAR SPECIES: Vaseygrass (*Paspalum urvillei* Steudel) [PASUR] and **bahiagrass** (*Paspalum notatum* J. Fleugge) [PASNO] are less common warm-season **tufted perennials with short rhizomes**, to 2 m and 1 m tall, respectively. Vaseygrass and bahiagrass are more prevalent in the southern United States but are expected to expand their range in California. Both typically inhabit disturbed moist places. Vaseygrass resembles dallisgrass, but unlike dallisgrass, it has inflorescences with **12–20 branches** and **spikelets mostly 1.5–3 mm long**. Vaseygrass occurs in

Dallisgrass (*Paspalum dilatatum*) seedling.

J. K. CLARK

Dallisgrass (*Paspalum dilatatum*) collar and sheath.   J. M. DITOMASO

California in the Sacramento Valley, northern Sierra Nevada foothills (Placerville area), and South Coast, to 1900 m. Introduced from South America. Bahiagrass resembles knotgrass, except bahiagrass upper glume backs are **glabrous**. In addition, bahiagrass is usually tufted and does not have 2-ranked leaves. Bahiagrass occurs in California in the southern Sacramento Valley, San Joaquin Valley, and South Coast, to 200 m. It is very common as a roadside and turf weed in the southern United States. Introduced from Mexico, Central America, and South America.

Dallisgrass (*Paspalum dilatatum*) florets and spikelets.   J. K. CLARK

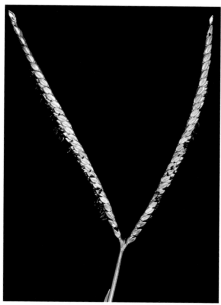

Knotgrass (*Paspalum distichum*) in native habitat along the bank of a stream.   J. M. DiTOMASO

Knotgrass (*Paspalum distichum*) inflorescence.
J. K. CLARK

Creeping stem of knotgrass *(Paspalum distichum)*.   J. M. DiTomaso

Knotgrass *(Paspalum distichum)* collar and sheath.   J. M. DiTomaso

Vaseygrass (*Paspalum urvillei*) inflorescence.

J. M. DiTomaso

Knotgrass (*Paspalum distichum*) florets (shiny structures) and spikelets.

J. K. CLARK

Vaseygrass (*Paspalum urvillei*) florets (shiny structures) and spikelets.

J. K. CLARK

Bahiagrass (*Paspalum notatum*) florets (arrows) and spikelets.

J. K. CLARK

Bahiagrass (*Paspalum notatum*) as a turf weed.

J. M. DiTomaso

Harding grass (*Phalaris aquatica* L.)

Noxious Weed Lists: CalEPPC: B

Synonyms: bulbous canarygrass; tuberous canarygrass; toowoomba grass; *Phalaris aquatica* L. var. *stenoptera* (Hack.) Burkart; *Phalaris commutata* Roem. & Schult.; *Phalaris stenoptera* Hackel; *Phalaris tuberosa* L.; *Phalaris tuberosa* L. var. *hirtiglumis* Batt. & Trabut; *Phalaris tuberosa* L. var. *stenoptera* (Hackel) A. Hitchc.; others

General Information: **Coarse tufted perennial** to 1.5 m tall, typically with **short rhizomes. Harding grass** and some other *Phalaris* species often have juice that oxidizes to a pinkish color when stems are broken. Harding grass was introduced to provide increased seasonal forage on pastures and rangeland. However, it has escaped cultivation in riparian areas and other moist places in California, Oregon, and Arizona. Harding grass is more invasive in coastal regions. In western states, it is designated as a facultative wetland species that is equally likely to grow on wetlands as uplands. Occasionally, Harding grass is **toxic** to livestock when consumed in quantity. Animals may develop a neurological condition known as phalaris staggers or may die suddenly due to cardiac failure. It is suspected that more than one mechanism causes livestock losses due to poisoning by *Phalaris* species. Depending on pasture conditions, toxicity may involve hydrocyanic acid, high levels of nitrates, or alkaloids specific to *Phalaris* species. Increased alkaloid content of leaves appears to be associated with drought conditions. Introduced from a cultivar grown in Australia but native to Mediterranean Europe.

Seedling: Foliage characteristics resemble those of mature plants, except size.

Harding grass (*Phalaris aquatica*) grows on both wet and dry sites.　　J. M. DiTomaso

Harding grass (*Phalaris aquatica*) inflorescence.　　J. M. DiTomaso

MATURE PLANT: Stems coarse, hollow, leafy, sometimes knotty at the base. Foliage glabrous. Blades rolled in bud, flat, 3–15 mm wide. Ligules membranous, delicate, mostly 5–12 mm long, ± truncate at the apex. Sheaths open, narrowly membranous along the upper margins. Auricles lacking. Collar region often pale.

ROOTS AND UNDERGROUND STRUCTURES: Tufts expand around the perimeter by short rhizomes but do not develop clonal patches of new plants. Under suitable conditions, rhizome fragments can develop into a new plant. Fibrous roots usually deep.

SPIKELETS AND FLORETS: May–September (–December). Panicles **dense, spikelike**, cylindrical to ovoid, sometimes interrupted near the base, mostly 1.5–11 cm long, 1–2.5 cm wide. Glumes **narrow-winged, tapered to tip**. Florets 2–3 per spikelet, 1 fertile, others reduced and sterile. Fertile florets lanceolate, 3–5 mm long, densely hairy, detach with sterile florets at base and without glumes. Sterile florets awl-like, **1 or 2 per spikelet, strongly unequal**, to 2 mm long. Observing sterile floret characteristics may require the aid of a 10× hand lens.

POSTSENESCENCE CHARACTERISTICS: Harding grass spikes typically remain intact for a period after senescence. Most seeds are shed at maturity.

HABITAT: Riparian areas, ditch banks, fields, and roadsides. Tolerates frost and drought.

DISTRIBUTION: Oregon, Arizona, and California in the northwestern region, central Sierra Nevada, Central Coast, and South Coast, to 1200 m. Few states in the southern and eastern United States.

PROPAGATION AND PHENOLOGY: **Reproduces by seed**. Seeds typically fall near the parent plant or disperse to greater distances with agricultural and other human activities, soil movement, water, and animals. Seeds germinate when moisture is available and temperatures are from 10°–30°C. Seedlings compete poorly with

Harding grass (*Phalaris aquatica*) florets (right) and spikelets (left).

J. K. CLARK

Harding grass (*Phalaris aquatica*) collar and sheath.

J. M. DITOMASO

established vegetation, but larger established plants readily displace native vegetation. In dry areas, plants become dormant in summer. Most active growth occurs fall through spring when moisture is plentiful.

MANAGEMENT FAVORING OR DISCOURAGING SURVIVAL: For disturbed sites in natural areas, enhancing the cover of desirable species can help prevent the establishment of Harding grass seedlings.

SIMILAR SPECIES: Reed canarygrass (*Phalaris arundinacea* L.) [TYPAR] (see table 14, page 296, for more information on canarygrass species) is a widespread **native perennial** to 1.5 m tall with **creeping rhizomes** from which it typically develops **clonal** patches. In natural areas, reed canarygrass is an important component of the ecosystem and provides food for seed-eating birds. However, it can

Harding grass (*Phalaris aquatica*) fertile floret with sterile florets at base.　　　　J. K. CLARK

Reed canarygrass (*Phalaris arundinacea*) in its native habitat along a river.　　　　J. M. DiTomaso

be troublesome in ditches, irrigation channels, and other controlled aquatic systems. In the Pacific Northwest, European cultivars of reed canarygrass have escaped cultivation and become particularly problematic. Some scientists are concerned that introgression with native populations may eventually eliminate the locally native type due to genetic assimilation. Hence, **reed canarygrass** is a C-listed noxious weed in Washington. Unlike Harding grass, reed canarygrass has **panicles with conspicuous spreading to erect branches, glumes that lack wings, 2 nearly equal awl-like sterile florets covered with long silky hairs,** and **creeping rhizomes.** In addition, panicles are green to purplish and are often interrupted near the base. Deeply buried seeds can survive up to 20 years. Reed canarygrass inhabits wet sites along streams and in grassland and woodlands throughout most of the United States, except some southern states. It occurs in all western states and is widespread in California, except in the deserts, to 1600 m. Reed canarygrass is designated as an obligate wetland indicator species in the western states, except Oregon, Washington, Idaho, western Montana, and western Wyoming, where it is a facultative wetland species that is more likely to occur on wetlands. It is sometimes cultivated for livestock forage.

Short-spike canarygrass (*Phalaris brachystachys* Link.) and **Carolina canarygrass** (*Phalaris caroliniana* Walt.) [PHACL] are **winter annuals** to 1 m tall. Short-spike canarygrass is distinguished by having an **annual life cycle, glumes broadly**

Reed canarygrass (*Phalaris arundinacea*) inflorescence.
J. M. DiTomaso

Reed canarygrass (*Phalaris arundinacea*) spikelets on inflorescence branches.
J. M. DiTomaso

Reed canarygrass (*Phalaris arundinacea*) collar and sheath.
J. M. DiTomaso

winged above the middle, fertile florets 4–6 mm long, and 2 sterile florets reduced to tiny fleshy or corky scales at the base of each fertile floret. Short-spike canarygrass inhabits wet disturbed sites and rice fields. It occurs in Oregon and California in the Sacramento Valley, San Francisco Bay region, and western South Coast Ranges, to 200 m. It is also found in a few southern states. Short-spike canarygrass has not been assigned any wetland indicator status. Introduced from Mediterranean Europe. **Carolina canarygrass** is distinguished by having an **annual life cycle, spikes tapered at the base and apex, and 2 nearly equal awl-like sterile florets about one-half the fertile floret length or slightly less.** Glumes are narrowly winged and tapered to the tip, like those of Harding grass. Carolina canarygrass inhabits wet or dry disturbed sites and is designated as a facultative wetland indicator species that is more likely to occur on wetlands in

Reed canarygrass (*Phalaris arundinacea*) florets (right) and spikelets (left).   J. K. CLARK

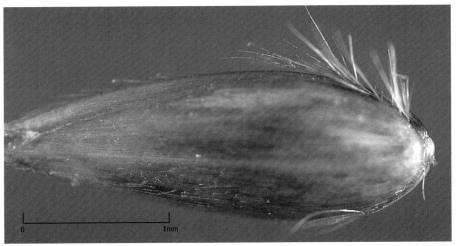

Reed canarygrass (*Phalaris arundinacea*) fertile floret with sterile florets at base.   J. K. CLARK

western states. It occurs in Oregon, Colorado, New Mexico, Arizona, Nevada, and California on the North and Central Coast, central Sierra Nevada foothills, western South Coast Ranges, and southwestern region, to 650 m. It is also found throughout the southern United States. Introduced from the southeastern United States.

Short-spike canarygrass (*Phalaris brachystachys*) florets (right) and spikelets (left).
J. K. CLARK

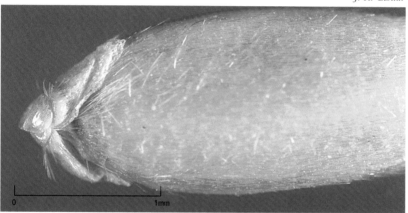

Short-spike canarygrass (*Phalaris brachystachys*) fertile floret with sterile florets at base.
J. K. CLARK

Carolina canarygrass (*Phalaris caroliniana*) florets (right) and spikelets (left).
J. K. CLARK

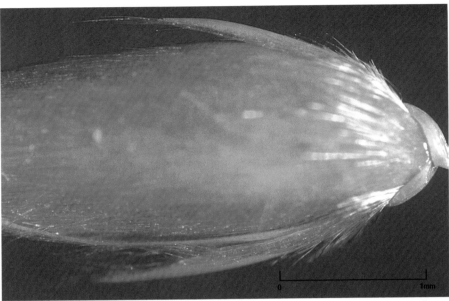

Carolina canarygrass (*Phalaris caroliniana*) floret with sterile bracts.   J. K. CLARK

Table 14. Canarygrass *(Phalaris)* species associated with aquatic sites

Species	Life cycle	Panicles	Glumes	Sterile florets at base of fertile floret	Fertile floret length (mm)
Harding grass (*P. aquatica*)	tufted perennial to 1.5 m tall ± with short rhizomes	spikelike, sometimes lumpy, 1.5–11 cm long	narrow-winged, tapered to tip	1(2), strongly unequal, awl-like	3–5
reed canarygrass (*P. arundinacea*)	perennial to 1.5 m tall with creeping rhizomes	branches usually conspicuous, interrupted near base, spreading to erect, 7–40 cm long	lack wings	2, ± equal, awl-like, long silky-hairy compared to fertile floret	3–5
short-spike canarygrass (*P. brachystachys*)	winter annual to 1 m tall	spikelike, 1.5–4 cm long	broad-winged above middle	2, reduced to tiny fleshy or corky scales at floret base	4–6
Carolina canarygrass (*P. caroliniana*)	winter annual to 1 m tall	spikelike, 1–7 cm long, tapered at base and apex	narrow-winged, tapered to tip	2, equal, awl-like, ± ½ floret length	3–5

Note: Identification to some species requires at least 10× magnification.

Rabbitfoot polypogon (*Polypogon monspeliensis* (L.) Desf.) [POHMO]

SYNONYMS: annual beardgrass; rabbitfootgrass; rabbitsfoot grass; tawny beard-grass; *Agrostis alopecuroides* Lam.; *Alopecurus aristatus* var. *monspeliensis* (L.) Huds.; *Alopecurus monspeliensis* L.; *Phleum crinitum* Schreb.; *Phleum monspeliense* Koel.; *Polypogon crinitus* (Schreb.) Nutt.; *Polypogon flavescens* J. Presl; *Santia monspeliensis* (L.) Parl.; a few others

GENERAL INFORMATION: Tufted **winter** or **summer annual** to 1 m tall, with **dense, soft-fuzzy panicles** reminiscent of a rabbit's foot. Rabbitfoot polypogon is a win-ter annual in regions with a mild climate and a summer annual at higher eleva-tions or in cold-winter areas. Plants sometimes spread by stolons and may appear perennial. Rabbitfoot polypogon is susceptible to certain grass rusts, pearl millet mosaic virus, and rice tungro virus. In Australia, rabbitfoot polypogon sometimes hosts toxic bacteria that can cause livestock poisoning, similar to that caused by **Italian ryegrass** (*Lolium multiflorum* Lam.). Introduced from southern and west-ern Europe.

SEEDLING: Foliage characteristics resemble those of mature plants, except some-times smaller.

MATURE PLANT: Culms erect or bent at the base (geniculate). Foliage glabrous. Blades rolled in bud, slightly rough to touch (scaberulous), yellowish green, flat, mostly 5–20 cm long, 3–8 mm wide. Ligules membranous, thin, (4)5–7 mm long, ± acute, ragged. Sheath open, smooth. Auricles lacking.

ROOTS AND UNDERGROUND STRUCTURES: Roots fibrous, ± shallow.

SPIKELETS AND FLORETS: April–October. **Panicles dense, spikelike**, branches mostly inconspicuous, ± ovoid, 1–17 cm long, 1–2.5 cm wide, pale green to yellowish tan. **Spikelets detach below glumes with part of the stalk**. Glumes equal,

Rabbitfoot polypogon (*Polypogon monspeliensis*) in a moist site.   J. M. DiTomaso

1–2.5 mm long, **slightly 2-lobed at the tip** with a fine, straight awn 3–10 mm long between the lobes, ± evenly covered with stiff hairs to 0.1 mm long. **Florets 1 per spikelet**, shorter than glumes. **Lemma membranous, translucent**, 5-veined, 0.5–1.5 mm long, truncate and toothed at the apex, with a slender **awn 0.5–5 mm long** that usually extends slightly beyond the glumes.

Rabbitfoot polypogon (*Polypogon monspeliensis*) emerged in an irrigation canal.
J. M. DiTomaso

Rabbitfoot polypogon (*Polypogon monspeliensis*) inflorescence.   J. M. DiTomaso

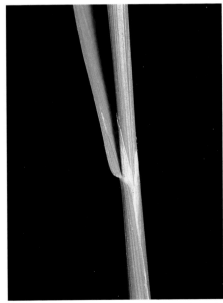

Rabbitfoot polypogon (*Polypogon monspeliensis*) collar and sheath.   J. M. DiTomaso

HABITAT: Moist to wet places, stream and pond margins, seasonally wet sites, ditches, pastures, agricultural fields, moist sites in orchards and vineyards, and roadsides.

Rabbitfoot polypogon (*Polypogon monspeliensis*) seedling.   J. K. CLARK

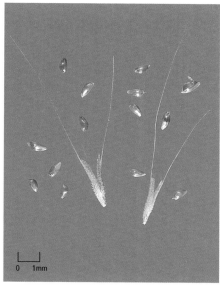

Rabbitfoot polypogon (*Polypogon monspeliensis*) spikelets and florets with seeds.   J. K. CLARK

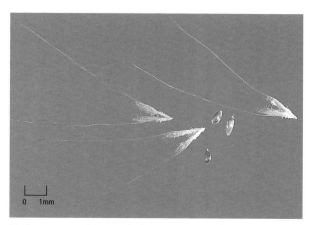

Mediterranean polypogon (*Polypogon maritimus*) spikelets and florets with seeds.   J. K. CLARK

Ditch polypogon (*Polypogon interruptus*) inflorescence.
J. M. DiTOMASO

DISTRIBUTION: Throughout most of North America, including all western states. Common throughout California to 2100 m.

PROPAGATION AND PHENOLOGY: Reproduces by seed. Seeds disperse with water, mud, agricultural activities, as a seed impurity, in hay, and by clinging to the feet,

Chilean polypogon (*Polypogon australis*) collar and sheath.   J. M. DITOMASO

Chilean polypogon (*Polypogon australis*) inflorescence.   J. M. DITOMASO

Ditch polypogon (*Polypogon interruptus*) spikelets and florets with seeds.

J. K. CLARK

fur, and feathers of animals and to the shoes and clothing of humans. Fluctuating temperature appears to stimulate germination.

SIMILAR SPECIES: There are a few *Polypogon* species in the western United States that resemble rabbitfoot polypogon and grow in similar habitats. Refer to table 15 to compare distinguishing features.

Mediterranean polypogon (*Polypogon maritimus* Willd.) occurs in California in the northwestern region, Sierra Nevada foothills, and Central Valley, to 600 m. It is also found in the southeastern United States. Introduced from Europe, the Mediterranean region, and Africa.

Ditch polypogon (*Polypogon interruptus* Kunth., synonym: *Polypogon lutosus* (Poir.) Hitchc.) [POHIN] is found in Oregon, Washington, Utah, New Mexico, Arizona, Nevada, and throughout California, to 1300 m. It is also sporadic in a few southern, central, and eastern states.

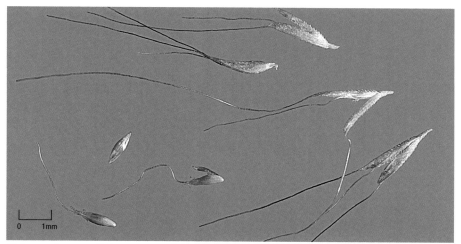

Chilean polypogon (*Polypogon australis*) spikelets and florets with seeds.　　J. K. CLARK

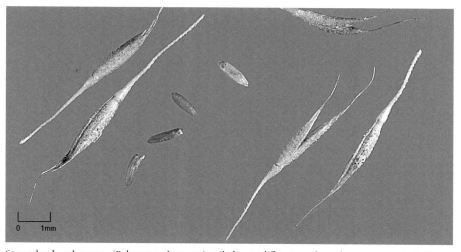

Streambank polypogon (*Polypogon elongatus*) spikelets and florets with seeds.　　J. K. CLARK

Chilean polypogon (*Polypogon australis* Brongn.) is often confused with ditch polypogon. Chilean polypogon occurs in Washington, Arizona, and California in the western North Coast Ranges, San Francisco Bay region, western South Coast Ranges, Sierra Nevada, Central Valley, and southwestern region, to 1000 m.

Streambank polypogon (*Polypogon elongatus* Kunth.) also grows in salt marshes and is uncommon compared to other *Polypogon* species. It occurs in Colorado, Arizona, and California, where it is sporadic in the San Francisco Bay region and South Coast Ranges, to 100 m. It is also found in Texas. Ditch, Chilean, and streambank polypogon are introduced from South America.

Water bent (*Polypogon viridis* (Gouan) Breistr., synonyms: *Agrostis viridis* Gouan; *Agrostis semiverticillata* (Forsk.) C. Christ., *Polypogon semiverticillatus* (Forsk.) Hyl.) [POHVI] is a ± **spreading perennial** to 0.75 m tall, with **long-trailing stems** that root at the lower nodes. It is easily distinguished from the other *Polypogon* species because its infloresence in less condensed and it lack awns. Water bent occurs throughout California to 2150 m. Water bent also has characteristics in common with the genus *Agrostis*. Introduced from Europe.

Water bent (*Polypogon viridis*) in a drainage canal. J. M. DiTomaso

Water bent *(Polypogon viridis)* inflorescence.

J. M. DiTomaso

Water bent *(Polypogon viridis)* spikelets and florets with seeds.

J. K. Clark

Table 15. *Polypogon* species

Species	Life cycle	Height (m)	Panicle	Glume tips with 20× magnification	Glume awn length (mm)	Lemma awn length (mm)	Ligule length (mm)	Other
rabbitfoot polypogon (*P. monspeliensis*)	annual	to 1	spikelike, branches mostly inconspicuous	slightly 2-lobed, lobe margins with bristly hairs to ± 0.1 mm long	3–10 ± straight	0.5–5	(4–) 5–7	blades mostly 3–8 mm wide
Mediterranean polypogon (*P. maritimus*)	annual	to 0.5	spikelike, branches inconspicuous	deeply 2-lobed, lobe margins with silky hairs ± 0.25 mm long	4–12 ± straight	0	4–6	blades mostly 1–3 mm wide
ditch polypogon (*P. interruptus*)	perennial	to 1	interrupted or lumpy, branches conspicuous	slightly rounded to barely lobed, ± purplish, with scabrous hairs less than 0.1 mm long	1–3(-5) mostly straight to curved	0.5–3	4–6 (–8)	spikelet stalks mostly 0.5–1 mm long
Chilean polypogon (*P. australis*)	perennial	to 1	interrupted or lumpy, branches conspicuous	rounded or slightly squared, often purplish, with scabrous hairs to 0.1 mm long	(2–)4–11 mostly curved to wavy	(1)2–7	1–3(4)	spikelet stalks sessile, to 0.5 mm long
streambank polypogon (*P. elongatus*)	perennial	to 1	interrupted	acute, tapered into awn, with scabrous hairs less than 0.1 mm long	1–3 straight	0–2	mostly 6–9	spikelet stalks usually more than 2 mm long

Smooth cordgrass (*Spartina alterniflora* Lois.) [SPTAL]

Noxious Weed Lists: Washington: B list; Oregon: A list, Wetland & Aquatic Weed Quarantine; CalEPPC: A-2

Synonyms: Atlantic cordgrass; saltmarsh cordgrass; saltwater cordgrass; *Spartina alterniflora* Lois. vars. *glabra* (Muhl. ex Bigelow) Fern and *pilosa* (Merr.) Fern.; *Spartina brasiliensis* Raddi; *Spartina glabra* Muhl.; *Spartina maritima* (Curt.) Fern. ssp. *glabra* (Muhl.) St.Y.; *Spartina stricta* vars. *alterniflora* (Lois.) A. Gray and *glabra* (Muhl. ex Elliot) A. Gray; *Trachynotia alterniflora* (Lois.) DC.; others

General Information: Slender to coarse **clumping** or sometimes solitary **perennial** to 2.5 m tall, with **creeping rhizomes**. Smooth cordgrass is a coastal species that invades salt marsh and mud flat habitats. One plant can develop into a large, dense, circular clonal patch to 20 m in diameter. Numerous individuals on barren mud flats can spread until no open space remains. Smooth cordgrass was unintentionally introduced from the Atlantic coast to Willapa Bay, Washington, sometime in the late 1800s to early 1900s and purposefully planted in the southern San Francisco Bay around the mid-1970s. From both points of introduction, smooth cordgrass has spread to cover large tracts of salt marsh habitat. In Washington, infestations threaten the oyster industry. In the late 1990s, a dwarf biotype was discovered in the upper intertidal zone of southern San Francisco Bay. Stems of the dwarf biotype grow only to 0.25 m tall. *Spartina* species utilize the C4 photosynthetic pathway.

Smooth cordgrass *(Spartina alterniflora)* along the San Francisco Bay.   D. Strong

Seedling: Only seedlings of hybrids between *Spartina alterniflora* and *S. foliosa* have been described: Glabrous. Blades straight, smooth, alternate in the same plane (distichous), to 30 cm long, ascend at an angle of 30°–40° with the stem. Ligules membranous, 0.5–3 mm long, top truncate and ragged or fringed. Collar region pale.

Mature Plant: Stems simple, erect, rigid, **0.5–1.5 cm in diameter at base**, and typically **1–2.5 m tall. Internodes fleshy.** Blades 20–55 cm long, **0.4–2.5 cm wide at the base**, mostly **flat**, sometimes **loosely in-rolled at the tips.** Angle between stem and blade 15°–35°. Margins smooth or rough to touch (scabrous).

Smooth cordgrass (*Spartina alterniflora*) (tall) growing with the native California cordgrass (*Spartina foliosa*) (short). J. M. DiTomaso

Hybrid between smooth cordgrass (*Spartina alterniflora*) and California cordgrass (*Spartina foliosa*). J. M. DiTomaso

Upper surface glabrous to sparsely long-hairy, longitudinally ridged with ± 6 ridges per millimeter. Lower surface glabrous. Sheaths open, longer than internodes, glabrous. Ligules consist of a fringe of hairs 0.5–2 mm long. Auricles lacking.

ROOTS AND UNDERGROUND STRUCTURES: Rhizomes deep, extensively creeping, soft, whitish, 4–8 mm in diameter, contain large air spaces, sparsely covered with inflated scales. Mats of rhizomes and roots increase sedimentation. Roots can associate with nitrogen-fixing bacteria. Uprooted plants typically have a persistent, unpleasant sulfurlike odor.

SPIKELETS AND FLORETS: June–November. Panicles 10–40 cm long, 0.7–2.2 cm wide, consist of 5–30 **spikelike branches** 4.5–13 cm long. Branches ± **erect to ascending at a 10°–20° angle** and **loosely overlapping** on a **straight central axis**. Branch axes **triangular**, with **2 rows of sessile, closely overlapping spikelets on the lower side**. Spikelets **strongly flattened, keeled**, lanceolate, 8–15 mm long, consist of 1 floret and a pair of **straight**, unequal glumes. Spikelets detach from below the glumes. Glume and lemma keels glabrous to sparsely covered with long soft hairs. Wind-pollinated. Primarily outcrossing but can occasionally self-pollinate.

HABITAT: Coastal salt marshes and associated drainage sloughs and mud flats.

DISTRIBUTION: Oregon in the Suislaw River estuary; Washington in Willapa Bay, Gray's Harbor, and Puget Sound; and California in the San Francisco Bay, to 10 m. Populations at Humboldt Bay have been eradicated. Expanding range elsewhere.

PROPAGATION AND PHENOLOGY: Reproduces **by seed** and **vegetatively from creeping rhizomes** and **rhizome fragments**. Seeds disperse primarily with water. An

Smooth cordgrass (*Spartina alterniflora*) inflorescence.   J. M. DITOMASO

Smooth cordgrass (*Spartina alterniflora*) collar and sheath.   J. M. DITOMASO

after-ripening period of a few months in cold seawater usually increases germination. Germination appears to require light. Seeds typically do not survive for more than 1 year. Viable seed production is often low where outcrossing is limited. Seed heads are susceptible to infection by an ergot fungus, which can also limit viable seed production.

ADDITIONAL ECOLOGICAL ASPECTS: Compared to the smaller native perennial **California cordgrass** (*Spartina foliosa* Trin.), smooth cordgrass spreads more rapidly, develops denser patches, grows in both high and low intertidal salt marshes and drainage sloughs, and tolerates higher water levels. These aspects change the

Smooth cordgrass (*Spartina alterniflora*) spikelets, indistinguishable from dense-flowered cordgrass (*S. densiflora*).   J. K. CLARK

California cordgrass (*Spartina foliosa*) in its native habitat in the San Francisco Bay, California.
J. M. DITOMASO

ecological dynamics of the mud flat and salt marsh communities. The ability of smooth cordgrass to exist in higher water allows it to colonize open mud flats that are normally devoid of vegetation and also to displace native vegetation closer to the shoreline in salt marshes. In San Francisco Bay, smooth cordgrass occasionally hybridizes with California cordgrass, and hybrids are fertile. Crosses display a variable spectrum of intermediate and parental characteristics, since hybrids readily backcross with either parent. Some hybrids appear to be more robust than either parent. The only way to distinguish such hybrids is with electrophoretic DNA analysis. Studies show that smooth cordgrass produces up to about 20 times more viable pollen than California cordgrass and that smooth cordgrass pollen is more fertile. Where both species coexist, seed set on California cordgrass is increased due to pollination by hybrid cordgrass. Up to nearly 8 times more hybrid seeds may set relative to pure California cordgrass seeds. Survival and growth of hybrid seedlings are also equal to or greater than that of California cordgrass seedlings. This evidence suggests that continued hybridization and introgression may eventually eliminate genetically pure California and smooth cordgrass through progressive genetic assimilation in areas where both species and/or hybrids occur.

MANAGEMENT FAVORING OR DISCOURAGING SURVIVAL: Limiting tidal action in salt ponds can help prevent seeds and rhizome fragments that are carried in the water from initiating new populations. Eradicating invading hybrid clones in native marshes is essential to maintaining the genetic integrity of the native species. Knowing the source and absolute identity of California cordgrass plants grown for salt marsh revegetation can help prevent the unintended introduction of indistinguishable smooth cordgrass hybrids into uninfested areas.

California cordgrass (*Spartina foliosa*) inflorescence.   J. M. DiTomaso

California cordgrass (*Spartina foliosa*) collar and sheath.   J. M. DiTomaso

SIMILAR SPECIES: Dense-flowered cordgrass, salt-meadow cordgrass, and common cordgrass are weedy salt marsh species that may be confused with smooth cordgrass. Refer to table 16 for a comparison of distinguishing characteristics.

Dense-flowered cordgrass (*Spartina densiflora* Brongn.) [Oregon: A list, CalEPPC: Red Alert) occurs in Humboldt Bay and at Corte Madera in the northwestern San Francisco Bay region. Introduced from southern South America.
Salt-meadow cordgrass (*Spartina patens* (Aiton) Muhlenb.) [SPTPA] [Washington: A list, Wetland & Aquatic Weed Quarantine, Oregon: B list, CalEPPC: Red Alert] occurs in Puget Sound, Washington, and at Cox Island and Suislaw River Estuary, Oregon. In California, only a small salt-meadow cordgrass

California cordgrass (*Spartina foliosa*) spikelets and seeds.   J. K. CLARK

Dense-flowered cordgrass (*Spartina densiflora*) infestation in Humboldt Bay, California.

J. M. DITOMASO

population exists at Southampton Marsh near Benicia in the northeastern San Francisco Bay region. Introduced from southeastern United States.

Common cordgrass (*Spartina anglica* C.E. Hubb.) [Oregon: A list, Washington: B list, Wetland & Aquatic Weed Quarantine, CalEPPC: Red Alert] is a recently evolved amphidiploid species derived from hybrids of smooth cordgrass and **small cordgrass** (*Spartina maritima* (Curtis) Fern. = *S. stricta* (Ait.) Roth) in

Dense-flowered cordgrass (*Spartina densiflora*) grows as a bunchgrass.   J. M. DiTomaso

Dense-flowered cordgrass (*Spartina densiflora*) inflorescence.   J. M. DiTomaso

Dense-flowered cordgrass (*Spartina densiflora*) collar and sheath.   J. M. DiTomaso

Britain. Smooth cordgrass was introduced into Britain in the early 1800s, where it hybridized with the native small cordgrass. Since its discovery in the late 1800s, common cordgrass has become the most widespread *Spartina* species in the United Kingdom. Common cordgrass occurs at Puget Sound, Washington, and in the northern San Francisco Bay region (Marin Co.), California. Introduced from the U.K. All species grow near sea level.

Salt-meadow cordgrass (*Spartina patens*) collar and sheath.   J. M. DiTomaso

Common cordgrass (*Spartina anglica*) collar and sheath.   J. M. DiTomaso

Newly emerging shoot of common cordgrass (*Spartina anglica*).   J. M. DiTomaso

Table 16. Cordgrass (Spartina) species

Species	Typical height at maturity (m)	Internode	Blade width at base (mm)	Blade	Blade/stem angle (°)	Ligule length (mm)	Inflorescence	Anthers length (mm)	Rhizome	Other
smooth cordgrass (S. alterniflora)	0.5–2.5 (dwarf form to 0.25 m)	fleshy	4–25	flat, margins ± loosely in-rolled at tip	± 15–35	0.5–2	slightly open; branches loosely erect to ascending, loosely overlapping	3–8	long, fleshy, 4–7 mm diameter	bases of flowering stems usually reddish
California cordgrass* (S. foliosa)	0.5–1.5	fleshy	5–17	flat, margins ± loosely in-rolled at tip	± 15–35	1–2	dense, ± cylindrical; branches tightly erect, closely overlapping	3–8	long, fleshy, 2–6 mm diameter	inflorescence branch axes often twisted; 1 or both glumes slightly curved; bases of flowering stems white (hybrids white, pink, or reddish)
common cordgrass (S. anglica)	0.3–1.3	fleshy	6–15	flat, margins ± loosely in-rolled at tip	± (30) 40–80	(1.5) 2–3	slightly open; branches loosely erect to ascending, loosely overlapping	8–13	long, fleshy	—
dense-flowered cordgrass (S. densiflora)	0.25–1.5	firm	4–8	margins in-rolled	± 15–35	1–2	narrow, ± dense, cylindrical; branches erect, overlapping	3–6	usually lacking, or short, thick (to ± 10 mm diameter)	stem bases hard, knotty
salt-meadow cordgrass (S. patens)	0.25–1.2	firm	1–4	margins in-rolled	± 45	± 0.5	open; branches spreading to ascending, lower usually not overlapping	3–6	lacking or long, wiry, 2–4 mm diameter	—

Note: *California cordgrass is not considered a weed and is included for identification purposes only.

313

Swamp smartweed (*Polygonum amphibium* L. var. *emersum* Mich.) [POLCC]

Pale smartweed (*Polygonum lapathifolium* L.) [POLLA]

Ladysthumb (*Polygonum persicaria* L.) [POLPE]

NOXIOUS WEED LISTS: swamp smartweed: California: C

SYNONYMS: A complete list of synonyms is beyond the scope of this publication.

Swamp smartweed: amphibious bistort; devil's shoestring; kelp; longroot smartweed; marsh smartweed; swamp knotweed; swamp persicaria; tanweed; water knotweed; water smartweed; *Persicaria amphibia* (L.) Gray; *Persicaria coccinea* (Muhl. ex Willd.) Greene; *Persicaria muhlenbergii* (S. Wats.) Small; *Polygonum coccineum* Muhl.; *Polygonum coccineum* Muhl. var. *pratincola* (Greene) Stanford; *Polygonum coccineum* Muhl. var. *terrestre* Willd.; *Polygonum emersum* Britton; *Polygonum muhlenbergii* S. Wats.

Pale smartweed: common knotweed; curltop ladysthumb; curlytop knotweed; dockleaf smartweed; nodding smartweed; pale persicaria; willow smartweed; willow-weed; wireweed; *Persicaria lapathifolia* S.F. Gray; *Polygonum nodosum* Pers.

Ladysthumb: heart-weed; lover's pride; persicary; red shanks; spotted knotweed; spotted smartweed; willow-weed; *Persicaria maculata* (Raf.) S.F. Gray; *Persicaria persicaria* (L.) Small; *Persicaria ruderalis* (Salisb.) C.F. Reed; *Persicaria vulgaris* Webb & Moq.; *Polygonum dubium* Stein.; *Polygonum fusiforme* E. Greene; *Polygonum minus* var. *subcontinum* (Meisn.) Fern.; *Polygonum persicaria* var.

Swamp smartweed (*Polygonum amphibium* var. *emersum*) in its native habitat in a pond.

J. M. DITOMASO

angustifolium Beckh.; *Polygonum persicaria* var. *ruderale* (Salisb.) Meisn.; *Polygonum puritanorum* Fern.

GENERAL INFORMATION: Coarse emergent aquatic to terrestrial herbs. Swamp smartweed and pale smartweed are widespread natives of North America that typically grow in or on the edges of ponds, marshes, lakes, streams, and areas subject to seasonal flooding or periodic standing water. In natural areas they are a desirable component of the flora. However, these species sometimes invade rice fields, pastures, orchards, and irrigated crops, and stands of emergent plants can impede the flow of water in irrigation ditches, canals, and drainage areas. All smartweed and ladysthumb seeds are an important food source for many species of songbirds, waterfowl, and mammals. Foliage provides cover for wildlife. Refer to table 17 (page 328) for a comparison of distinguishing characteristics.

Swamp smartweed: Colonizing **perennial with creeping rhizomes** and erect to spreading stems to 1.5 m tall. Plants are highly plastic depending on environmental conditions. Aquatic plants with floating stems and leaves at flowering are often known as **water smartweed** (*Polygonum amphibium* L. var. *stipulaceum* Coleman) [POLAM]. Terrestrial and aquatic varieties intergrade, and some populations appear to convert from one variety to the other when environmental conditions change over time. Swamp smartweed is designated as an obligate wetland indicator species in the western United States.

Pale smartweed: Erect **summer annual**, to 1.5 m tall. Pale smartweed is designated a facultative wetland indicator plant in the northwestern states (Oregon, Washington, Idaho, Montana, and Wyoming) and as an obligate wetland species elsewhere in the western United States.

Swamp smartweed (*Polygonum amphibium* var. *emersum*) flowering stem.   J. M. DiTOMASO

315

Ladysthumb: Erect to spreading **summer annual**, to 1 m tall. Ladysthumb is designated as a facultative wetland indicator species in the western United States. Ladysthumb hybridizes with pale smartweed. Compared with ladysthumb, hybrid plants have narrower flower spikes and flatter achenes. Introduced from Europe.

SEEDLING: Cotyledons **narrowly elliptic-oblong**, with short stalks fused at bases. First and subsequent leaves alternate, elliptic.

Swamp smartweed (*Polygonum amphibium* var. *emersum*) achenes and dried flowers with achenes intact.   J. K. CLARK

Water smartweed (*Polygonum amphibium* var. *stipulaceum*) in its native habitat in a pond. Leaves are floating, unlike erect leaves of *P. a.* var. *emersum*.   J. M. DiTOMASO

Swamp smartweed: Cotyledons 7–18 mm long, covered with minute stiff translucent hairs. First leaf lower surface has minute stiff hairs along margins and veins. Roots tough and brown by second-leaf stage. Ocrea (sheath at leaf base) ± glabrous, ragged at the top.

Pale smartweed (*Polygonum lapathifolium*) infestation in an irrigation canal.   J. M. DiTomaso

Pale smartweed (*Polygonum lapathifolium*) flowering stem.   J. M. DiTomaso

Pale smartweed: Cotyledons 3–12 mm long, 1–3 mm wide, ± glabrous, surfaces sparsely covered with minute, flat, glandular dots. First leaf 10–30 mm long, 2–5 mm wide, surfaces usually sparsely covered with flat to slightly raised glandular dots and long flattened ± interwoven nonglandular hairs. Ocrea ± glabrous, ragged at the top.

Ladysthumb: Cotyledons 8–12 mm long, with a few short glandular hairs on the margins near the base. First leaves glabrous or sparsely covered with a few soft nonglandular hairs. Ocrea fringed with erect hairs at the top.

MATURE PLANT: Stems **coarse, swollen at the nodes,** typically **rooting at lower nodes,** openly branched, often reddish. Leaves alternate, **lanceolate to elliptic.** Leaf stalks 0.5–2 cm long.

Swamp smartweed: Leaves typically evenly covered with minute stiff translucent hairs (low magnification), sometimes ± glabrous, to **35 cm long,** often 3–8(10) **cm wide.** Leaf **bases rounded, truncate, or abruptly tapered.** Leaf stalks 1–5 cm long. Ocrea often 1.5–3 cm long, ± glabrous, ragged at the top. Water smartweed stems grow to 12 m long, with floating leaves **glabrous, oblong, less than 10 cm long.**

Pale smartweed: Leaves 2.5–20 cm long, 0.5–4 cm wide, **bases tapered. Lower leaf surfaces dotted with minute sunken glands** (low magnification), typically covered with short hairs. Upper surfaces ± glabrous, except minute stiff hairs on veins. Ocrea ± **glabrous,** 0.5–2 cm long, ragged at the top.

Ladysthumb: Plants often form large clumps. Leaves 2.5–20 cm long, 0.5–4 cm wide, **bases tapered.** Surfaces glabrous to sparsely covered with minute stiff hairs, typically with a dark purplish central spot. Other smartweed species, including Pennsylvania smartweed, may also have a dark central leaf spot. Leaf surfaces, especially lower, usually **dotted with minute, barely raised glands** (requires magnification). Ocrea 0.5–2 cm long, covered with **flattened, short,**

Pale smartweed (*Polygonum lapathifolium*) inflorescence.   J. K. CLARK

stiff hairs (strigose), often whitish, fringed at the top with stiff hairs 1–2 mm long.

ROOTS AND UNDERGROUND STRUCTURES: Lower stems typically root at the nodes.

Swamp smartweed: Rhizomes long (to 13 m in aquatic plants), horizontal, slender, tough, woody, with shoot buds and fibrous roots at regular intervals. In

Swollen node and ocrea of pale smartweed
(*Polygonum lapathifolium*).   J. K. CLARK

Pale smartweed (*Polygonum lapathifolium*)
seedling.   J. K. CLARK

Pale smartweed (*Polygonum lapathifolium*) achenes and dried flowers with achenes intact.

J. K. CLARK

319

fertile soils, rhizomes can grow more than 5 cm per day. Rhizome fragments can develop new shoots. Typically nonmycorrhizal.

Pale smartweed: Taproots shallow, branched, with fibrous secondary roots.

Ladysthumb (*Polygonum persicaria*) in a rice field.   J. K. CLARK

Ladysthumb (*Polygonum persicaria*) flowering stem.   J. M. DITOMASO

Ladysthumb (*Polygonum persicaria*) inflorescence.   J. K. CLARK

Ladysthumb: Taproots resemble those of pale smartweed. Mycorrhizal.

FLOWERS: Perianth (sepals and/or petals) fused ± one-third the length, with a 5-lobed glandular disk at the base.

Swamp smartweed: June–October. Spikes **erect, dense**, cylindrical, 4–15 cm long, 0.5–1.5 cm wide, with densely glandular stalks. Perianth (sepals and/or

Ladysthumb (*Polygonum persicaria*) leaves and stem.   J. M. DiTomaso

Ladysthumb (*Polygonum persicaria*) node with ocrea.   J. M. DiTomaso

Ladysthumb (*Polygonum persicaria*) seedling.   J. K. Clark

petals) 5-lobed, **bright reddish pink, 4–6 mm long,** open at maturity. Glandular disc orange-red. Water smartweed has ovoid spikes < 3.5 cm long. Insect-pollinated. Self-incompatible.

Pale smartweed: June–October. Spikes **drooping, dense,** cylindrical, 3–8 cm long, 0.2–0.6 cm wide. Perianth 4(5)-lobed, **greenish to pale pink,** ± 2 mm long,

Ladysthumb (*Polygonum persicaria*) achenes and dried flowers with achenes intact.   J. K. CLARK

Marshpepper smartweed (*Polygonum hydropiper*) flowering stem.   J. M. DiTOMASO

Marshpepper smartweed (*Polygonum hydropiper*) inflorescence.   J. M. DiTOMASO

strongly veined in fruit, remain loosely **closed** at maturity. Veins of outer lobes forked and curved outward at tips. Flower stalks glabrous to sparsely glandular. Insect- and self-pollinated.

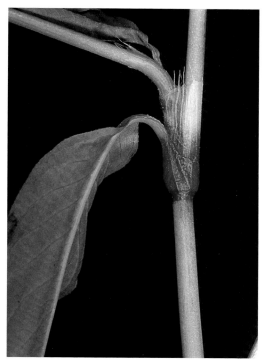

Marshpepper smartweed (*Polygonum hydropiper*) node with ocrea.   J. M. DiTomaso

Marshpepper smartweed (*Polygonum hydropiper*) achenes and dried flowers with achenes intact.   J. K. Clark

Ladysthumb: June–November. Spikes **erect, dense, oblong,** 1–3 cm long, 0.7–1.2 cm wide, sometimes interrupted below. Perianth 5-lobed, **deep pink to rarely white,** ± 2 mm long, open at maturity. Glandular disc yellow-green. Flower stalks glabrous. Insect- and self-pollinated.

Pennsylvania smartweed *(Polygonum pensylvanicum)* node with ocrea.   J. M. DiTomaso

Pennsylvania smartweed *(Polygonum pensylvanicum)* inflorescence.   J. M. DiTomaso

Pennsylvania smartweed *(Polygonum pensylvanicum)* achenes and dried flowers with achenes intact.
J. K. Clark

FRUITS AND SEEDS: Achenes glossy, brown to black.

Swamp smartweed: Achenes nearly round, flattened, 2.5–3 mm diameter.

Pale smartweed: Achenes broadly ovate, flattened, occasionally 3-sided, ± 2 mm long, slightly concave on both sides.

Mild smartweed (*Polygonum hydropiperoides*) at the margin of an irrigation canal.   J. M. DiTOMASO

Mild smartweed (*Polygonum hydropiperoides*) achenes and dried flowers with achenes intact.
J. K. CLARK

Mild smartweed (*Polygonum hydropiperoides*) inflorescence.   J. M. DiTOMASO

Ladysthumb: Achenes broadly ovate, flattened or ± 3-sided, ± 2 mm long.

POSTSENESCENCE CHARACTERISTICS: Pale smartweed, ladysthumb, and the foliage of swamp smartweed are killed by the first frost. Foliage turns brown to reddish and does not persist through the cold season. Rhizomes of swamp smartweed survive cold winter climates.

HABITAT: Edges of ponds, shallow lakes, marshes, and streams, wet fields, areas subject to seasonal flooding, irrigation ditches, pastures, orchards, rice fields, grain fields, and irrigated crops. Plants typically grow in wet to moist soils but tolerate periods of dryness. Terrestrial plants grow best in disturbed places with fertile soils and minimal competition. Plants do not tolerate highly acidic soils.

Swamp smartweed: Aquatic plants (water smartweed) typically grow in 1–5 m of water.

Pale smartweed: Dense stands often grow on loose, rich, slightly acidic soils high in organic matter.

Ladysthumb: Often follows human disturbance and also inhabits moist urban places.

DISTRIBUTION: All occur throughout most of the United States, including all western states. All are found throughout California, to 1500 m, except swamp smartweed does not occur in the Great Basin region and western Mojave Desert.

PROPAGATION AND PHENOLOGY: Seeds fall near and/or remain on the parent plant or disperse to greater distances with water, animals, in soil movement, agricultural machinery, and as contaminants of crop seeds. Seeds are dormant when shed and require a cold, moist period to break dormancy. Seeds germinate in spring. Seed longevity in the field is poorly documented. Under certain conditions, fragmented stems regenerate into new plants.

Swamp smartweed: Reproduces vegetatively from rhizomes and fragmented stems and **by seed.** Stem pieces develop roots rapidly and can disperse great distances along watercourses to initiate new colonies. Populations derived from a single clone do not set seeds. Seed production is typically lower in terrestrial plants. Seeds stored in cold water (2°C) survive ± 1 year.

Dotted smartweed (*Polygonum punctatum*) inflorescence.　　　　J. M. DiTomaso

Pale smartweed: Reproduces by seed. Plants produce about 800–1500 seeds per season, but under optimal conditions an individual may produce up to 19,000 seeds. Seed viability is variable. Under drought conditions seed production is often low, and many seeds may be nonviable. Seeds typically germinate March–June. Most seeds germinate within the first year. Seeds in dry storage can remain viable for up to 6 years.

Ladysthumb: Reproduces by seed. Seeds often remain on the parent plant until ingested or scattered by animals or disturbance. A persistent soil seed bank usually accumulates. Length of initial seed dormancy varies widely on individual plants and between populations. Seeds that do not germinate the first season enter secondary dormancy.

MANAGEMENT FAVORING OR DISCOURAGING SURVIVAL: Cultivation and mowing during the dry season and improving drainage can help control populations.

SIMILAR SPECIES: Marshpepper smartweed, Pennsylvania smartweed, mild smartweed, and dotted smartweed also occur in California and other western states. Refer to table 17 (page 328) for a comparison of important distinguishing characteristics. All inhabit marshes, margins of ponds and lakes, and other wet, often-disturbed places. Marshpepper, mild, and dotted smartweed are designated as obligate wetland indicator plants in the western United States. Pennsylvania smartweed is considered a facultative wetland species in the northwestern region (Oregon, Washington, Idaho, Montana, and Wyoming) and an obligate wetland species elsewhere in the western United States.

Marshpepper smartweed (*Polygonum hydropiper* L.) [POLHY]: Throughout most of the United States, including all western states except Arizona and New Mexico. Scattered in California throughout the northwestern region, Cascade Ranges, central-western region, Central Valley, and Sierra Nevada, to 1500 m. Introduced from Europe.

Pennsylvania smartweed (*Polygonum pensylvanicum* L.) [POLPY]: Montana, Wyoming, Colorado, New Mexico, Arizona, Nevada, and California in the eastern Sacramento Valley, where it is expected to expand range. Central and eastern United States. Native to the eastern United States.

Dotted smartweed (*Polygonum punctatum*) achenes and dried flowers with achenes intact.

J. K. CLARK

Mild smartweed (*Polygonum hydropiperoides* Michaux) [POLHP]: Oregon, Washington, Idaho, New Mexico, Arizona, Nevada, and throughout much of California to 1500 m, except Great Basin region, deserts, and east of the Sierra Nevada. Central and eastern United States. A widespread native.

Dotted smartweed (*Polygonum punctatum* Elliott) [POLPT]: Throughout most of the United States, including all western states except Utah and Nevada. Throughout California to 1500 m. A widespread native.

Table 17. Smartweed *(Polygonum)* species

Species	Life cycle	Flower spikes	Perianth (petals/sepals)	Glandular dots on perianth	Achenes (fruits)	Stipule margins	Other
swamp smartweed (*P. amphibium*)	perennial with rhizomes	erect, dense	deep or reddish pink, 4–6 mm long	no	flat	usually glabrous	stems often floating; leaves broad
marshpepper smartweed (*P. hydropiper*)	summer annual	drooping, loose-flowered	± green with red margins, ± 3 mm long	yes	2–3-angled	bristly-hairy	fruits dull, taste spicy or peppery when chewed
mild smartweed (*P. hydropiperoides*)	perennial with rhizomes	erect or with drooping tips, loose-flowered	pale pink to white, ± 3 mm long	no	3-angled	bristly-hairy	perianth opens, veins inconspicuous in fruit
pale smartweed (*P. lapathifolium*)	summer annual	drooping, dense	greenish to pale pink, ± 2 mm long	no	flat occasionally 3-angled	nearly glabrous	perianth remains closed, veins forked and prominent in fruit; fruits concave on both sides
Pennsylvania smartweed (*P. pensylvanicum*)	summer annual	erect, dense	light to deep pink, 4–5 mm long	no	flat	nearly glabrous	flower stalks have long-stalked glands; fruits concave on 1 side
ladysthumb (*P. persicaria*)	summer annual	erect, dense	deep pink, rarely white, ± 2 mm long	no	flat to 3-angled	bristly-hairy	hybridizes with pale smartweed
dotted smartweed (*P. punctatum*)	annual or perennial with rhizomes	erect or with drooping tips, loose-flowered	± green with white margins 2–3 mm long	yes	2–3-angled	bristly-hairy	fruits glossy, no peppery taste when chewed

Curly dock (*Rumex crispus* L.) [RUMCR]

Broadleaf dock (*Rumex obtusifolius* L.) [RUMOB]

SYNONYMS:

Curly dock: curled dock; curly-leaved dock; narrowleaf dock; narrow-leaved dock; sour dock; yellow dock

Broadleaf dock: bitter dock

GENERAL INFORMATION: Variable erect **perennials** with **whorls of fruits** at upper nodes. Each fruit is enclosed by **3 distinctively winged perianth parts** (sepals or petals) that are important for species identification. Refer to table 18 (page 341) for a comparison of distinguishing characteristics for 6 species often associated with aquatic systems. Curly and broadleaf dock are designated as facultative wetland indicator plants in California and most of the western United States. Under certain conditions, *Rumex* species may accumulate **toxic** levels of soluble oxalates, and plants may be **poisonous** to livestock when ingested in quantity. However, animals will seldom consume docks when more palatable forage is available. Both curly dock and broadleaf dock grow to 1.5 m tall. In most regions, these species are more likely to inhabit wetlands than uplands. Both are agronomic weeds nearly worldwide and can hybridize with one another and other European species. Curly dock is a state-listed secondary noxious weed in Iowa and Minnesota. Introduced from Eurasia and western Europe, respectively.

Curly dock (*Rumex crispus*) along river floodplain.   J. M. DITOMASO

Curly dock (*Rumex crispus*) fruiting inflorescence.   J. M. DITOMASO

SEEDLING: Cotyledons narrowly lanceolate to oblong, 4–14 mm long, 1–3 mm wide, tip ± rounded, base tapered to a short stalk. Seedling leaves alternate, form a rosette, have a stalk about as long or longer than the blade.

Curly dock: First few leaves ovate to elliptic, 10–15 mm long, tip rounded, base tapered.

Broadleaf dock: First few leaves broadly ovate, 10–15 mm long, tip broadly rounded, base slightly rounded to weakly heart-shaped. Often with red to purple spotting on upper surface.

MATURE PLANT: Foliage glabrous. Leaves alternate, oblong to oblong-lanceolate. Lower leaves long-stalked. Stipules (ocrea) membranous, fused, sheathing stem above nodes, fragile.

Curly dock: Leaves to 50 cm long, **base tapered, margins strongly ruffled, especially at the base**. Stems ± thick.

Curly dock *(Rumex crispus)* basal rosette.   J. K. CLARK

Curly dock *(Rumex crispus)* seedling.   J. K. CLARK

Broadleaf dock: Leaves to 75 cm long, flat, **base heart-shaped to truncate**, margins smooth to finely ruffled. Stems thick.

ROOTS AND UNDERGROUND STRUCTURES: Basal portion of the stem is typically pulled 3–5 cm below the soil surface by root contraction as seedlings develop. Under favorable conditions, underground stems fragmented during agricultural operations can develop into new plants. Carbohydrate reserves in the roots of curly dock and broadleaf dock increase most rapidly when flowering stems attain a height of ± 30 cm through the end of flowering. Carbohydrate reserves remain

Curly dock (*Rumex crispus*) achenes and dried perianth parts with achenes intact.   J. K. CLARK

Broadleaf dock (*Rumex obtusifolius*) habitat.
J. M. DiTomaso

Broadleaf dock (*Rumex obtusifolius*) leaf.   J. M. DiTomaso

fairly level as seeds ripen and are lowest just after new shoots emerge in winter/spring or after cutting.

Curly dock: Taproots slender, simple or few-branched, can grow to 3 m deep, only upper 4 cm can develop new shoots. Secondary roots numerous, fine, ± horizontal, near the soil surface and much deeper.

Broadleaf dock: Taproots typically branched, thick up to 30 cm deep, slender to 2 m deep, only upper 8 cm can generate new shoots. Secondary roots not usually near the soil surface.

FLOWERS: Bisexual, small, greenish, in whorled clusters at upper stem nodes. Perianth parts (sepals and/or petals) 6. **Inner 3 perianth parts enlarge, harden, and enclose developing fruits** and are usually required for identification (refer to **FRUITS AND SEEDS**, below). Stamens 6. Stigmas 3, feathery.

Comparison between leaves of broadleaf dock (*Rumex obtusifolius*) (left) and curly dock (*R. crispus*) (right).   R. UVA

Broadleaf dock (*Rumex obtusifolius*) seedling.   J. M. DiTOMASO

Curly dock: Nearly year-round. Flower clusters typically **dense, closely spaced along stems**, sometimes lowest few clusters widely spaced. Flowering branches erect.

Broadleaf dock: June–December. **Flower clusters** narrowly to widely spaced. Flowering branches erect.

FRUITS AND SEEDS: Fruit wings (inner perianth parts) ± veiny, often with a **raised tubercle at the center**, enclose one achene. Achenes ovate, triangular in cross-section, smooth, glossy, reddish brown.

Curly dock: Fruit stalks mostly longer than fruits. Fruit wings **triangular to heart-shaped**, 4–6 mm long. **Margins smooth to inconspicuously toothed.** Tubercles usually (1)3, equal or unequal. Achenes 2–2.5 mm long, the length near 1.5 times the width. Achene base short, ± stalklike.

Broadleaf dock: Fruit stalks nearly twice as long as fruits. Fruit wings **narrowly ovate-triangular**, 3–5 mm long. Margins typically have a **few spreading spinelike teeth 0.5–2 mm long** or rarely lack teeth. Teeth **broader at the base**. Tubercles typically 1, occasionally 3, unequal. Achenes 2–3 mm long, the length more than 1.5 times the width. Achene base short, ± stalklike.

POSTSENESCENCE CHARACTERISTICS: Fruiting stems die in mid to late summer and fruits and stems turn a **distinctive rusty-brown**. All typically persist for a few months. New rosettes grow from root crowns in early winter.

HABITAT: Ditches, roadsides, wetlands, periodically flooded areas, pastures, agronomic crops (especially perennial crops such as alfalfa), orchards, and moist

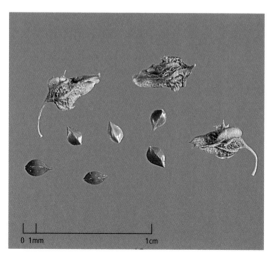

Broadleaf dock (*Rumex obtusifolius*) achenes and dried perianth parts with achenes intact.　　　J. K. CLARK

Cluster dock (*Rumex conglomeratus*) flowering stem.　　　J. M. DiTOMASO

waste places. Established plants tolerate drought. Curly dock seldom grows in acidic soils.

DISTRIBUTION:

Curly dock: Throughout the United States, including all western states. Throughout California to 2500 m. Nearly worldwide.

Cluster dock (*Rumex conglomeratus*) fruit cluster.   J. M. DiTOMASO

Cluster dock (*Rumex conglomeratus*) seedling.   J. M. DiTOMASO

Cluster dock (*Rumex conglomeratus*) achenes and dried perianth parts with achenes intact.   J. K. CLARK

334

Broadleaf dock: Throughout most of the United States, including all western states except Nevada and Wyoming. Throughout California to 1500 m. Nearly worldwide.

Toothed dock (*Rumex dentatus*) flowering stem.
J. M. DiTomaso

Toothed dock (*Rumex dentatus*) fruit clusters.
J. M. DiTomaso

PROPAGATION AND PHENOLOGY: Reproduce primarily by seed. Seeds fall near the parent plant or disperse to greater distances with water, soil movement, animals, agricultural activities, and as a seed or feed contaminant. Fruit wing tubercles help fruits float in water. Seedlings are most likely to establish in open disturbed places and exist as rosettes while their root systems develop. Plants develop flowering stems during their first or second spring. Seed production is typically high. Germination requires light and/or fluctuating temperature and is enhanced by scarification. Seeds from the same plant are highly variable, even under optimal conditions. Germination is typically intermittent with main flushes occurring in fall and spring. Newly matured curly dock seeds exhibit little dormancy compared to those of broadleaf dock. However, buried seeds of both species can remain viable for 20 years or more. Seeds survive ingestion by cattle and small birds but not chickens. Fall seedlings appear to establish better than spring-germinating seedlings.

Toothed dock (*Rumex dentatus*) seedling.
J. M. DiTomaso

Kerner's dock (*Rumex kerneri*) habit.
J. M. DiTomaso

Toothed dock (*Rumex dentatus*) achenes and dried perianth parts with achenes intact.
J. K. CLARK

MANAGEMENT FAVORING OR DISCOURAGING SURVIVAL: Mechanically or hand-cutting plants below the portion of the root that is able to resprout can control infestations. Systemic herbicides are most effective when applied to plants late in the growing season from the beginning of flowering through postseed development.

Kerner's dock *(Rumex kerneri)* basal rosette.   J. M. DiTOMASO

Kerner's dock *(Rumex kerneri)* immature fruiting clusters.   J. M. DiTOMASO

SIMILAR SPECIES: Refer to table 18 (page 341) for a comparison of distinguishing characteristics. **Cluster dock** or green dock (*Rumex conglomeratus* Murray) [RUMCO] is an erect **perennial** to 1.5 m tall. It is designated as a facultative wetland indicator plant in the western United States. Cluster dock occurs in Oregon, Washington, Nevada, Arizona, and throughout much of California to 1500 m, except the Great Basin region, deserts, and east side of the Sierra Nevada. Cluster dock is a state-listed noxious weed in parts of southwestern Australia. Introduced from Europe.

Toothed dock (*Rumex dentatus* L.) is an infrequent **annual or biennial** with slender stems to 0.75 m tall. It is designated as an obligate wetland species in California, where it was first discovered. Toothed dock occurs in Oregon,

Kerner's dock *(Rumex kerneri)* mature fruiting cluster.   J. M. DiTomaso

Kerner's dock *(Rumex kerneri)* seedling.   J. M. DiTomaso

Arizona, Utah, and California, where it grows in disturbed wet places and rice fields in the northern Sacramento Valley and northern San Joaquin Valley, to 30 m. Toothed dock is expanding its range and is also found in Missouri and Illinois. Introduced from Eurasia.

Kerner's dock *(Rumex kerneri)* achenes and dried perianth parts with achenes intact
J. K. CLARK

Fiddleleaf dock *(Rumex pulcher)* habit in drier environments.
J. M. DiTOMASO

Kerner's dock (*Rumex kerneri* Borbás) is a **perennial** with slender stems to 1.5 m tall. Kerner's dock occurs in California. It inhabits disturbed wet places on the Central Coast, to 50 m. Wetland indicator status has not been assigned to Kerner's dock. Introduced from southeastern Europe.

Fiddleleaf dock (*Rumex pulcher* L.) [RUMPU] can inhabit wetlands but is more commonly found on upland dry areas. It occurs in Oregon, New Mexico, and throughout California to 1500 m. Introduced from the Mediterranean region.

Fiddleleaf dock *(Rumex pulcher)* inflorescence with fruit.   J. M. DiTomaso

Fiddleleaf dock *(Rumex pulcher)* achenes and dried perianth parts with achenes intact.   J. K. Clark

Table 18. Dock *(Rumex)* species

Species	Life cycle	Lower leaf bases	Flower clusters	Fruit wing teeth	Fruit wing shape	Other
cluster dock *(R. conglomeratus)*	perennial	heart-shaped to truncate	widely spaced throughout	none	narrow, oblong, 2–3 mm long	largest tubercle covers ± half of fruit wing width
curly dock *(R. crispus)*	perennial	tapered	usually dense, closely spaced, except near base	none or inconspicuous	triangular to heart-shaped, 4–6 mm long	leaf margins strongly ruffled, especially at base
toothed dock *(R. dentatus)*	annual to biennial	heart-shaped to tapered	widely spaced throughout	± 1.5 mm long, slender	narrow, ovate, 4–5 mm long	flower branches ascending-erect
Kerner's dock *(R. kerneri)*	perennial	± heart-shaped to truncate	lower half widely spaced, closely or widely spaced above	± none to ± 0.5 mm long, broad at base	broad, heart-shaped to round, 5–7 mm long	largest leaves less than 20 cm long, achenes 3 mm long
broadleaf dock *(R. obtusifolius)*	perennial	heart-shaped to truncate	closely to widely spaced	none or 0.5–2 mm long, broad at base	narrow, ovate-triangular, 3–5 mm long	flower stalks near twice fruit length; largest leaves usually more than 20 cm long
fiddleleaf dock *(R. pulcher)*	perennial	heart-shaped to truncate	widely spaced throughout	at least some ± 1.5 mm long, slender to base	ovate, 3–5 mm long	flower branches spreading, nearly horizontal; largest leaves less than 15 cm long, some lower leaves narrowed near middle

Ducksalad (*Heteranthera limosa* (Sw.) Willd.) [HETLI]

Monochoria (*Monochoria vaginalis* (Burm. f.) K. Presl ex Kunth) [MOOVA]

NOXIOUS WEED LISTS: monochoria: Federal Noxious Weed

SYNONYMS:

Ducksalad: blue mudplantain; longleaf mudplantain; *Heteranthera alismoides* Humb. ex Link; *Heteranthera rotundifolia* (Kunth) Griseb.; *Leptanthus ovalis* Michx.; *Pontederia limosa* Sw.; others

Monochoria: heartshape false pickerelweed; *Monochoria africana* (Solms-Laub.) N.E. Brown; *Monochoria brevipetiolata* Verdc.; *Monochoria linearis* Miq.; *Monochoria plantaginia* Kunth; *Pontederia vaginalis* Burm. f.

GENERAL INFORMATION: Erect, ± tufted annuals to perennials to 0.5 m tall. Ducksalad and monochoria often form dense colonies in shallow water. Both species typically grow as **summer annuals** in California rice fields, particularly where rice establishment is poor.

Ducksalad: Typically **emersed**, sometimes terrestrial on mud banks where water has receded. Plants sometimes develop creeping horizontal stems. Introduced from the central and eastern United States. Ducksalad is expanding range as a rice weed in Asia.

Ducksalad (*Heteranthera limosa*) infestation in a rice field.   J. K. CLARK

Monochoria: Emersed to submersed, usually with creeping stems. Perennial colonies are typically more problematic than annual populations. In addition to its inclusion on the federal noxious weed list, monochoria is a state-listed class 1 and class A noxious weed in Florida and North Carolina, respectively. Introduced from tropical Australia and Asia, where it is regionally consumed as a vegetable and used medicinally.

SEEDLING: Glabrous, submerged, typically a rosette of narrow ribbonlike leaves. Leaves are sometimes floating in more developed juveniles.

White-flowering form of ducksalad (*Heteranthera limosa*).   J. M. DiTomaso

Blue-flowering form of ducksalad (*Heteranthera limosa*).   J. M. DiTomaso

Ducksalad: Cotyledon elliptic to lanceolate, long-stalked, typically floating. Immature leaves lacking or with reduced blades.

Monochoria: Cotyledon blade oval, ± 1 mm long, on a slender sheathing stalk 8–10 mm long. First leaf linear, 10–15 mm long, 1–2 mm wide, with 3 parallel veins, sheathing at the base, rounded at the tip. Subsequent leaves resemble first leaf.

MATURE PLANT: Foliage glabrous, variable. Leaves alternate, mostly ± basal.

Ducksalad: Blades ovate to elliptic, more than 4 cm long, base ± rounded to truncate, on long stalks (>15 cm long).

Ducksalad (*Heteranthera limosa*) seedling.   J. M. DiTomaso

Ducksalad (*Heteranthera limosa*) seeds.   J. K. Clark

Monochoria: Blades ovate to narrowly lanceolate, 3–11 cm long, base usually rounded, sometimes heart-shaped, on stalks 4–70 cm long.

ROOTS AND UNDERGROUND STRUCTURES: Roots fibrous. Both species may develop creeping stems that root at the nodes.

FLOWERS: Inflorescences are **positioned below terminal leaf blades** and arise from the uppermost leaf sheath (spathe). Insect- and/or self-pollinated.

Monochoria (*Monochoria vaginalis*) in flower.   J. M. DiTomaso

Monochoria (*Monochoria vaginalis*) in a rice field.   J. M. DiTomaso

Ducksalad: April–July. Flowers **solitary on a long stalk**. Perianth (petals or sepals as a unit) bluish purple to white, ± **trumpet-shaped** (salverform), 6-lobed, **tube 1.5–3 cm long. Stamens 3**. Anthers yellow, with 1 slightly larger and sometimes pale blue. Ovary 1-chambered. Flowers open above water.

Monochoria: June–August. Racemes consist of **2–7**(1–20) **closely clustered flowers on a short stalk**. Perianth blue, ± **saucer-shaped** (rotate), with 6 nearly separate lobes, **tube less than 1 cm long. Stamens 6**, with 5 yellow anthers and 1 larger blue anther. Ovary 3-chambered. Flowers typically open under water.

Monochoria (*Monochoria vaginalis*) fruit.   J. M. DiTomaso

Monochoria (*Monochoria vaginalis*) seedling.   J. M. DiTomaso

FRUITS AND SEEDS: Capsules ellipsoid, contain numerous seeds. Seeds brown, ellipsoid to ovoid, longitudinally thin-ribbed, with fine transverse striations between.

Ducksalad: Capsules erect, membranous, ± 2 cm long, open by splitting down 1 side. Seeds 1 mm long.

Monochoria: Fruiting stalks reflex downward. Capsules ± 1 cm long, open by 3 valves, sometimes explosively ejecting seeds. Capsules may disperse before opening. Seeds ± 0.5–1 mm long.

HABITAT: Rice fields, ditches, and pond and lake margins.

DISTRIBUTION: Uncommon.

Ducksalad: Arizona, Colorado, New Mexico, and California in the Sacramento Valley, to 100 m. Central and part of the southern United States.

Monochoria: Much less common than ducksalad. In the west, found only in California in the Sacramento Valley, to 100 m. Has spread from the rice experimental station in Biggs (Butte Co.) to other rice fields in Butte, Glenn, Sutter, and Yuba Cos.

PROPAGATION AND PHENOLOGY: Reproduce primarily by seed. Capsules and seeds disperse with water, mud, and agricultural equipment. Seeds germinate under water.

SIMILAR SPECIES: Water hyacinth (*Eichhornia crassipes* (Mart.) Solms) is distinguished by its **free-floating habit, ± inflated leaf stalks,** and inflorescences that typically consist of **many flowers held above the leaves.** Refer to the **Water Hyacinth** entry (page 52) for more information.

Monochoria (*Monochoria vaginalis*) seeds.   J. K. CLARK

Himalaya blackberry (*Rubus armeniacus* Focke = *R. discolor* Weihe & Nees) [RUBDI]

Cutleaf blackberry (*Rubus laciniatus* Willd.) [RUBLA]

NOXIOUS WEED LISTS:

Himalaya blackberry: Oregon: B; CalEPPC: A-1

SYNONYMS:

Himalaya blackberry: Himalayaberry; Himalayan blackberry; *Rubus procerus* auct. non P. J. Muell. *Rubus discolor* is an incorrectly applied name, but widely used.

Cutleaf blackberry: cut-leaved blackberry; evergreen blackberry; *Rubus vulgaris* Weihe & Nees var. *laciniatus* Dippel

GENERAL INFORMATION: Erect, mounded, climbing, or trailing **shrubs** to 3 m tall, with stout prickles and edible fruits. Himalaya blackberry is a vigorous cultivar introduced from Eurasia and is the most common non-native bramble invading riparian areas in California and the Pacific Northwest. It originated from Armenia and spread as a common garden escape throughout much of Europe and elsewhere, including New Zealand, Australia, and South Africa. Cutleaf blackberry is a closely related cultivar introduced from Europe. Fruits of *Rubus* species are an important food source for wildlife, particularly birds. The genus *Rubus* is comprised of numerous variable and taxonomically difficult species and types, many of which are native to the western states. *Rubus fruticosus* L. agg. (referred to as European blackberry) is sometimes used to refer to a complex of closely related European and eastern North American species, which includes Himalaya and cutleaf blackberry.

Himalaya blackberry *(Rubus armeniacus)* shrub.   J. M. DITOMASO

Himalaya blackberry *(Rubus armeniacus)* flowers and foliage.
J. M. DiTomaso

Himalaya blackberry *(Rubus armeniacus)* fruit and whitish color on back of leaflet.   J. M. DiTomaso

MATURE PLANT: First-year stems (primocanes) **strongly angled**, typically acquire length. Primocane prickles straight or curved, **thick-based**. Second year stems (floricanes) produce flowers and fruits and often have leaves with a different number of leaflets. Floricanes usually die after fruiting, except in some European species. Primocanes of many species may root at the tips when touching the ground. Leaves compound, ± evergreen. Leaflets 3–5, toothed.

Himalaya blackberry: Some leaflets **shallow-lobed, broadest above middle (ovate), lower surfaces white** and densely covered with short white hairs.

Cutleaf blackberry: Leaflets **deeply incised to compound**, lower surfaces green, sparse to moderately hairy.

Prickly and angled stem of Himalaya blackberry *(Rubus armeniacus).* J. M. DiTOMASO

Cutleaf blackberry *(Rubus laciniatus)* foliage. J. M. DiTOMASO

350

Roots and Underground Structures: While canes are typically biennial, roots are perennial. Most roots are in the top 50 cm of soil, but some may grow up to 2 m deep in loose soils. New shoots can grow from buds on the roots. Under favorable conditions, root fragments may develop into new plants.

Flowers: White to pinkish. Petals and sepals 5. Stamens and ovaries numerous. Insect-pollinated. Self-fertile. Some *Rubus* species may hybridize where their ranges overlap.

Himalaya blackberry: May–September. Flowers bisexual, numerous, in non-glandular panicles. **Sepal tips ± 1 mm long, petals 10–15 mm long.**

Cutleaf blackberry: May–July. Flowers bisexual, numerous, in glandular or non-glandular panicles. **Sepal tips 2–8 mm long, petals 5–7 mm long.**

Fruits and Seeds: Fruits consist of an aggregate of drupelets. Blackberries have fruits that adhere to the fleshy receptacle (fruit-bearing axis).

Himalaya blackberry: Mature berries black, ovoid to oblong, to 2 cm long, glossy, glabrous or minutely pubescent. Berries typically ripen later in the season than those of native blackberries.

Cutleaf blackberry: Mature berries black, round to ovoid, to 1.5 cm in diameter, glabrous.

Postsenescence Characteristics: Dense thickets typically contain numerous dead canes that can persist for an extended period.

Habitat: The blackberries typically inhabit disturbed moist open sites, roadsides, fencerows, fields, canal and ditch banks, and riparian areas in many plant communities. Himalaya blackberrry tolerates periodic flooding with brackish water.

Distribution:

Himalaya blackberry: British Columbia, Oregon, Washington, Idaho, Utah, New Mexico, Arizona, Nevada, and throughout California, except deserts, to 1600 m. Scattered in the eastern United States.

Cutleaf blackberry: Oregon, Washington, Idaho, Montana, Wyoming, Colorado, and scattered in California in the northwestern region, Cascade Range, Sierra Nevada, San Francisco Bay region, and Peninsular Ranges, to 1900 m. Northeastern United States.

Propagation and Phenology: Reproduce by seed, root sprouts, and stem tip rooting. Fruits typically disperse to greater distances with animals, especially birds. Seeds without the succulent flesh may also disperse with water and soil movement. Seed germination occurs mainly in spring. Seedlings grow slowly, and those of most species typically grow poorly in dense shade. Primocanes emerge from roots and/or the crowns in late winter/early spring.

Management Favoring or Discouraging Survival: Small infestations may be controlled effectively by manual removal. However, removing only the aboveground portion of plants usually stimulates the growth of root sprouts. Cutting or burning plants can be effective tools if root sprouts are controlled while small. Repeated cutting, especially at flowering time, can help exhaust root stores. Cutting in fall can prevent stems from tip rooting. Goats readily consume *Rubus* species, and their browsing may also help control infestations, especially new growth.

SIMILAR SPECIES: Elmleaf blackberry (*Rubus ulmifolius* Schott var. *inermis* (Willd.) W.O. Focke) is a less common species that resembles Himalaya blackberry. Unlike Himalaya blackberry, elmleaf blackberry **lacks prickles** on the stems. Elmleaf blackberry occurs sporadically in Arizona and California in the southern northwestern region, central-western region, Sacramento Valley, and northern part of the southwestern region, to 500 m. It was introduced from Europe as a garden cultivar. There are many native *Rubus* species in the western states that can also resemble non-native species.

Cutleaf blackberry *(Rubus laciniatus)* fruit.   J. M. DiTOMASO

Cutleaf blackberry *(Rubus laciniatus)* prickly stem.   J. M. DiTOMASO

Coyote willow (*Salix exigua* Nutt.) [SAXEX]

Goodding's black willow (*Salix gooddingii* C. Ball)

Red willow (*Salix laevigata* Bebb)

Arroyo willow (*Salix lasiolepis* Benth.)

SYNONYMS: Many willows are widespread and highly variable, resulting in much taxonomic confusion. A complete list of synonyms for some species is extensive and beyond the scope of this publication.

Coyote willow: narrowleaf willow; sandbar willow; *Salix agrophylla* Nutt.; *Salix hindsiana* Benth.; *Salix linearifolia* Rydb.; *Salix nevadensis* S. Wats.; *Salix parishiana* Rowlee; *Salix sessifolia* Nutt. var. *hindsiana* (Benth.) Anderss. and var. *leucodendroides* (Rowlee) Schneid.; *Salix thurberi* Rowlee; others

Goodding's black willow: Goodding's willow; *Salix gooddingii* var. *variabilis* Ball; *Salix nigra* var. *vallicola* Dudl.; *Salix vallicola* (Dudl.) Britt. & Shafer

Red willow: polished willow; *Salix congesta* (Bebb ex Rothrock) J.T. Howell; others

Arroyo willow: Tracy's willow; *Salix bakeri* von Seem.; *Salix lutea* Nutt. var. *nivaria* Jeps.; *Salix tracyi* C. Ball; others

GENERAL INFORMATION: Mostly **winter deciduous native shrubs or small trees** to 15 m tall, with **flowers in catkins**. There are numerous native willow species in western states. All are an important component of riparian ecosystems. However,

Coyote willow *(Salix exigua)* with male flower clusters. J. M. DiTomaso

some native willow species are occasionally weedy in irrigation and drainage ditches and other controlled aquatic systems. **Coyote, Goodding's black, red**, and **arroyo willows** are commonly encountered willows in many western states. Refer to table 19 for a comparison of distinguishing features for these species.

MATURE PLANT: Bark bitter-tasting. Twigs ± flexible, hairy to glabrous. Leaves alternate, longer than wide, pinnately veined, on short stalks. Margins entire to toothed. Surfaces glabrous to hairy. Stipules usually deciduous, sometimes large. **Winter buds have a single scale.**

Coyote willow (*Salix exigua*) with female flower clusters.   J. M. DiTomaso

Goodding's black willow (*Salix gooddingii*) with male flower clusters.   J. M. DiTomaso

ROOTS AND UNDERGROUND STRUCTURES: Roots woody, ± spreading, can develop new shoots from basal rootstock. **Coyote willow** typically develops clonal thickets from root sprouts.

FLOWERS: March–May. **Catkins consist of numerous male or female flowers. Male and female catkins develop on separate plants (dioecious). Flowers lack sepals and petals. Each flower is subtended by a single bract.** Female flowers consist of a simple pistil. Male flowers consist only of stamens. Insect- and/or wind-pollinated.

Red willow (*Salix laevigata*) with male flower clusters.

J. M. DITOMASO

Female flower cluster of red willow (*Salix laevigata*).

J. M. DITOMASO

355

Red willow (*Salix laevigata*) with stipules and whitish color on back of leaves.   J. M. DiTomaso

Arroyo willow (*Salix lasiolepis*) with female flower clusters.   J. M. DiTomaso

FRUITS AND SEEDS: Capsules ovoid to lanceolate, 3–9 mm long, most open by 2 valves, contain numerous seeds. Seeds elliptic, ± 1 mm long, with a tuft of long hair at the apex.

HABITAT: Riparian areas, washes, flood plains, moist meadows, lake and pond margins, marshes, springs, and irrigation and drainage ditches.

DISTRIBUTION:

Coyote willow: All western states. Throughout California to 2700 m. Texas, Nebraska.

Goodding's black willow: Utah, New Mexico, Arizona, Nevada, and California in the eastern North Coast Ranges, Cascade Range foothills, Sierra Nevada foothills, Central Valley, South Coast, Peninsular Ranges, and deserts, mostly to 500 m but occasionally as high as 1600 m. Texas.

Red willow: Oregon, Utah, Arizona, Nevada, and throughout California to 1700 m.

Arroyo willow: Oregon, Washington, Idaho, Utah, New Mexico, Arizona, Nevada, and throughout California to 2800 m.

PROPAGATION AND PHENOLOGY: Reproduce by seed and vegetatively from root sprouts and stem fragments. Seeds disperse primarily with wind and water. Seeds typically germinate within 24 hours after landing on a suitable substrate. Otherwise, seeds survive a few weeks at most. Stem fragments deposited in moist substrate from flooding or other disturbance can grow into a new plant. Plants

Drooping branches of weeping willow (*Salix babylonica*).   J. M. DITOMASO

Weeping willow (*Salix babylonica*) leaves.
                    J. M. DITOMASO

readily resprout from the crown following mechanical damage such as cutting or fire.

SIMILAR SPECIES: Weeping willow (*Salix babylonica* L.) [SAXBA] is a non-native tree that has occasionally escaped cultivation in disturbed areas and riparian sites around urban areas. It is easily distinguished from other willows by its drooping branches and foliage.

Seepwillow (*Baccharis salicifolia* (Ruíz Lopez & Pavón) Pers.) [BACGL] is a native **shrub** in the Asteraceae (sunflower family) with **whitish flower heads in clusters**. In its vegetative state, seepwillow may be confused with willow species. Unlike willow species, seepwillow leaves have **3 veins from the base, with the outer 2 veins near the margins**. Seepwillow often grows in riparian areas in Colorado, Utah, New Mexico, Arizona, Nevada, and California in the north-western region, Cascade Range foothills, Sierra Nevada foothills, Central Valley, Tehachapi Mountains, central-western and southwestern regions, and deserts, to 1250 m. It is occasionally a weed problem in irrigation canals, ditches, or controlled aquatic systems. See the **Seepwillow** entry on page 162 for more information.

Table 19. Common willows (*Salix* spp.)

Species	Habit	Axillary bud scale margins	Leaf shape	Mature leaf upper surface	Mature leaf lower surface	Stamens per flower	Ovary	Flower timing
coyote willow (*S. exigua*)	shrub to 7 m tall	fused	linear to narrowly elliptic	silky-hairy	green or glaucous, (silvery) silky-hairy	2	glabrous or hairy	with or after leaf emergence
Goodding's black willow (*S. gooddingii*)	tree to 30 m tall	free, overlapping	narrowly lanceolate or narrowly ovate	gray-green, glabrous or nearly glabrous	gray-green, glabrous	4–8	glabrous or hairy	with leaf emergence
red willow (*S. laevigata*)	tree to 15 m tall	free, overlapping	lanceolate to elliptic, broadest below middle	green, glabrous, glossy	glaucous, glabrous	5	glabrous	with or after leaf emergence
arroyo willow (*S. lasiolepis*)	shrub or small tree to 10 m tall	fused	oblanceolate to elliptic, broadest above middle	dark green, glabrous, glossy	glaucous, glabrous to densely short-hairy, hairs white and/or rust-colored	2	glabrous	before leaf emergence

Eisen waterhyssop (*Bacopa eisenii* (Kellogg) Pennell) [BAOEI]

SYNONYMS: bacopa; Gila River waterhyssop; western hydraulthele

GENERAL INFORMATION: Native **perennial to annual** growing in shallow water or on mud, typically with creeping stems to 0.6 m long and **opposite leaves**. Stems sometimes form floating mats. In natural areas it is usually considered a desirable component of the vegetation. However, Eisen waterhyssop is sometimes a minor weed in wet agricultural ditches and rice fields.

SEEDLING: Typically submerged. Cotyledons lanceolate. First leaves elliptic to nearly round, sessile, developing on a short to long stem (depending on water depth).

MATURE PLANT: Stems prostrate to ascending or floating, branched, fleshy, hollow, sometimes constricted at the nodes, glabrous to soft-hairy. Leaves sessile, **obovate to nearly round**, **12–36 mm long**, **14–20 mm wide**, with **10–12 veins** radiating fanlike from the base.

ROOTS AND UNDERGROUND STRUCTURES: Stems usually develop roots at the lower nodes.

FLOWERS: June–September. Flowers solitary in leaf axils, held above the water surface **on stalks longer than leaves (15–50 mm long)**. Corolla ± bell-shaped, **10–15 mm long**, 5-lobed, white with a yellow throat. **Sepals 5**, separate, **upper sepal ovate to round**, conspicuously broader than the others. Stamens usually 4(2–5).

Eisen waterhyssop (*Bacopa eisenii*) in a rice field.　　　　　　　　J. M. DiTOMASO

FRUITS AND SEEDS: Capsules ± round, 4–5 mm long, with 2 valves, each 2-parted, typically submersed when mature. Seeds numerous, cylindrical, 0.5 mm long, 0.2–0.3 mm wide, with a bladdery seed coat (testa).

HABITAT: Rice fields, ponds, ditches, and wet places in shallow water or on mud.

DISTRIBUTION: Nevada and California in the Central Valley, southern central-western region, and Sierra Nevada, to 1200 m on the east side of the Sierra Nevada and to 100 m on the west side.

PROPAGATION AND PHENOLOGY: Reproduces by seed. Plants may sometimes

Eisen waterhyssop (*Bacopa eisenii*) flowering stems.   J. M. DiTOMASO

Eisen waterhyssop (*Bacopa eisenii*) flowers.   J. M. DiTOMASO

reproduce vegetatively from stem fragments. Seeds disperse with water, soil movement, and by clinging to agricultural machinery.

SIMILAR SPECIES: Unlike Eisen waterhyssop, **Monnier waterhyssop** (*Bacopa monnieri* (L.) Pennell) [BAOMO] has **narrow leaves with 1 vein** and **a pair of linear bractlets below each** white to pink **flower**. Monnier waterhyssop occurs in Arizona and California in the Sonoran Desert (especially Riverside Co.) to 100 m. It is native to tropical and subtropical regions nearly worldwide, where it is a widespread minor weed in rice fields.

Eisen waterhyssop (*Bacopa eisenii*) seedling.   J. M. DiTomaso

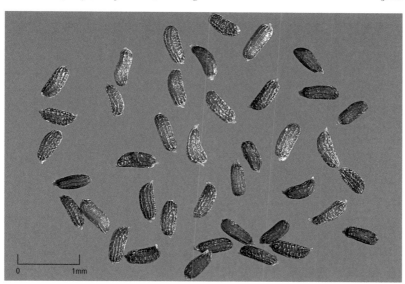

Eisen waterhyssop (*Bacopa eisenii*) seeds.   J. K. Clark

Disc waterhyssop (*Bacopa rotundifolia* (Michaux) Wettst., synonym: *Bacopa nobsiana* H. Mason) [BAORO] is distinguished by having **flower stalks ± shorter than leaves (5–18 mm long)** and **corollas 5–8 mm long**. Disc waterhyssop occurs in Idaho, Montana, Wyoming, Colorado, Utah, New Mexico, Arizona, and California in the Central Valley to 100 m. It is a widespread native of the central United States, including all the western states previously listed except California, where it is considered an introduced species.

Creeping waterhyssop (*Bacopa repens* (Sw.) Wettst.) is distinguished from other hyssop species by typically having **4 sepals** (occasionally 5), the **largest with**

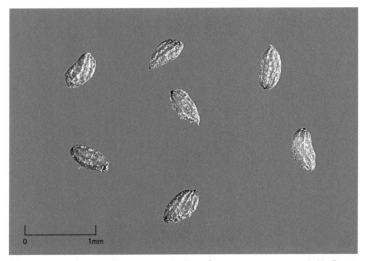

Monnier waterhyssop (*Bacopa monnieri*) seeds.   J. K. CLARK

Disc waterhyssop (*Bacopa rotundifolia*) plants.   J. M. DiTomaso

hairs along the margin (ciliate), and **leaves 8–12 mm wide**. Flowers are white or pink-tinged. Creeping waterhyssop is mostly associated with rice fields and other wet agronomic fields. It occurs in California in the Sacramento Valley to 100 m. Introduced from Central America and/or the Caribbean.

Disc waterhyssop (*Bacopa rotundifolia*) flowers.   J. K. CLARK

Disc waterhyssop (*Bacopa rotundifolia*) seedling.   J. M. DiTOMASO

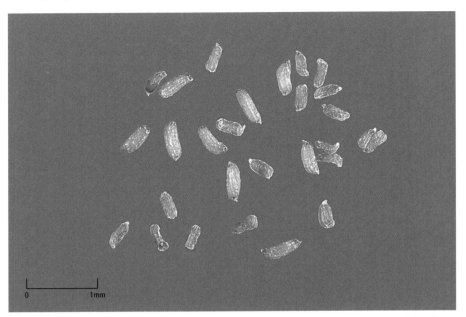

Disc waterhyssop *(Bacopa rotundifolia)* seeds.

J. K. CLARK

Water speedwell (*Veronica anagallis-aquatica* L.) [VERAA]

SYNONYMS: great water speedwell; *Veronica anagallis* L. in some references

GENERAL INFORMATION: Emergent **biennial or perennial**, with **opposite leaves** and small **pale lavender-blue flowers**, to 1 m tall. Introduced from Europe.

SEEDLING: Cotyledons oval, 2–4 mm long. First leaves opposite, oblong to elliptic, with rounded tips.

MATURE PLANT: Foliage glabrous. Stems erect to spreading, sometimes creeping and rooting at lower nodes. Leaves **sessile** (except lower sometimes short-stalked), **lanceolate or elliptic to ovate**, ± **lobed at the base and clasping the stem**, light green, 2–8 cm long, with the **length 1.5–3 times the width**. Margins smooth to serrate.

ROOTS AND UNDERGROUND STRUCTURES: Plants typically spread from **creeping rhizomes** and/or **stolons**. Stems usually develop roots at the lower nodes.

FLOWERS: May–September. **Racemes axillary**, **opposite**, glabrous or minutely glandular, bracts alternate. Flower stalks (pedicels) 4–8 mm long. Corolla (petals as a unit) deeply 4-lobed, upper lobe widest, 5–10 mm diameter, **pale lavender-blue**, **lined with violet**. Sepals 4–5, separate, unequal, 3–5.5 mm long, usually **longer than capsules**.

FRUITS AND SEEDS: Capsules flattened, **nearly round, barely notched** (to 0.1 mm) **at the apex**, 2-chambered, 2.5–4 mm long, smooth, style 1.5–3 mm long, with numerous seeds. Sepals are usually longer than capsules. Seeds ± ovoid, flat on

Water speedwell (*Veronica anagallis-aquatica*) infestation in an irrigation ditch.   J. M. DiTOMASO

one side, rounded on the other, ± 0.5 mm long. Surface finely reticulate with magnification.

HABITAT: Ditches, slow streams, pond and stream margins, wet meadows, and marshy places.

DISTRIBUTION: All western states. Throughout most of California, except deserts and Great Basin region, to 2500 m. Throughout United States, except some southern states. South America.

Water speedwell *(Veronica anagallis-aquatica)* in flower.   J. M. DiTOMASO

Water speedwell *(Veronica anagallis-aquatica)* inflorescence.   J. M. DiTOMASO

PROPAGATION AND PHENOLOGY: Reproduces by seed and vegetatively from creeping rhizomes and/or stolons. Seeds disperse in water and mud and can germinate year-round under favorable conditions.

SIMILAR SPECIES: Chain speedwell (*Veronica catenata* Pennell, synonyms: *Veronica comosa* Richt.; *Veronica connata* var. *glaberrima* Penn.) and **European speedwell** (*Veronica beccabunga* L.) are **glabrous perennials** with **rhizomes** that grow in habitats similar to those of the more common water speedwell. Unlike water speedwell, chain speedwell has **pale pink flowers 4–5 mm diameter**, capsules

Water speedwell (*Veronica anagallis-aquatica*) seedling. J. M. DiTomaso

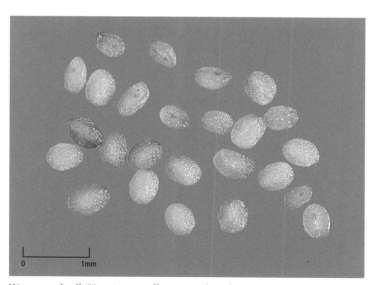

Water speedwell (*Veronica anagallis-aquatica*) seeds. J. K. CLARK

with an **apical notch 0.1–0.3 mm** deep, sepals usually **equal to or shorter than capsules**, and **leaf length 3–5 times the width**. Chain speedwell is often **mostly submersed** and has stems to ± 1 m long or tall. Chain speedwell occurs in Washington, Oregon, Utah, Colorado, Nevada, New Mexico, Arizona, and throughout California, except deserts and Great Basin region, to 2500 m. Chain speedwell may also occur in Idaho, Montana, and Wyoming and can hybridize with water speedwell, where intermediate plants can be encountered where both species occur.

European speedwell has stems to 60 cm long and is distinguished from chain speedwell by having **obovate to nearly round leaves on short petioles** 2–10 mm long. In addition, European speedwell flowers are blue to violet with sepals 2.5–3.5 mm long, and with ± **spherical capsules on stalks 3–6 mm long**. European speedwell occurs in Nevada and California east of the Sierra Nevada (primarily Mono Co.), to 2000 m. European and chain speedwell are introduced from Europe.

American speedwell or brooklime (*Veronica americana* (Raf.) Schwein.) is a **widespread native aquatic perennial** with **short-stalked leaves** that closely resembles European speedwell. Unlike European speedwell, American speedwell has **ovate to lanceolate leaves that are longer than wide** and **capsules round and moderately flattened on stalks 5–10 mm long**. American speedwell flowers are bright blue with a white center. It is a desirable component of natural aquatic ecosystems and is not considered a weed under most circumstances throughout the western states.

American speedwell (*Veronica americana*) foliage
and flowers.   J. M. DiTomaso

Smallflower tamarisk (*Tamarix parviflora* DC.) [TAAPA]

Saltcedar (*Tamarix ramosissima* Ledeb.) [TAARA]

Athel tamarisk (*Tamarix aphylla* (L.) Karst.) [TAAAP]

NOXIOUS WEED LISTS:

Smallflower tamarisk: California: C; Colorado: A; Wyoming: Noxious Weed; CalEPPC: A-1

Saltcedar: California: C; Washington: A; Montana: 2; Colorado: A; Wyoming and Nevada: Noxious Weed; CalEPPC: A-1

Athel tamarisk: CalEPPC: Need More Information

SYNONYMS:

Smallflower tamarisk: early tamarisk; *Tamarix cretica* Bge.; *Tamarix lucronensis* Sennen & Elias; *Tamarix petteri* Presl ex Bge.; *Tamarix rubella* Batt.; *Tamarix tetranda* auct. non Pall.; others. Plants are sometimes sold in California as *Tamarix africana* Poir, which is a different species.

Saltcedar: five-stamen tamarisk; late tamarisk; tamarisk; *Tamarix altaica* Nied.; *Tamarix ewersmannii* C. Presl ex Bunge; *Tamarix gallica* L. vars. *micrantha* Ledeb. and *pallasii* Dyer; *Tamarix odessana* Stev. ex Bunge; *Tamarix pallasii* Desv.; *Tamarix pentandra* Pall.; others

Athel tamarisk: athel pine; athel tree; flowering cypress; tamarisk salt tree; *Tamarix articulata* Vahl; *Tamarix orientalis* Forssk.; *Thuja aphylla* L.

Smallflower tamarisk (*Tamarix parviflora*) in flower in a riparian site.   J. M. DITOMASO

GENERAL INFORMATION: Tree (athel tamarisk) **or shrubs** with **tiny scale- or awl-like leaves.** *Tamarix* species typically develop an efficient, deep, extensive root system. Plants have a high evapotranspiration rate in arid climates during the warm season when deep soil moisture is accessible. Unlike willows and cotton-woods, roots can extract water from both saturated and unsaturated soils, which increases their competitive ability. The presence of numerous trees along riparian corridors or around desert springs can seriously reduce underground water tables. Roots extract salts from deep soil layers and excrete them from the leaves.

Smallflower tamarisk (*Tamarix parviflora*) flowering branch.   J. M. DiTOMASO

Smallflower tamarisk (*Tamarix parviflora*) resprouting from stem fragment.   J. M. DiTOMASO

Salt is deposited on the soil surface following rainfall or with leaf litter. The increased salinity of the upper soil profile inhibits the growth, survival, and recruitment of desirable native vegetation. Although some animals will seek cover or nest in *Tamarix* thickets, most wildlife does not consume *Tamarix* foliage, fruits, or seeds. Many insects, however, use *Tamarix* as a source of pollen and nectar. *Tamarix* species can increase flooding in riparian areas by narrowing channel width. In addition, plants are flammable and can introduce fire into wetland and riparian communities that are not adapted to periodic burning.

Smallflower tamarisk (*Tamarix parviflora*) seed. J. K. Clark

Saltcedar (*Tamarix ramosissima*) infestation along a riparian site in the southwestern United States.
C. Bell

Collectively, *Tamarix* species occupy over 450,000 hectares of sensitive habitat in western North America. Smallflower tamarisk and saltcedar are common invasive species in western states and were introduced from southeastern Europe and eastern Asia, respectively, as landscape ornamentals and soil stabilizers. Athel tamarisk is less invasive than either smallflower tamarisk or saltcedar. Athel

New saplings of saltcedar *(Tamarix ramosissima)* along an intermittenly dry creekbed.

J. M. DiTomaso

Saltcedar *(Tamarix ramosissima)* in flower.

J. M. DiTomaso

tamarisk is a widespread ornamental in southwestern states, including Southern California. It is introduced from northern Africa to the Middle East and India.

SEEDLING: Cotyledons and young seedlings inconspicuous. Seedlings 1 cm tall have leaves that resemble those of mature plants. Seedlings may grow 2–3 m in 1 year under favorable conditions.

MATURE PLANT: Trunk(s) short, sometimes twisted. Branches erect to spreading, with a dense canopy of slender, often arched or drooping twigs. Twig leaves tiny, alternate, sessile, gray-green depending on the amount of salt excretion. Foliage of deciduous species turns yellow to orange-red in fall.

Smallflower tamarisk: To 5 m tall, deciduous. Multiple trunks with a more roundish shape. Bark brown, reddish brown, or deep purplish brown. Twig leaves awl-like, **ovate to lanceolate**, 2–3 mm long, **strongly overlapping**, tip long-pinched-in (long-acuminate), base narrow.

Saltcedar: To 8 m tall, deciduous, variable. May have multiple trunks but more treelike in appearance than smallflower tamarisk. Bark reddish brown. Branches often purplish. Twig leaves awl-like, **ovate to lanceolate**, 1.5–3.5 mm long, **strongly overlapping**, tip acute or pinched-in, base narrow. Foliage is usually more bluish green than smallflower tamarisk.

Athel tamarisk: To 12 m tall, **evergreen**. Usually a single dominant trunk. Bark reddish brown to gray. Twigs appear **jointed**, grayish. Twig leaves scalelike, ± 2 mm long, **not or barely overlapping**, **completely sheathing twig**, except for the minute, abruptly pointed tip.

Saltcedar (*Tamarix ramosissima*) flowering branch.   J. M. DITOMASO

Saltcedar (*Tamarix ramosissima*) flowers.
                              J. M. DITOMASO

Saltcedar (*Tamarix ramosissima*) seedlings.　　　　　J. M. DiTomaso

Athel tamarisk (*Tamarix aphylla*) along shoreline of Lake
Mead, Nevada.　　　　　J. M. DiTomaso

ROOTS AND UNDERGROUND STRUCTURES: Taproots typically grow to 5 m deep or more to access the water table. Once the water table is located, the taproot branches profusely into numerous lateral roots to several meters long. Large amounts of water are stored in the roots of athel tamarisk. In sand dunes the extensive root system prevents the natural shifting of the dune.

FLOWERS: Racemes 3–5 mm wide, simple or compound and panicle-like. Simple racemes develop on previous year's growth, usually before or at the same time as leaves emerge. Compound racemes develop on current year's growth, typically after leaves emerge in spring.

Smallflower tamarisk: Mostly March–May. Racemes simple. Flowers typically pale to dark pink, usually with **4 sepals, petals, and stamens.** Nectar disc fused and continuous with stamen bases, such that stamen bases appear broadened and starfishlike. Petals ± persist on fruits.

Saltcedar: Mostly April–August, but plants may flower throughout much of the year in some areas. Racemes usually compound, some simple. Flowers white or pale to dark pink, mostly with **5 sepals, petals, and stamens. Inner 2–3 sepals minutely irregular-toothed** (erose). Sepal tips acute. Nectar disc lobes broader than long, alternate with stamens. **Petals persist on fruits.**

Athel tamarisk: Mostly May–July. Racemes mostly compound, some simple. Flowers white to pale pink, mostly with **5 sepals, petals, and stamens.** Sepal tips rounded. Nectar disc lobes broader than long, alternate with stamens. Petals deciduous or ± persist on fruits.

FRUITS AND SEEDS: Capsules small, often less than 5 mm long, open by 3 valves to release numerous minute seeds. Seeds ± cylindrical, ± 0.1–0.2 mm long, with a tuft of long hairs at the apex. Athel tamarisk does not appear to produce seeds in North America, which may account for its reduced invasiveness.

HABITAT: River, lake, and pond margins, washes, roadsides, ditches, flats, sand dunes, and desert springs. Grows well in neutral and alkaline soil but tolerates salinity and acidity. Mature plants survive desert heat, below freezing temperatures, periodic flooding, drought, and burning.

DISTRIBUTION:

Smallflower tamarisk: All western states, except Wyoming. More prevalent in Northern California, and is found in the southern North Coast Ranges, southern Sierra Nevada foothills, eastern Sierra Nevada, Tehachapi Mountains, Central Valley, San Francisco Bay region, eastern South Coast Ranges, South Coast, and deserts, to 800 m. Many southern and eastern states.

Saltcedar: Utah, Colorado, New Mexico, Arizona, Nevada, central Washington, and California in the southern Klamath Ranges (Whiskeytown area), Central Valley, eastern Sierra Nevada, Tehachapi Mountains, western Transverse Ranges, South Coast, and deserts, to 2100 m. Central United States, some southern states. Mexico (Baja California).

Athel tamarisk: Utah, Arizona, Nevada, and California in the Sacramento and San Joaquin Valley, eastern South Coast, deserts, to 200 m. Texas.

PROPAGATION AND PHENOLOGY: Reproduce by seed and sometimes vegetatively from root sprouts and stem fragments. Seeds disperse primarily with wind and water. Germination occurs shortly after seed dispersal in spring through summer.

Seeds lack a dormancy period, and most germinate within 24 hours after imbibing water. Salinity does not inhibit germination. Seed viability is typically ± 5 weeks during hot summer months, but seeds that mature during late summer may survive winter and germinate the following spring. One mature plant can produce up to 500,000 seeds per year. Robust seedlings may flower at the end of the first year's growth. However, seedling survival is typically low. Seedling roots develop slowly and cannot tolerate dry conditions for even 1 day, and water currents can wash seedlings away. Seedlings often survive submergence in still water for a few weeks. Plants that are burned or cut down usually develop new shoots from adventitious buds on the lateral roots. Stem fragments can produce roots when buried in a moist substrate, as might occur after a flooding event. Individual trees can live 75–100 years or more.

Comparison of foliage of Athel tamarisk (*Tamarix aphylla*) (left) and saltcedar (*Tamarix ramosissima*) (right).   J. M. DiTomaso

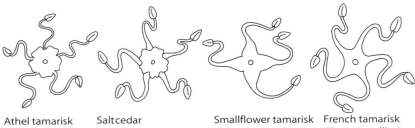

| Athel tamarisk (*Tamarix aphylla*) | Saltcedar (*Tamarix ramosissima*) (*T. chinensis* very similar) Male flower showing nectar disc (without petals). After Baum 1978. | Smallflower tamarisk (*Tamarix parviflora*) | French tamarisk (*Tamarix gallica*) |

MANAGEMENT FAVORING OR DISCOURAGING SURVIVAL: Plants cut or burned to the ground typically regenerate from the roots. Manually removing or killing the root system with chemical treatment is required to effectively control infestations. After treatment or removal of mature plants, seedlings must be removed during the first year to prevent re-infestation. Seedlings and small plants are easily hand-pulled when growing in sandy soils. Managing the hydrology of an area to maintain natural water regimes with periodic flooding can inhibit establishment and dominance of *Tamarix* species, and favor natives.

SIMILAR SPECIES: French tamarisk (*Tamarix gallica* L.) [TAAGA] [CDFA list: C, CalEPPC: A-1] and **Chinese tamarisk** (*Tamarix chinensis* Lour.) [TAACH] [CDFA list: C, CalEPPC: A-1] have leaves that resemble those of saltcedar and **floral parts mostly in 5's**. Separating these species is difficult. Unlike saltcedar, French tamarisk has **nectar disc lobes that are fused and continuous with the stamen bases**, such that the **stamen bases appear broadened** and **starfishlike**. In addition, **petals are deciduous from fruits**. French tamarisk inhabits washes, flats, and roadsides in New Mexico and California in the southern North Coast Ranges, San Joaquin Valley, San Francisco Bay region, South Coast, and northern Mojave Desert (Death Valley), to 300 m. Introduced from southern Europe. Chinese tamarisk is distinguished from saltcedar by having **oblong to linear-lanceolate leaves** and **all sepals with entire margins**. Some botanists believe Chinese tamarisk may be a variety of, or the same species as, saltcedar. Chinese tamarisk inhabits canyons, river margins, and roadsides in Oregon, Montana, Wyoming, Colorado, Utah, New Mexico, Arizona, Nevada, and California on the South Coast and deserts, to 200 m. Introduced from Asia.

Athel tamarisk (*Tamarix aphylla*) flowers.   J. M. DiTomaso

Common cattail (*Typha latifolia* L.) [TYHLA]

SYNONYMS: Broadleaf cattail; broad-leaved cattail

GENERAL INFORMATION: Coarse emergent perennial to 3 m tall, with stout **creeping rhizomes**. Plants typically develop dense colonies in shallow water to 0.5 m deep but are sometimes terrestrial on mud. Common cattail is a widespread native of Eurasia, North Africa, and North America, with many variable biotypes. In natural areas it is usually not considered a weed. Plants prevent erosion of shorelines, help remove excessive quantities of nutrients from water, and are a valuable source of food and shelter for wildlife. However, common cattail can be problematic in irrigation ditches, canals, rice fields, and other controlled aquatic systems. The pollen is a common allergen. Young shoots, rhizomes, pollen, and seeds are edible. Flour produced from the rhizomes is as nutritious as rice or corn flour. Leaves are a source of soft fiber that can be used to make paper, rope, baskets, and other items. Seeds contain oil that is similar in quality to linseed oil. All plant parts have been used medicinally.

Common cattail (*Typha latifolia*) infestation along an irrigation canal.

J. M. DiTomaso

378

SEEDLING: Cotyledon linear, threadlike, ± 1 cm long, usually strongly curved, often with the yellowish brown seed coat (testa) remaining on the tip. First 2–4 leaves linear, glabrous, ± 0.5–1.5 cm long, with a single midvein and distinct cross-veins. Subsequent few leaves ribbonlike, floating.

MATURE PLANT: Glabrous. Stems erect, unbranched, rigid, solid. Leaves alternate, mostly near stem base, linear, sheathing at the base, sheaths open. Blades light green, thick, ± spongy, **distal portion flat**, 1–2.5 cm wide, to 120 cm long, **tapered to the sheath or shoulderlike** (truncate).

ROOTS AND UNDERGROUND STRUCTURES: Rhizomes tough, creeping, branched, white, 1–3 cm or more in diameter at the base, to 70 cm long, with fibrous scale leaves. Tips of rhizomes terminate in a leafy shoot. Roots from rhizomes fibrous, shallow.

FLOWERS: May–August. Spikes usually taller than leaves, densely covered with numerous tiny male and female unisexual flowers (monoecious), with male flowers in the upper portion and female flowers in the lower portion. Male and female flowers are **usually contiguous**, but sometimes there is a bare section up to 8 cm long. Female portions of spikes dark greenish brown to red-brown. Male flowers reddish to black-brown, consist of 2–7 deciduous stamens and tiny **color-less hairlike bracts** (bracteoles). Pollen is shed in clusters of 4 grains (tetrads). Female flowers **dark brown**, **lack tiny bracts**, consist of 1 ovary on a slender hairy stalk **1.5–3 mm long**, with a persistent **broadly lanceolate stigma** at the apex. Wind-pollinated. Self-compatible.

FRUITS AND SEEDS: Spikes ± 2.8–3.6 cm **wide** in fruit. Fruits achene- or follicle-

Common cattail (*Typha latifolia*) infestation in a rice field.   J. K. CLARK

like, minute, football-shaped, thin-walled, with a persistent stigma and hairy stalk at the base. Fruits contain 1 seed and eventually split open in water. Seeds yellowish brown, ellipsoid, blunt at 1 end, ± 1.5 mm long, with coat striated, scaly, or covered with minute papillae.

POSTSENESCENCE CHARACTERISTICS: The stem crown and associated rhizome typically die after flowering. Dead stems and flower spikes often persist through winter.

HABITAT: Marshes, ponds, lake margins, estuaries, wet meadows, irrigation channels, and rice fields in substrates that remain wet through most of the growing season. Tolerates acidic, alkaline, and slightly saline conditions.

DISTRIBUTION: All western states. Throughout California to 2000 m. Nearly worldwide in temperate to tropical climates.

PROPAGATION AND PHENOLOGY: Reproduces by seed but spreads mainly vegetatively from rhizomes. Plants produce abundant fruits. Fruits fall near the parent plant or disperse to greater distances with wind, water, soil movement, human activities, and by clinging with mud to the feet, fur, or feathers of animals. Seeds can germinate at maturity if adequate moisture is available and other conditions are favorable. Rupturing of the seed coat usually stimulates germination, but germination of intact seeds of some biotypes appears to require warmth, a long

Mature common cattail (*Typha latifolia*) inflorescence.   J. M. DiTomaso

Immature common cattail (*Typha latifolia*) inflorescence.   J. M. DiTomaso

Common cattail (*Typha latifolia*) rhizome.   J. M. DiTomaso

Common cattail (*Typha latifolia*) seedling.   J. K. Clark

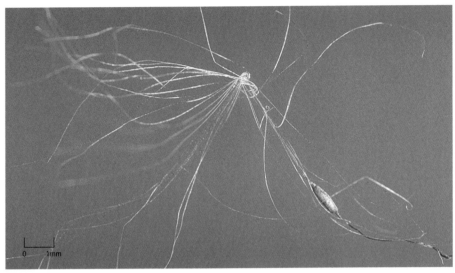

Common cattail *(Typha latifolia)* seed.   J. K. Clark

Narrowleaf cattail *(Typha angustifolia)* inflorescence with gap
between male and female flower clusters.   J. M. DiTomaso

Narrowleaf cattail (*Typha angustifolia*) sheath with lobes at junction with blade.

J. M. DiTomaso

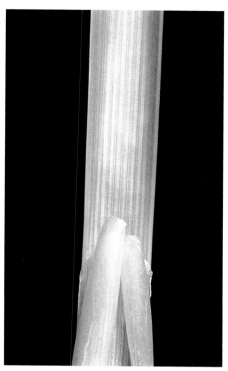

Narrowleaf cattail (*Typha angustifolia*) sheath lacking obvious dark glandular dots on inside surface.

J. M. DiTomaso

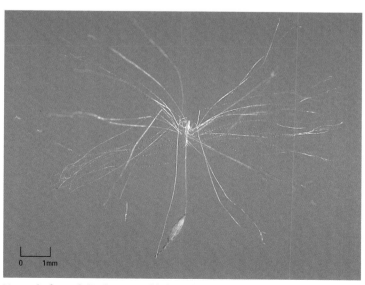

Narrowleaf cattail (*Typha angustifolia*) seed.

J. K. Clark

light period, and reduced levels of oxygen, or nitrogen in combination with fluctuating temperature. Seeds germinate primarily in late spring. Most seedlings emerge from the substrate surface in water to 35 cm deep, but some may emerge from water up to ± 75 cm deep. Seedling establishment can be inhibited by wave action and sedimentation. Plants usually do not flower the first year. Local reproduction is primarily vegetative from rhizomes. Most rhizomes survive for less than 3 years. Rhizome fragments frequently disperse with tillage, water, or substrate movement and develop into new plants.

MANAGEMENT FAVORING OR DISCOURAGING SURVIVAL: Repeated mowing or lowering water levels for mechanical removal, exposure to freezing in cold-winter areas, or burning followed by deep flooding in spring can help control unwanted stands. Plants cut below the water surface cannot respire, and most die within ± 2 weeks. Cutting at the end of flowering is most effective since rhizome carbohydrate levels are low and few seeds are mature.

SIMILAR SPECIES: Narrowleaf cattail (*Typha angustifolia* L.) [TYHAN] and southern cattail (*Typha domingensis* Pers.) [TYHDO] are widespread, although less common, **native perennials** closely related to common cattail. Unlike common cattail, narrowleaf and southern cattail have leaves that are **convex on the back**, spikes that typically have a **bare section 1–8 cm long separating male and female flowers**, female flowers on stalks ± 5 mm long with **minute bracts** and a

Southern cattail (*Typha domingensis*) inflorescence with gap between male and female flower clusters.   J. M. DiTomaso

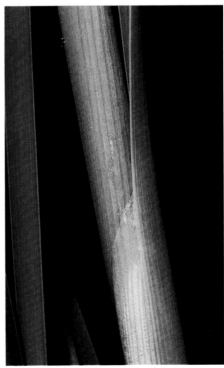

Southern cattail (*Typha domingensis*) sheath lacking lobes at junction with blade.
J. M. DiTomaso

deciduous linear stigma, and some pollen grains shed singly (monads). In addition, narrowleaf cattail has female flowers with **rounded dark brown bracts**, rhizomes that usually survive for more than 3 years, and **dark green leaves** that are typically **longer than female portions of spikes** and are up to **1 cm wide** with earlike lobes (auricles) at the collar region. Southern cattail has **yellow to orange-brown female portions of spikes**, female flowers with **acute, yellow to orange-brown bracts**, and **bases of blades facing stem and inner side of sheaths dotted with glands**. Narrowleaf and southern cattail often grow in water deeper than 0.5 m and tolerate a higher degree of salinity than common cattail. Common cattail rhizomes typically grow more vigorously and produce more

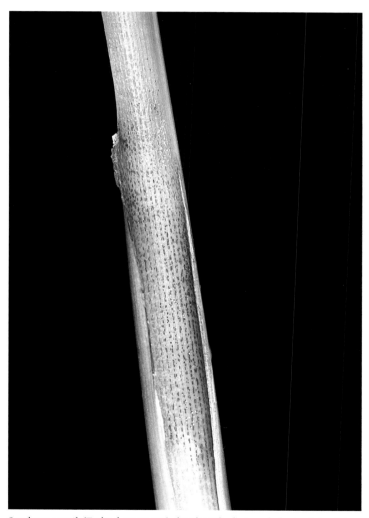

Southern cattail (*Typha domingensis*) sheath with obvious dark glandular dots on inside surface.   J. M. DiTomaso

shoots than those of narrowleaf cattail. Narrowleaf cattail occurs in Oregon, western and central Washington, Montana, Wyoming, Colorado, New Mexico, Nevada, and California in the Central Valley, Central Coast, San Francisco Bay region, South Coast, and Lake Tahoe area of the Sierra Nevada, to 2000 m. Southern cattail occurs in Oregon, Wyoming, Utah, Colorado, New Mexico, Arizona, Nevada, and California in the western North Coast Ranges, North Coast, Central Valley, central-western region, southwestern region, deserts, and Great Basin, to 1500 m. It is encroaching in salt marsh areas in San Diego County. All three species appear to hybridize in California. Hybrids between common and narrowleaf cattail have been called *Typha* × *glauca* Godron (blue cattail) [TYHGL].

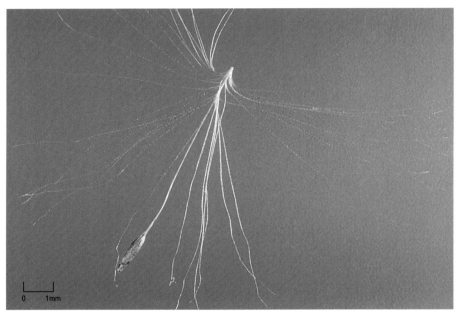

Southern cattail (*Typha domingensis*) seed.   J. K. CLARK

Tall vervain (*Verbena bonariensis* L.) [VEBBO]

Seashore vervain (*Verbena litoralis* Kunth) [VEBLI]

NOXIOUS WEED LISTS:

Tall and seashore vervain: CalEPPC: Need More Information

SYNONYMS:

Tall vervain: Argentine vervain; blue vervain; cluster-flowered verbena; purple-top vervain

Seashore vervain: *Verbena bonariensis* L. var. *litoralis* (Kunth) Hook.; *Verbena brasiliensis* Vell.; *Verbena caracasana* Kunth; *Verbena hansenii* Greene; a few others; often incorrectly spelled *Verbena littoralis*

GENERAL INFORMATION: Erect summer annuals, biennials, or short-lived perennials to ± 1.5 m tall, with opposite leaves and short terminal spikes of purple flowers. Both species often inhabit riparian areas but are also found in dry or seasonally moist places. Tall vervain is introduced from South America. Seashore vervain is introduced from Central and South America.

Tall vervain (*Verbena bonariensis*) along an irrigation canal.
J. M. DITOMASO

SEEDLING:

Tall vervain: Cotyledons oval, covered with short glandular hairs. First leaves opposite, ovate, covered with short hairs, darker green below, margins coarsely toothed.

Seashore vervain: Very similar to tall vervain.

MATURE PLANT: Stems erect, few or single, **4-angled or square**, glabrous or sparsely covered with short stiff hairs. Leaves **opposite**, elliptic to lanceolate, 3–15 cm long, sparsely covered with short stiff hairs.

Tall vervain (*Verbena bonariensis*) inflorescence.   J. M. DiTomaso

Tall vervain (*Verbena bonariensis*) stem with opposite leaves clasping stem at base.   J. M. DiTomaso

Tall vervain: Leaf margins coarsely toothed. **Leaf bases sessile, truncate to weakly lobed, ± clasping stem.**

Seashore vervain: Leaf margins irregularly toothed. **Leaf bases tapered, nearly sessile to short-stalked.** Stalk ± winged.

ROOTS AND UNDERGROUND STRUCTURES: Taprooted.

FLOWERS: Spikes in terminal clusters, initially short, becoming elongated in fruit. Calyx (sepals as a unit) tubular, 5-angled, **3–4 mm long, 5-toothed.** Corollas

Tall vervain (*Verbena bonariensis*) seedling.   J. M. DiTomaso

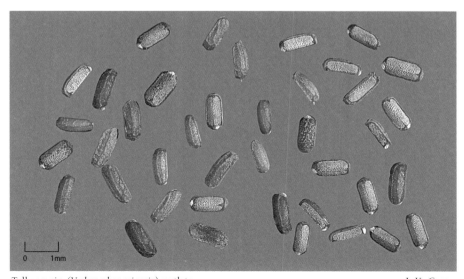

Tall vervain (*Verbena bonariensis*) nutlets.   J. K. Clark

(petals as a unit) typically purple (sometimes white in **tall vervain**), **5-lobed, ± radial, 4–6 mm long, to 5 mm wide**. Stamens 4. Ovary superior, 4-lobed. Bract below each flower **3–3.5 mm long**, usually **shorter than the calyx above**.

Tall vervain: Mostly June–October. Spikes dense, mostly **5–6 mm wide**.

Seashore vervain: Nearly year-round in some places. Spikes dense to open in the lower portion, mostly **3–4 mm wide**.

FRUITS AND SEEDS: Fruits consist of 4 nutlets that are concealed by the calyx. Each nutlet is equivalent to 1 seed. Nutlets oblong, ± truncate at the ends, 1–1.5 mm long, with white papillose bumps on the inner surface.

Tall vervain: Spikes 1.5–12.5 cm long.

Seashore vervain: Spikes 3–7 cm long.

HABITAT: Riparian areas, ditches, irrigation canals, roadsides, fields (including margins and levees of rice fields), and other disturbed places. These species typically inhabit disturbed wet sites but can also be found in dry places.

DISTRIBUTION: Both species appear to be expanding range.

Seashore vervain (*Verbena litoralis*) adjacent to irrigation canal.   J. M. DiTomaso

Tall vervain: Arizona, Oregon, and California in the Central Valley, and northern San Francisco Bay region, to 200 m. Southern United States, parts of northeastern United States.

Seashore vervain: Oregon and California at the southern North Coast, Central Coast, Central Valley, and northern and central Sierra Nevada foothills, to 200 m. Southern United States.

PROPAGATION AND PHENOLOGY: Reproduce by seed. The biology of these species is poorly understood.

Seashore vervain (*Verbena litoralis*) inflorescence.   J. M. DiTomaso

Seashore vervain (*Verbena litoralis*) stem with opposite leaves tapered at base.   J. M. DiTomaso

SIMILAR SPECIES: Some native *Verbena* species, including a rare one in the central Sierra Nevada foothills (Tuolumne Co.) of California, often grow in wet places and may be confused with tall vervain and seashore vervain. Native *Verbena* species are a desirable component of natural riparian ecosystems. Most native *Verbena* species are distinguished by having at least one of the following characteristics: **leaves lobed or dissected, middle and lower leaves with stalks 1– 2.5 cm long, fruiting spikes with fruits widely spaced and not overlapping in the lower portion of the spike, or flower bracts that are longer than the calyx.**

Seashore vervain (*Verbena litoralis*) seedling.　　　　　　　J. M. DiTomaso

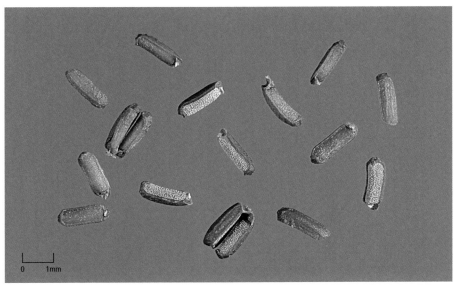

Seashore vervain (*Verbena litoralis*) nutlets.　　　　　　　J. K. Clark

Appendix: Federally Listed Noxious Weeds in Aquatic Habitats

Species	Common name	Family	General information
Alternanthera sessilis (L.) R. Br. ex DC.	sessile joy-weed [ALRSE]	Amaranthaceae	Prefers wet conditions. A serious weed of upland and paddy rice in other parts of the world. A weed of some aquatic systems in the United States. Distribution limited to the far southern United States and an area along the East Coast; could occur in the Monongahela National Forest. Reported in Alabama, Florida, Georgia, Hawaii, Louisiana, and Maryland. Browsed by cattle and deer in the far southern United States.
Azolla pinnata R. Br.	pinnate mos-quitofern [AZOPI]	Azollaceae	Floating annual, nonflowering plant, mat forming. Used in Asian countries as a nitrogen-fixer with rice. Distribution in the United States limited to the far south.
Eichhornia azurea (Sw.) Kunth	anchored waterhyacinth [EICAZ]	Pontederiaceae	Rhizomatous aquatic plants with floating or submerged leaves. Flowers dimorphic. A weed in South America and a major weed in India. In the United States, reported in Florida and Puerto Rico. Similar to the more common *E. crassipes* (waterhyacinth).
Heracleum mantegazzianum Sommier & Levier	giant hog-weed [HERMZ]	Apiaceae	A cultivated ornamental, native to the Caucasus, now naturalized in Europe. See Giant Hogweed entry (page 156) for more information.
Hydrilla verticillata (L.f.) Royle	hydrilla [HYLLI]	Hydrocharitaceae	See Hydrilla entry (page 96) for more information.
Hygrophila polysperma (Roxb.) T. Anderson	Indian hygrophila or Miramar weed [HYGPO]	Acanthaceae	Native to southeast Asia, *H. polysperma* is used as a cultivated ornamental or aquaria in the United States. The stems are upright, submerged or emergent, with opposite leaves. All portions of the plants, even leaves, can produce new plants when separated. The plant is particularly troublesome in Florida, where it may be found in flood-control channels, lakes, and rivers. The sale of this plant is prohibited in Florida. Also found in northern Texas and Virginia.
Ipomoea aquatica Forsk.	swamp morn-ingglory or water-spinach [IPOAQ]	Convolvulaceae	Cultivated in the Old World tropics as human and animal food. A perennial aquatic weed that may cover water surfaces in lakes or ditches, interfering with fisheries and impeding water flow. Produces a large white morningglory-like flower. Distribution includes an infestation on the East Coast, possibly extending to the Monongahela National Forest. Does not tolerate frost or snow and grows poorly when cold.
Ischaemum rugosum Salisb.	saramolla-grass or murainograss [ISCRU]	Poaceae	An aggressive annual grass of both wet and dry habitats. A serious weed in rice fields; sometimes used as famine food. A serious to occasional weed in many tropical parts of the world, including southeast Asia, Brazil, Madagascar, Jamaica, and Trinidad. Not yet introduced in North America.
Lagarosiphon major (Ridley) Moss	African elodea or oxygen weed	Hydrocharitaceae	Submerged aquatic plant with elongated, branched stems and crowded, serrate leaves. A cultivated ornamental for aquaria, but apparently not distributed in the United States. A principal weed in New Zealand.

Federally Listed Noxious Weeds in Aquatic Habitats, cont.

Species	Common name	Family	General information
Leptochloa chinensis (L.) Nees	Chinese sprangletop [LEFCH]	Poaceae	An annual grass. A weed in irrigated channels and cultivated bean fields. A serious weed in southeast Asia, New Guinea, and southeast Africa. Not known in North America.
Limnophila sessiliflora (Vahl) Blume	limnophila [LIOSE]	Scrophulariaceae	Perennial herb with dissected leaves; terresrial or sometimes aquatic; common in inundated ditches, flooded rice paddies, and wet areas along rivers. A common weed in India, Japan, and elsewhere in southeast Asia. In the United States, reported in Florida, Georgia, and Texas. A hybrid with this species and *L. indica* has been found in rice irrigation ditches in California (*L. ×ludoviciana*). See the Coontail entry (page 78) for more information.
Melaleuca quinquen-ervia (Cav.) S.T. Blake [= *M. leuca-dendra* (L.) L.]	melaleuca [MLAQU]	Myrtaceae	Cultivated tree used for timber and medicinal oil. In New Caledonia, the trees form almost pure stands after the native vegetation is destroyed by fire. A principal weed in Australia. In the United States, reported as a weed in Florida, Hawaii, Louisiana, and Puerto Rico.
Monochoria hastata (L.) Solms-Laub.	arrowleaved monochoria [MOOHA]	Pontederiaceae	A serious weed in southeast Asia. Not known in North America.
Monochoria vaginalis (Burm. f.) Kunth	monochoria [MOOVA]	Pontederiaceae	A perennial weed with decumbent stems, cordate leaves, and bright blue flowers. A serious weed of rice paddies in much of southeast Asia; a principal weed in Hawaii. In the United States, reported in California and Hawaii. See the Monochoria entry (page 342) for more information.
Oryza longistami-nata A. Chev. & Roehr.	red rice	Poaceae	A weed of rice fields. West African progenitor of *O. glabberrima* (red rice). Not known in North America.
Oryza punc-tata Kotschy ex Steudel	red rice	Poaceae	Annual tufted grass. A weed of rice fields in tropical Africa. Not known in North America.
Oryza rufi-pogon Griff.	red rice	Poaceae	Perennial, tufted grass. A weed of rice fields in southeast Asia. Progenitor wild species of *O. sativa*. In the United States, reported in California and Florida. Probably eradicated in California. Some taxonomists believe that true *O. rufipogon* was never in California, and what was thought to be *O. rufipogon* was actually a hybrid between *O. rufipogon* and a rice cultivar.
Ottelia alismoides (L.) Pers.	duck-lettuce	Hydrocharitaceae	Aquatic herb, rooted submerged in water to 60 cm deep, to 35 cm tall. In rice paddies, ditches, fields, swamps, small ponds, open places, and waterholes. A weed in southeast Asia, Australia, Egypt, Honduras, and Lake Charles, Louisiana. In the United States, reported in California, Louisiana, and Texas.

Federally Listed Noxious Weeds in Aquatic Habitats, cont.

Species	Common name	Family	General information
Paspalum scrobicula-tum L. [= *P. orbiculare* Forst.]	ricegrass pas-palum [PASOR]	Poaceae	Perennial grass, culms loosely tufted. In moist places, old fields, pastures where grazed by cattle, rice marshes, and roadsides. South American origin, introduced agricultural grass in tropical areas of southeast Asia, Africa, and Australia. In the United States, reported in Florida, Hawaii, Texas, Maryland, and New Jersey.
Pennisetum macrourum Trin.	African feathergrass	Poaceae	Perennial grass with erect stems from a rhizome. Swampy places and along streams and damp cultivated areas. South Africa, Australia. In the United States, reported in California and Hawaii.
Rubus fruti-cosus L.	European blackberry [RUBFR]	Rosaceae	Shrub with prickles, compound leaves, and edible compound fruits. The name *Rubus fruticosus* L. is no longer accepted as a single species. Current treatments consider it an aggregate of related species. *Rubus discolor* Weihe & Nees is considered a member of this group. See the Himalaya blackberry entry (page 348) for more information.
Rubus moluccanus L.	Molucca raspberry [RUBMO]	Rosaceae	Forests, especially regrowth, and in thickets along streams. A principal weed in Mauritius, Hawaii, Madagascar; also in Australia, Fiji, and India. Not known in North America.
Sagittaria sagittifolia L.	arrowhead [SAGSA]	Alismataceae	A nuisance in irrigation systems and drains. Produces an attractive inflorescence with male and female flowers. Alters its morphology depending on environment. Mostly occurs in quiet, shallow waters along river banks and in bays. Flooding disperses the stolons. Europe, southeast Asia, Hawaii, Argentina, Australia, and Mexico.
Salvinia biloba Raddi	lobed salvinia	Salviniaceae	Aquatic floating fern with water-repellent hairs on upper surface and sporocarps on submerged modified leaves. Coastal areas of Eastern Brazil. Not known in North America.
Salvinia her-zogii de la Sota	Herzog salvinia	Salviniaceae	Aquatic floating fern with water-repellent hairs on upper surface and sporocarps on submerged modified leaves. Uruguay, northeastern Argentina, southern Brazil, Paraguay. Not known in North America.
Salvinia molesta D. Mitchell	giant salvinia [SAVMO]	Salviniaceae	A sterile species and a weed of waterways in Africa, where it was probably introduced as a cultivated ornamental. Also in southeast Brazil, Sri Lanka, India, South Africa, North America, and Australia. See the Salvinia entry (page 57) for more information.
Sparganium erectum L.	branched burreed [SPGER]	Sparganiaceae	Erect perennial aquatic herb. Occurs on the margins of ponds, lakes, and streams, in ditches, and swamps and along shores. Nearly throughout Europe to Russia, Tyrol, and Caucasus. Often confused with *Sparganium simplex*. Not known in North America, although at least one reference has applied this name to native North American plants.

Glossary

achene. A single-seeded dry fruit that does not open when mature (fig. 10).

acuminate. Leaf tip that tapers to a point; the sides are concave and tip is extended (fig. 2).

acute. Leaf tip that tapers to a point but is less tapering than acuminate; the angle of the sides is less than 90° (fig. 2).

adventitious. Tissue that is not growing in the typical location on the plant, such as roots growing from stem nodes or leaf tissues.

after-rippening. A period of dormancy in which seed germination does not occur under ideal conditions. Seeds may require specific conditions for germination to occur or embryo to develop. Dormancy can vary from weeks to years.

alkaline. Basic conditions (high pH); a substance that neutralizes an acid.

allelopathy. Release of a substance by a plant that typically inhibits (or, occasionally, stimulates) the germination or growth of another plant. Release can be through glands, residue, root exudate, or volatilization.

allergen. An agent or chemical capable of inducing an allergic response.

allopolyploid. *See* amphidiploid.

alternate. Attachment of leaves to the stem in which one leaf is attached to each stem node (fig. 6).

ament. *See* **catkin.**

amphidiploid. Duplication of chromosome number resulting from hybridization of two species. Also referred to as **allopolyploid.**

annual. Plant whose life cycle is completed within a single year.

anoxic. Oxygen-depleted.

anther. Pollen-bearing portion of a stamen (figs. 9, 10, and 12).

antheridia. Plant structure that produces male gametes.

apex. Upper or terminal end part of a tissue, as in the tip of a leaf, stem, or root.

apiculate. Short, flexible, abruptly ending leaf tip (fig. 2).

apomictic. Plant or organism that produces seeds without fertilization or genetic exchange with another plant.

apomixis. Process by which seeds are produced without fertilization or genetic exchange with another plant.

appressed. Hairs on a plant that lie flat against the stem or leaf.

aril. An appendage at or near the point of attachment (hilium) of the seed.

attenuate. Long, gradual taper at the tip (apex) or base of a leaf (fig. 2).

auricle. An ear-shaped appendage usually associated with the collar region of grasses (fig. 11) or the sheath of some submerged aquatic plants.

awn. A slender bristle attached to a tissue; usually refers to grass florets, primarily lemmas and glumes.

axil. The junction between the stem and the upper leaf base.

axillary bud. A bud originating in a leaf axil.

backcrossing. Mating of a hybrid with one of the original parent lines.

banner. Uppermost petal of a flower in the Fabaceae (pea or bean family).

beak. A prominent sterile projection at the tip of a fruit.

biennial. Herbaceous plant whose life cycle is completed within two years. In the first year, plants germinate and typically exist as basal rosettes. In the second year, plants bolt, flower, and die.

bilateral. Two-sided; an irregular-shaped flower that can be divided into two equal parts with one dissection.

biotype. A distinct genotype of a species, such as a herbicide-resistant population of a weed.

bipinnate. Twice pinnate; leaves that are branched twice with leaflets on the second branch (fig. 5).

bisexual. Flower that has both male and female parts.

blade. Flattened, expanded portion of a leaf (fig. 11).

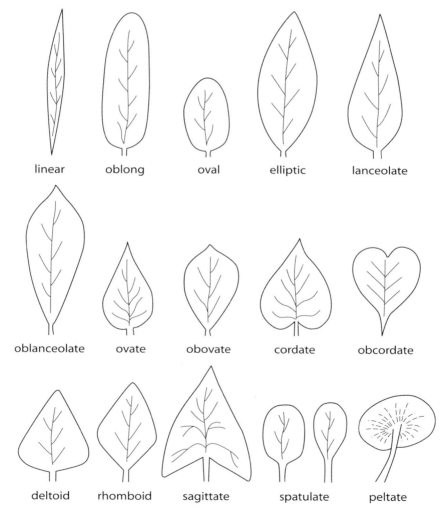

Figure 1. Simple leaf shapes.

bolting. Producing erect, elongated flowering stems from a basal rosette of leaves, usually associated with winter annual or biennials.

brackish. Salty water, but with salt concentrations less than that of sea water.

bract. A very reduced leaflike structure, usually associated with the base of a flower or inflorescence.

bracteole. *See* bractlet.

bractlet. A secondary bract that is often associated with a subunit of a compound inflorescence. Usually smaller than a bract. Also referred to as a **bracteole.**

C3. Photosynthetic pathway of a plant that initially fixes carbon dioxide into a 3-carbon chain (3-PGA). C3 plants are typically not as well adapted to high heat and low moisture as C4 plants.

C4. Photosynthetic pathway of a plant that initially fixes carbon dioxide into a 4-carbon chain (oxaloacetic acid). C4 plants are typically better adapted to high heat and low moisture than C3 plants.

calyx. Sepals collectively.

capsule. A dry fruit structure that opens by means of slits, lids, pores, or teeth to release its seeds.

carbohydrate. Starch or sugars within a plant.

carpel. Female structure of a flower that bears the ovules.

caryopsis. A single-seeded fruit that does not open when mature (indehiscent); typically used to describe the fruits of grasses.

catkin. A pendant cluster of flowers that is typically unisexual, lacking petals, and associated with a small bract at the base of each flower. Also referred to as an **ament.**

chaff (chaffy bracts). Small thin, dry scales or bristles on the receptacle of the flower head of many members of the Asteraceae (sunflower family).

chloroplast. A plastid that contains chlorophyll and functions primarily in photosynthesis.

ciliate. Having a fringe of hairs on the margin of a plant structure.

clasping. Having a lower section of a leaf that is partly or entirely surrounding the stem.

collar. Outer side of a grass leaf that marks the junction between the blade and the sheath (fig. 11).

composite. A member of the Asteraceae (sunflower family); flower structure arranged in dense heads (fig. 10).

compound leaf. A leaf with two or more leaflets (fig. 5).

compressed. Flattened, often in reference to the stem (culm) of a grass.

concave. Hollow, curved, or depressed.

conical. Cone-shaped.

convex. Curved or rounded on the surface.

cordate. Heart-shaped (figs. 1 and 3).

corm. Short, thick underground vertical stem surrounded by dry papery leaf bases.

corolla. Petals collectively, either separate or fused (fig. 10).

corymb. A flat-topped or rounded inflorescence that is unbranched or branched (compound corymb) with pedicels of varying lengths (fig. 8).

cotyledon. Primary leaf or leaves of the embryo.

crenate. Leaf margin with shallow, rounded teeth (fig. 4).

culm. Stem of a grass (fig. 11).

cuneate. Wedge-shaped (fig. 3).

cuspidate. Sharp, abruptly pointed tip of a leaf (fig. 2).

cyanobacterium. Photosynthetic bacterium that lives in water.

cyme. A flat-topped or convex inflorescence type in which the flowers bloom from the center outward (fig. 8).

deciduous. Falling off, usually in reference to flower parts or leaves that fall off in the fall.

decumbent. Stems that lie prostrate on the ground but with the tip pointed upward.

decussate. Opposite leaves (two leaves per node) attached at right angle to a pair of opposite leaves at adjacent nodes. Leaves are in four rows along stem (fig. 6).

deltoid. Equilaterally triangular (fig. 1).

dessication. Dried thoroughly, usually due to lack of moisture.

dioecious. Having male and female flowers on separate plants.

disk flower. Tubular flowers associated with the flower heads of many species in the Asteraceae (sunflower family) (fig. 10).

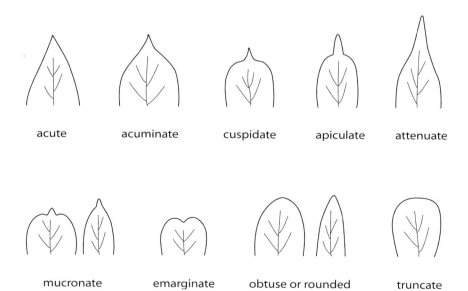

acute   acuminate   cuspidate   apiculate   attenuate

mucronate   emarginate   obtuse or rounded   truncate

Figure 2. Leaf tips.

dissected. Leaves irregularly, sharply, or deeply cut but not compound (fig. 4).

dormancy. Inactive state; otherwise viable seeds that do not germinate.

drupe. A fleshy fruit that contains a single seed in a stony endocarp.

drupelet. A small drupe; usually refers to a cluster of drupelets that form a fruiting structure.

electrophoretic. A technique where charged molecules or particles are separated by differential migration through a dispersion medium.

elliptic. Football-shaped; a flattened circle more than twice as long as wide (fig. 1).

emarginate. Having a shallow notch at the tip of a leaf (fig. 2).

embryo. Developing plant within a seed.

endocarp. Inner layer of the walls of the ovary (pericarp).

entire. Having leaves with smooth margins (lacking teeth) (fig. 4).

ephemeral. Short-lived.

erose. Having a margin with a gnawed appearance.

ethylene. Plant growth regulator associated with flower withering, fruit ripening, and other plant responses.

eutrophic. Water body with a minimum amount of dissolved oxygen and high levels of organic matter.

evapotranspiration. Combined water loss from evaporation from soil and transpiration from the plant.

evergreen. Having leaves that remain green on plant year-round; not deciduous.

fertilization. In plants, combining the chromosomes of the ovule with the pollen cell to form a viable seed.

filament. Fine threadlike portion of the stamen below the anther (fig. 9).

filiform. Very thin or threadlike.

flagella. Long, slender, whiplike structure that aids in the locomotion of some bacteria, algae, protozoans, choanocytes, and reproductive cells.

floret. Usually the flower (lemma and palea) of a grass (fig. 12). The combination of florets and glumes is a **spikelet**. Also used to describe small flowers in the Asteraceae (sunflower family).

floricane. Flowering and fruiting shoots of members of the genus *Rubus* (blackberry, raspberry, brambles).

frond. Leaf of a fern or a palm.

fusiform. Widest at the middle and tapering at both ends.

geniculate. Abruptly bent, as in a knee.

glabrous. Lacking hairs (fig. 7).

glandular. Containing glands; often sticky (fig. 7).

glaucous. Having a whitish or bluish green color due to the deposition of waxes.

glume. Sterile bract or bracts (2) at the base of a grass spikelet (fig. 12).

hastate. Leaves arrow-shaped, with the two basal lobes angled away from the long axis (fig. 3).

hemispherical. Half of a sphere.

herbaceous. Plant lacking woody parts. Usually dies to the ground each year; can be an annual or perennial.

heterostyly. With styles of differing lengths or shapes.

hilium. Point of attachment of a seed.

hybridize. Cross-pollination between two different species.

hydathode. A minute, specialized pore in which water is extruded from the surface of uninjured leaves (guttation).

hypanthium. A cuplike elongation or enlargement of the floral structure on which the calyx, corolla, and often stamens are attached (fig. 9).

hypocotyl. Portion of the plant seedling that lies below the cotyledons but above the roots.

hypoxic. Generally referring to sediments with low (but not zero) oxygen levels. Sometimes refers to deep lake waters with very low oxygen or waters in which the abundance of submersed plants reduces oxygen levels, particularly from midnight to early morning.

imbibe. To absorb water; usually in reference to seeds.

indehiscent. Fruit that does not open to release seeds when mature.

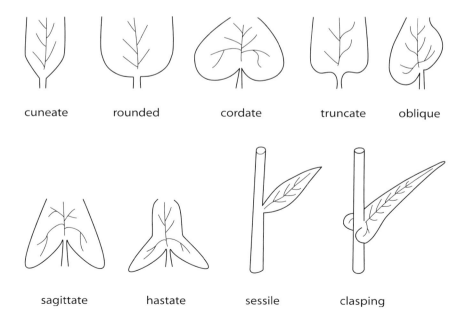

Figure 3. Leaf bases.

inferior ovary. Ovary that is below the attachment of the flower parts (perianth) (fig. 9).

inflorescence. Collected cluster or arrangement of flowers on a plant.

internode. Region of the stem between the nodes.

introgression. Introduction of a gene from one gene complex to another, as in the mixing of the gene pool between two normally separate populations or ecotypes.

involucre. Group of bracts together as a unit and subtending a flower, cluster of flowers (as in the Asteraceae), or fruit (fig. 10).

keel. Prominent ridge in the center of a structure such as the leaf or flower part (i.e., lemma).

lanceolate. Leaf shape that is narrow, widest in the middle, and tapering at both ends. Much longer than wide; narrower than fusiform (fig. 1).

leaflet. A subunit of a compound leaf (fig. 5).

legume. Member of the Fabaceae (pea or bean family). Also refers to the fruit type of this family.

lemma. Larger outer bract of a grass floret (fig. 12).

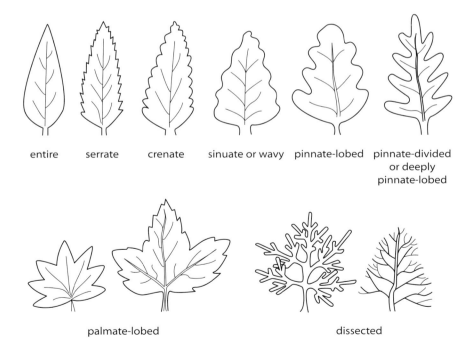

entire   serrate   crenate   sinuate or wavy   pinnate-lobed   pinnate-divided or deeply pinnate-lobed

palmate-lobed   dissected

Figure 4. Leaf margins and lobing.

ligulate flower. Flower type in the Asteraceae (sunflower family). Bilateral, fertile flower with long straplike corolla that is 5-lobed. Only occurs when all flowers in a head are ligulate (fig. 10).

ligule. In grasses, the membranous projection at the inner junction of the blade and sheath (fig. 11). In the Asteraceae (sunflower family), the showy irregularly shaped straplike flowers, also known as ray flowers.

linear. Long, narrow, and of uniform width (fig. 1).

membranous. Thin, soft, and transparent or translucent.

mericarp. Individual one-seeded segment of a schizocarp.

midrib. Central rib of a leaf.

midvein. Central vein of a leaf.

monad. A group of one, such as single pollen grains rather than clusters.

monoecious. Male and female flowers separate but on the same plant.

mucronate. Having a small, short, abrupt tip at the apex of a leaf, leaflet, or bract (fig. 2).

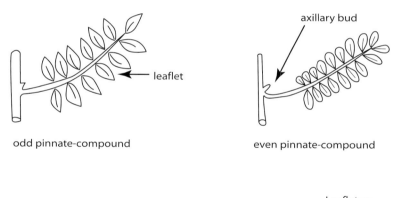

odd pinnate-compound

even pinnate-compound

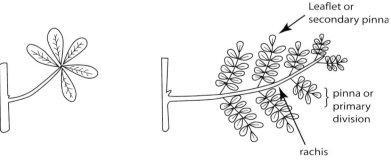

palmate-compound

bipinnate- or twice pinnate-compound

Figure 5. Compound leaves.

mulch. Living or dead plant tissue or synthetic material used to cover the soil. Often used to suppress weed growth by blocking light penetration.

mycorrhiza. A fungus that forms a symbiotic relationship with the roots of most plants. The fungus benefits from carbohydrate production by plants and the plants benefit from increased access to nutrients and moisture through hyphae of the fungus.

nectary. An organ, usually associated with a flower, that secretes nectar.

node. Plant joints where leaves are usually attached (fig. 11).

nutlet. A small nut that consists of a dry, thick-walled indehiscent structure with a single seed.

obcordate. In the shape of an inverted heart (fig. 1).

oblanceolate. Much longer than wide, and tapering at both ends. Similar to lanceolate but widest above the middle (fig. 1).

oblique. Sides unequal; often referring to base of leaf, leaflet, or flowers (fig. 3).

oblong. Much longer than wide; sides parallel and more or less rectangular (fig. 1).

obovate or obovoid. Widest at or above the middle and tapering at the base; egg-shaped (fig. 1).

obtuse. Rounded or blunt at the apex or tip (fig. 2).

ocrea. A papery sheath that encloses the stem at the nodes and is formed from the fusion of two stipules. Typical of many members of the Polygonaceae (buckwheat family).

oogonia. Single-celled structures in algae that produce the female gamete.

oospore. A resting zygote in various algae or fungi.

opposite. Attachment of two leaves across from each other at each node (fig. 6).

outcrossing. Exchange of genes between two individuals of the same species. Also referred to as cross-pollination.

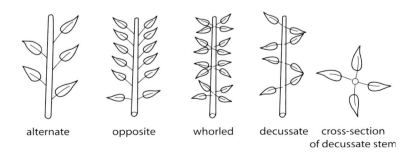

alternate   opposite   whorled   decussate   cross-section
of decussate stem

Figure 6. Leaf arrangement.

oval. Broadest at the middle and equally tapered on both ends; broader than elliptic; length not over twice the width (fig.1).

ovary. Ovule-bearing portion of a pistil; develops into the fruit (figs. 9 and 12).

ovate or ovoid. Widest at or below the middle and tapering at the apex; egg-shaped (fig. 1).

ovule. Structure within the ovary that, after fertilization, will become the seed.

palea. Inner bract of a grass floret that is usually partially or totally enclosed by the lemma (fig. 12).

palmate. Branches, lobes, leaflets, or veins arising from a common point; similar to the palm of a hand (figs. 4 and 5).

panicle. Inflorescence branched more than once with flowers attached at the terminal end of the branchlets; branches can be short and give the inflorescence a spikelike appearance (fig. 8).

papillose or papillate. Having small nipplelike projections on the tissue surface (fig. 7).

pappus. Modified calyx of the flower of species in the Asteraceae (sunflower family) that can take the form of bristles, feathery structures, scales, awns, or a low crown; typically facilitate wind or animal dispersal (fig. 10).

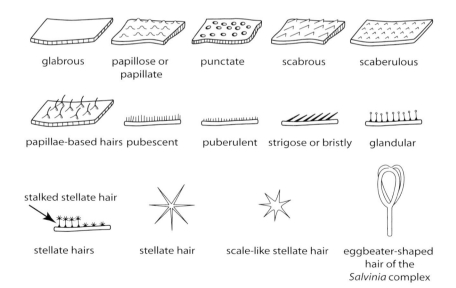

Figure 7. Surface characteristics and some hair types.

pedicel. Stalk of an individual flower (fig. 9).

peduncle. Stalk of a flower cluster, inflorescence, or flower head.

peltate. Having a petiole attached to the center of a leaf blade, much like a shield (fig. 1).

pendant. Drooping or hanging down, as in a fruit, flower, or inflorescence.

perennial. Plant with a life cycle that extends beyond two years.

perianth. The calyx (sepals) and corolla (petals) collectively.

pericarp. Outer wall of the ovary.

persistent. Remaining attached, as in a leaf or fruit.

petal. Individual part of the corolla, usually colored (fig. 9).

petiole. Stalk of a leaf; the area of the leaf below the blade.

pH. An expression of the concentration of hydrogen (H^+)or hydroxyl (OH^-) ions used to measure acidity (pH <7) or alkalinity (pH >7) of a solution.

photosensitizer. A chemical that causes a sensitive reaction, such as a dermatitis or poisoning, in an animal after the contacted area is exposed to light.

photosynthesis. Light-requiring process in the chloroplast of green plants in which carbon dioxide and water are metabolized to form sugar and oxygen.

phyllary. One of many bracts subtending the flower head of species in the Asteraceae (sunflower family). Collectively called an involucre (fig. 10).

pinna. A leaflet or primary division of a pinnate leaf (fig. 5).

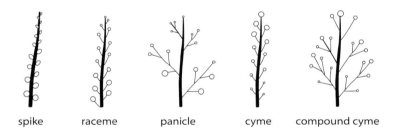

spike raceme panicle cyme compound cyme

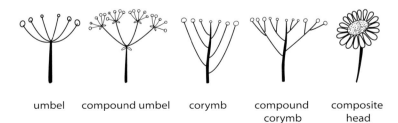

umbel compound umbel corymb compound corymb composite head

Figure 8. Inflorescence types (largest circles represent oldest flowers).

pinnate. Having leaflets arranged on either side of a common axis (figs. 4 and 5).

pistil. Female structure of a flower; includes stigma, style, and ovary (fig. 6).

pistillate. Having a female flower and lacking functional male parts.

plumose. Featherlike; usually refers to the pappus of flowers and achenes in the Asteraceae (sunflower family).

pod. Fruit of species in the Fabaceae (pea or bean family).

pollination. Transfer of pollen from an anther to a stigma.

polyploid. Species or taxa that contain a chromosome number more than twice the haploid (base chromosome number).

prickle. Sharp-pointed structure on a plant that usually originates as an outgrowth of the epidermis (e.g., hairs or rose thorns).

primocane. Nonflowering shoots of members of the genus *Rubus* (blackberry, raspberry, brambles). Usually first-year growth in shoots.

prostrate. Lying flat on the ground.

puberulent. Having hairs that are soft, short, straight, and erect (fig. 7).

pubescent. With hairs (fig. 7).

punctate. Having plant tissue with dots, pits, or depressions on the surface (fig. 7).

pustule. A small pimplelike elevation on the surface of a plant tissue.

pyramidal. Pyramid-shaped.

raceme. Elongated inflorescence with stalked flowers arising along the unbranched central axis (fig. 8).

rachilla. A small secondary axis to a rachis. Usually refers to the axis of a grass spikelet (fig. 12).

rachis. Central or main axis of an inflorescence or pinnately compound leaf (fig. 5).

ray flower. Flower type in the Asteraceae (sunflower family). Bilateral sterile or female flower with long straplike corolla that has up to 3 lobes. Associated with flower heads that also contain disk flowers (fig. 10).

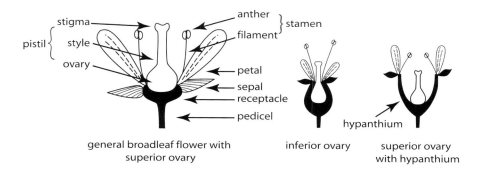

Figure 9. General broadleaf flower structures.

spatulate. Spatula- or spoon-shaped; broader and rounded near the tip and tapered at the base (fig. 1).

spherical. Rounded three-dimensionally, as a globe.

spike. An inflorescence with sessile flowers attached along an unbranched elongated rachis (fig. 8).

spikelet. Inflorescence of a grass or sedge that consists of glumes at the base and one or more sterile or fertile florets attached along an unbranched rachilla (fig. 12).

sporangia. Specialized structures where spores are produced in lower vascular plants such as ferns and mosses.

spore. Asexual reproductive structure of lower vascular plants such as ferns and mosses. Leads to the development of a new plant.

sporocarp. A structure that encases the spores or sporangia in aquatic ferns.

sporophyll. A spore-bearing leaf, typical of ferns.

stamen. The male tissue of a flower that consists of filaments attached to anthers, which contain the pollen (fig. 9).

staminate. Having a male flower but lacking functional female parts.

staminode, pl. staminodia. A sterile stamen, usually lacking an anther and always lacking viable pollen.

stellate. Star-shaped, as in a hair with three or more branches radiating from the same point (fig. 7).

stigma. Upper region of the pistil that receives the pollen (figs. 9, 10, and 12).

stipulate. Having stipules.

stipule. Appendage at the base of the petiole or leaf; usually in pairs, sometimes thin and inconspicuous, other times leaflike.

stolon. Aboveground trailing shoot; roots form at the nodes.

stratification. In plant propagation, exposure of seeds to cold or wet treatments to stimulate germination.

strigose. Covered with sharp, straight, stiff, appressed hairs; bristly (fig. 7).

strobile. Having a cone or conelike aggregate of sporophylls; often associated with the reproductive structures of horsetails or scouringrushes in the Equisetaceae (horsetail family).

style. Elongated structure above the ovary and below the stigma of the female portion of the flower (fig. 9).

subterranean. Underground.

superior ovary. Ovary that is above the attachment of the flower parts (perianth) (fig. 9).

taproot. Dominant and primary descending root of a plant; much larger than the fibrous (smaller, thinner) roots.

tegument. The covering of a structure; integument.

temperate. Nontropical; having distinct seasons.

tertiary. Third order, as in the third level of branching in a panicle inflorescence or a compound leaf.

testa. Outer coating or covering on a seed.

tetrad. A group of four, as in four pollen grains together.

thiamine. Vitamin B_1, produced by plants.

tiller. A new sprout or branch that grows from the base of a grass or other monocot.

trichome. Any hair growing on the epidermis.

triploid. Having three times the haploid number of chromosomes; the organism is usually sterile.

truncate. Having a straight base or apex that gives the appearance of having been cut off (figs. 2 and 3).

tuber. A swollen underground stem tip or tip of a rhizome (e.g., potato).

tubercle. A small wartlike projection.

tufted. Growing in a cluster or tuft.

turbid. Clouded; not clear.

turion. A small, scaly overwintering structure of a stem or rhizome.

umbel. Flower cluster in which the stalks or pedicels arise from a common point. Referred to as compound umbel when stalks of each cluster (peduncle) arise from a common point (fig. 8).

unisexual. Having organs of only one sex, either male or female flowers.

utricle. A thin-walled indehiscent 1-seeded fruit that is usually inflated.

vernal pool. A depression in grasslands that have a shallow hardpan; collects water and is associated with early-spring-flowering wildflowers.

verticil (verticillate). A whorl or circle of similar parts such as leaves, petals, or inflorescence branches.

vestigial. A small, degenerate nonfunctioning organ or tissue.

whorl. More than two leaves or flowers attached at a node (fig. 6).

zoospore. A spore with a flagellum that is capable of moving.

zygote. A fertilized egg or ovum.

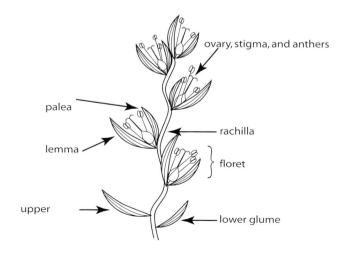

Figure 12. General grass spikelet.

Bibliography

General References

Abrams, L., and R. S. Ferris. 1961. Illustrated flora of the Pacific states. Stanford: Stanford University Press.

Aulbach-Smith, C. A., and S. J. D. Kozlowski. 1996. Aquatic and wetland plants of South Carolina. Columbia: S.C. Department of Natural Resources.

Bailey, L. H. 1951. Manual of cultivated plants. 2nd ed. New York: Macmillan.

Barnard, C. M., and L. D. Potter. 1984. New Mexico grasses: A vegetative key. Albuquerque: University of New Mexico Press.

Barrett, S. C. H., and D. E. Seaman. 1980. The weed flora of Californian rice fields. Aquatic Bot. 9:351–376.

Borman, S., R. Korth, and J. Temte. 1997. Through the looking glass: A field guide to aquatic plants. Stevens Point: Wisconsin Lakes Partnership, University of Wisconsin.

Bossard, C., J. Randall, and M. Hershovsky, eds. 2000. Invasive weeds of California's wildlands. Berkeley: University of California Press.

Composite list of weeds. 2003 (in press). Lawrence, KS: Weed Science Society of America.

Cook, C. D. K. 1990. Aquatic plant book. The Hague: SPB Academic Publishers.

Cook, C. D. K. 1996. Aquatic and wetland plants of India. Oxford: Oxford University Press.

Correll, D. S., and H. B. Correll. 1972. Aquatic and wetland plants of south-western United States. Water Pollution Control Research Series 16030 DNL 01/72. Environmental Protection Agency: Research and Monitoring. 866–868.

Crampton, B. 1974. Grasses in California. Berkeley: University of California Press.

Cronquist, A. 1972. Intermountain flora: Vascular plants of the Intermountain West. New York: Hafner.

Delorit, R. J. 1970. Illustrated taxonomy manual of weed seeds. River Falls, WI: Agronomy Publications.

Fischer, B. B., J. McCaskill, A. H. Lange, B. Crampton, W. T. Lanini, and S. C. Scardaci. 1978–2000. The grower's weed identification handbook. Oakland: University of California Agriculture and Natural Resources Publication 4030.

Flora Europaea. 1993. Vols. 1–4. London: Cambridge University Press.

Fuller, T. C., and E. McClintock. 1986. Poisonous plants of California. Berkeley: University of California Press.

Gleason, H. A., and A. Cronquist. 1991. Manual of vascular plants of northeastern United States and adjacent Canada. 2nd ed. New York: New York Botanical Garden.

Godfrey, R. K., and J. W. Wooten. 1979. Aquatic and wetland plants of southeastern United States. Athens: University of Georgia Press.

Gould, F. W. 1975. The grasses of Texas. Kingsville: Texas A & M University Press.

Hellquist, C. B., and G. E. Crow. 1980. Aquatic vascular plants of New England: Part 1. Zosteraceae, Potamogetonaceae, Zannichelliaceae, Najadaceae. Durham: University of New Hampshire Agricultural Experiment Station Bulletin 515.

Hickman, J. C. (ed.) 1993. The Jepson manual: Higher plants of California. Berkeley: University of California Press.

Hitchcock, A. S., and A. Chase. 1950. Manual of the grasses of the United States. 2nd ed. New York: Dover.

Hitchcock, C. L. 1969. Key to the grasses of the Pacific Northwest based upon vegetative characters. Seattle: University of Washington Press.

Hitchcock, C. L., and A. Cronquist. 1973. Flora of the Pacific Northwest: An illustrated manual. Seattle: University of Washington Press.

Holm, L., J. Doll, E. Holm, J. Pancho, and J. Herberger. 1997. World weeds. New York: Wiley.

Holm, L. G., D. L. Plucknett, J. V. Pancho, and J. P. Herberger. 1977. The world's worst weeds: Distribution and biology. Honolulu: University of Hawaii Press.

Kingsbury, J. M. 1964. Poisonous plants of the United States and Canada. Englewood Cliffs, N.J.: Prentice Hall.

Kummer, A. 1951. Weed seedlings. Chicago: University of Chicago Press.

Martin, A. C., H. S. Zim, and A. L. Nelson. 1951. American wildlife and plants: A guide to wildlife food habits. New York: Dover.

Mason, H. L. 1957. A flora of the marshes of California. Berkeley: University of California Press.

Muenscher, W. C. 1955. Weeds. 2nd ed. Ithaca: Cornell University Press.

Muller, F. M. 1978. Seedlings of the north-western European lowland: A flora of seedlings. Boston: W. Junk B. V.

Parsons, W. T., and E. G. Cuthbertson. 1992. Noxious weeds of Australia. Melbourne: Inkata Press.

Preston, C. D., and J. M. Croft. 1997. Aquatic plants in Britain and Ireland. Colchester, England: Harley Books.

Reed, C. F. 1977. Economically important foreign weeds: Potential problems in the United States. Washington, D.C.: USDA Agricultural Research Service Agricultural Handbook 498.

Robbins, W. W., M. K. Bellue, and W. S. Ball. 1951. Weeds of California. Sacramento: California State Department of Agriculture.

Sainty, G. R., and S. W. L. Jacobs. 1994. Water plants in Australia: A field guide. 3rd ed. Darlinghurst: Sainty and Associates.

Tarver, T. P., J. A. Rodgers, M. J. Mahler, and R. L. Lazor. 1979. Aquatic and wetland plants of Florida. 2nd ed. Tallahassee: Florida Department of Natural Resources.

U.S. Department of Agriculture, Agricultural Research Service 1971. Common weeds of the United States. New York: Dover.

U.S. Department of Agriculture, National Resource Conservation Service. 2001. The Plants Database, Version 3.1 (http://plants.usda.gov). National Plant Data Center, Baton Rouge, LA 70874-4490 USA.

Uva, R. H., J. C. Neal, and J. M. DiTomaso. 1997. Weeds of the Northeast. Ithaca: Cornell University Press.

Weeds of rice in Indonesia. 1987. Jakarta: Balai Pustaka.

Whitley, J. R., B. Bassett, J. G. Dillard, and R. A. Haefner. 1990. Water plants for Missouri ponds: Identification, unique features, values and uses, and non-chemical control. St. Louis: Missouri Department of Conservation.

References to Specific Genera

Alternanthera

Buckingham, G. R. 1996. Biological control of alligatorweed, *Alternanthera philoxeroides*, the world's first aquatic weed success story. Castanea 61:232–243.

Clark, W. R. 1973. Alligatorweed. Proc. Calif. Weed Conf. 25:49–50.

Coulson, J. R. 1977. Biological control of alligatorweed, 1959–72. A review and evaluation. USDA Technical Bulletin 1547.

Goeden, R. D., and D. W. Ricker. 1971. Imported alligatorweed insect enemies precluded from establishment in California. J. Econ. Entomol. 64:329–330.

Hill, W. G., and R. G. Donley. 1973. Alligatorweed report: Los Angeles County. Proc. Calif. Weed Conf. 25:43–48.

Julien, M. H., and J. E. Broadbent. 1980. The biology of Australian weeds. *Alternanthera philoxeroides* (Mart.) Griseb. J. Aust. Inst. Agric. Sci. 46:150–155.

Kay, S. H., and W. T. Haller. 1982. Evidence for the existence for distinct alligatorweed biotypes. J. Aquatic Plant Manage. 20:37–41.

Maddox, D. M., and A. Mayfield. 1979. Biology and life history of *Amynothrips andersoni*, a thrip for the biological control of alligatorweed *Alternanthera philoxeroides*. Ann. Entomol. Soc. Am. 72:136–140.

Roberts, L. I., C. J. Winks, O. R. Sutherland, and R. A. Galbreath. 1984. Progress of biological control of alligator weed in New Zealand. Proc. N. Z. Weed Pest. Control. Conf. Pp. 50–54.

Room, P. M. 1993. Biological control of floating weeds in the Pacific: History and status. Micronesica. 41–47.

Wellborn, T. L. 1979. Aquatic weed identification and control: Alligator weed *Alternanthera philoxeroides*, *Hydrilla verticillata*. Inf. Sheet. Coop. Ext. Serv. Miss. State Univ. 1034.

Amorpha

Glad, J. B., and R. R. Halse. 1993. Invasion of *Amorpha fruticosa* L. (Leguminosae) along the Columbia and Snake rivers in Oregon and Washington. Madroño 40:62–63.

Wang, E. T., P. V. Berkum, X. H. Sui, D. Beyene, W. X. Chen, and E. Martinez Romero. 1999. Diversity of rhizobia associated with *Amorpha fruticosa* isolated from Chinese soils and description of *Mesorhizobium amorphae* sp. nov. Int. J. Syst. Bacteriol. 49:51–65.

Wilbur, R. L. 1975. A revision of the North American genus *Amorpha* (Leguminosae-Psoraleae). Rhodora 77:337–409.

Arundo, Phragmites

Boose, A. B., and J. S. Holt. 1999. Environmental effects on asexual reproduction in *Arundo donax*. Weed Res. Oxford 39:117–127.

Ekstam, B., and A. Forseby. 1999. Germination response of *Phragmites australis* and *Typha latifolia* to diurnal fluctuations in temperature. Seed Sci. Res. 9:157–163.

Ekstam, B., R. Johannesson, and P. Milberg. 1999. The effect of light and number of diurnal temperature fluctuations on germination of *Phragmites australis*. Seed Sci. Res. 9:165–170.

Jackson, N. E., P. Frandsen, and S. Duthoit. 1994. *Arundo donax*. Workshop Proc., San Diego, CA. California Exotic Pest Plant Council.

Marks, M., B. Lapin, and J. Randall. 1994. *Phragmites australis* (*P. communis*): Threats, management and monitoring. Natural Areas J. 14:285–294.

Matoh, T., N. Matsushita, and E. Takahashi. 1988. Salt tolerance of the reed plant *Phragmites communis*. Physiologia Plantarum 72:8–14.

Van der Merwe C. G., H. J. Schoonbee, and J. Pretorius. 1990. Observations on concentrations of the heavy metals zinc, manganese, nickel and iron in the water, in the sediments and in two aquatic macrophytes, *Typha capensis* (Rohrb.) N.E. Br. and *Arundo donax* L., of a stream affected by goldmine and industrial effluents. Water S. Africa 16:119–124.

Rezk, M. R., and T. Y. Edany. 1979. Comparative responses of two reed species to water table levels. Egyptian J. Bot. 22:157–172.

Baccharis

Perry, B. 1981. Trees and shrubs for dry California landscapes: Plants for water conservation. San Dimas, CA: Land Design Publ.

Caulerpa

Anderson, L. W. J., and S. Keppner. 2001. *Caulerpa taxifolia*: Marine algal invader provides quick response in U.S. waters. ANS Digest 4(2):1, 21–22.

Eubank, L. L. 1947. Hawaiian representatives of the genus *Caulerpa*. Univ. Calif. Publ. Bot. 18:409–431.

Meinesz, A. 1999. Killer algae. Trans. D. Simberloff. Chicago: University of Chicago Press.

Raloff, J. 1998. Rogue algae. Science News 154:8–10.

Taylor, W. R. 1960. Marine algae of the eastern tropical and subtropical coasts of the Americas. Ann Arbor: University of Michigan Press.

Chara, Nitella

Bold, H. C., and M. J. Wynne. 1985. Introduction to the algae: Structure and reproduction. 2nd ed. Englewood Cliffs, NJ: Prentice-Hall.

Entwisle, T. J., J. A. Sonneman, and S. H. Lewis. 1997. Freshwater algae in Australia: A guide to conspicuous genera. New South Wales: Sainty and Associates.

Prescott, G. W. 1964. How to know the freshwater algae. 2nd ed. Dubuque, IA: Wm. C. Brown.

Wood, R. D. 1967. Charophytes of North America: A guide to the species of Charophyta of North America, Central America, and the West Indies. Kingston: University of Rhode Island.

Cotula

Toorn, J. J. 1982. On the ecology of *Cotula coronopifolia* L. and *Ranunculus sceleratus* L. II. Experiments on germination, seed longevity, and seedling survival. Acta Oecol. 3:409–418.

Cyperus

Hafliger, E. 1982. Monocot weeds. Vol. 3 . Basle, Switzerland: CIBA-GEIGY.

Kim, J. S., and B. L. Mercado. 1987. Viability and emergence of buried seeds of *Echinochloa glabrescens*, *Monochoria vaginalis* and *Cyperus difformis*. Proc. 11th Asian Pacific Weed Sci. Soc. Conf. 469–476.

Echinochloa

Barrett, C. H., and B. F. Wilson. 1981. Colonizing ability in the *Echinochloa crus-galli* complex (barnyardgrass). I. Variation in life history. Can. J. Bot. 59:1844–1860.

Crampton, B. 1964. Notes and news: *Echinochloa oryzicola* in California. Madroño 17:294–295.

Gould, F. W., M. A. Ali, and D. E. Fairbrothers. 1972. A revision of *Echinochloa* in the United States. College Station: Tx. Agr. Exp. St. Tech. Bull. 8804. 36–59.

Kim, J. S., and B. L. Mercado. 1987. Viability and emergence of buried seeds of *Echinochloa glabrescens*, *Monochoria vaginalis* and *Cyperus difformis*. Proc. 11th Asian Pacific Weed Sci. Soc. Conf. 469–476.

Maun, M. A., and C. H. Barrett. 1986. The biology of Canadian weeds. 77. *Echinochloa crus-galli* (L.) Beauv. Can. J. Plant Sci. 66:739–759.

Michael, P. W. 1983. Taxonomy and distribution of *Echinochloa* species with special reference to their occurrence as weeds of rice. In Weed control in rice, 1981. Los Banos, Philippines: International Rice Research Institute. 291–306.

Michael, P. W. 1991. The discovery of *Echinochloa oryzicola* (Vasing.) Vasing. In 13th Conf. Asian Pacific Weed Sci. 223–224.

Rumpho, M. E., and R. A. Kenney. 1981. Anaerobic metabolism in germinating seeds of *Echinochloa crus-galli* (barnyard grass): metabolite and enzyme studies. Plant Physiol. 68:165–168.

Yabuno, T. 1981. Cytological relationship between *Echinochloa oryzicola* Vasing. and the French strain of *E. phyllopogon* Stapf subsp. *oryzicola* (Vasing.) Koss. Cytologia 46:393–396.

———. 1984. A biosystematic study on *Echinochloa oryzoides* (Ard.) Fritsch. Cytologia 49:673–678.

Eichhornia

Barrett, S. H. 1980. Sexual reproduction in *Eichhornia crassipes* (water hyacinth). II. Seed production in natural populations. J. Appl. Ecol. 17:113–124.

Forno, I. W., and A. D. Wright. 1981. The biology of Australian weeds. 5. *Eichhornia crassipes* (Mart.) Solms. J. Australian Inst. Agric. Sci. 47:21–28.

Pieterse, A. H. 1978. The water hyacinth (*Eichhornia crassipes*)—A review. Abstr. Trop. Agric. 4:9–42.

Elaeagnus

Brown, C. R. 1990. Avian use of native and exotic riparian habitats on the Snake River, Idaho. Ft. Collins: Colorado State University.

Graham, S. A. 1964. The Elaeagnaceae in the Southeastern United States. J. Arnold Arboretum 45:274–278.

Hamilton, D. F., and P. L. Carpenter. 1976. Regulation of seed dormancy in *Elaeagnus angustifolia* by endogenous growth substances. Can. J. Bot. 54:1068–1073.

Howe, W. H., and F. L. Knopf. 1991. On the imminent decline of Rio Grande cottonwoods in Central New Mexico. Southwestern Naturalist 36:218–224.

Knopf, F. L., and T. E. Olson. 1984. Naturalization of Russian-olive: implications to Rocky Mountain wildlife. Wildl. Soc. Bull. 12:289–298.

Lesica, P., and S. Miles. 1999. Russian olive invasion into cottonwood forests along a regulated river in north-central Montana. Can. J. Bot. 77:1077–1083.

Olson, T. E., and F. L. Knopf. 1986. Naturalization of Russian-olive in the western United States. West. J. Applied For. 1:65–69.

Riffle, J. W. 1977. First report of vesicular-arbuscular mycorrhizae on *Elaeagnus angustifolia*. Mycologia 69:1200–1203.

Schopmeyer, C. S. 1974. Seeds of woody plants in the United States. USDA Agric. Handbook 450.

Shafroth, P. B., G. T. Auble, and M. L. Scott. 1995. Germination and establishment of the native plains cottonwood (*Populus deltoides* Marshall subsp. *monilifera*) and the exotic Russian-olive (*Elaeagnus angustifolia* L.). Conserv. Biol. 9:1169–1175.

Zitzer, S. F., J. O. Dawson, G. Z. Gertner, G. Rink, and C. A. Budelsky. 1989. Seasonal changes in nitrogen fixation activity of European black alder and Russian olive. 7th Central Hardwood Forest Conf., No. NC-132:134–140.

Eleocharis

Ashton, F. M., J. M. DiTomaso, and L. W. J. Anderson. 1985. Spikerush (*Eleocharis* spp.): A source of allelopathy for the control of undesirable aquatic plants. In A. C. Thompson, ed., The chemistry of allelopathy biochemical interactions among plants. Am. Chem. Soc. Sym. Ser. 268. 401–414.

Routledge, R. D. 1987. Rhizome architecture for dispersal in *Eleocharis palustris*. Can. J. Bot. 65:1218–1223.

Elodea

Cook, C. D. K., and K. Urmi-Konig. 1985. A revision of the genus *Elodea* (Hydrocharitaceae). Aquatic Bot. 21:111–156.

Equisetum

Cody, W. J., and V. Wagner. 1981. The biology of Canadian weeds. 49. *Equisetum arvense* L. Can. J. Plant Sci. 61:123–133.

Heracleum

Anonymous. 2001. Giant hogweed (*Heracleum mantegazzianum*)—A noxious plant in Washington. Olympia: Washington Department of Ecology Water Quality Program Non-native Aquatic Plants Web site. http://www.ecy.wa.gov/programs/wq/plants/weeds/aqua012.html

Camm, E., H. W. L. Buck, and J. C. Mitchell. 1976. Phytodermatitis from *Heracleum mantegazzianum*. Contact Dermatitis 2:68–72.

Heteranthera, Monochoria

Horn, C. N. 1984. Variation in the adaptations to the aquatic environment during seedling growth in the genus *Heteranthera* (Pontederiaceae). Amer. J. Bot. 71:172.

Kim, J. S., and B. L. Mercado. 1987. Viability and emergence of buried seeds of *Echinochloa glabrescens, Monochoria vaginalis* and *Cyperus difformis*. Proc. 11th Asian Pacific Weed Sci. Soc. Conf. 469–476.

Rosatti, T. J. 1987. The genera of Pontederiaceae in the southeastern United States. J. Arnold Arboretum 68:35–71.

Steyermark, J. A. 1963. Flora of Missouri. Ames: Iowa State University Press.

Stutzenbaker, C. D. 1999. Aquatic and wetland plants of the western Gulf Coast. Austin: Texas Parks and Wildlife Press.

Hydrilla

Anderson, L. W. J., and N. Dechoretz. 1982. Growth, reproduction and control of *Hydrilla verticillata* Royle (l.f.) in an irrigation system in southwestern U.S. Proc. 6th Int. Sym. Aquatic Weeds [European Weed Res. Soc.]. 54–61.

Blackbrun, R. D., L. W. Weldon, R. R. Yeo, and T. M. Taylor. 1969. Identification and distribution of certain similar-appearing submersed aquatic weeds in Florida. Hyacinth Control J. 8(1):17–21.

Cook, C. D. K., and R. Luond. 1982. A revision of the genus *Hydrilla* (Hydrocharitaceae). Aquatic Bot. 13:485–504.

Miller, J. D., W. T. Haller, and M. S. Glenn. 1993. Turion production by dioecious hydrilla in north Florida. J. Aquatic Plant Manage. 31:101–105.

Netherland, M. D. 1997. Turion ecology of *Hydrilla*. J. Aquat. Plant Manage. 35:1–10.

Spencer, D. F., and L. J. Anderson. 1986. Photoperiodic responses in monoecious and dioecious *Hydrilla verticillata*. Weed Sci. 34:551–557.

Sutton, D. L., T. K. Van, and K. M. Portier. 1992. Growth of dioecious and monoecious hydrilla from single tubers. J. Aquatic Plant Manage. 30:15–20.

Thullen, J. S. 1990. Production of axillary turions by the dioecious *Hydrilla verticillata*. J. Aquatic Plant Manage. 28:11–15.

Van, T. K. 1989. Differential responses to photoperiods in monoecious and dioecious *Hydrilla verticillata*. Weed Sci. 37:552–556.

Van, T. K., W. T. Haller, and L. A. Garrard. 1978. The effect of daylength and temperature on hydrilla growth and tuber production. J. Aquatic Plant Manage. 16:57–59.

Wellborn, T. L. 1979. Aquatic weed identification and control: Alligator weed *Alternanthera philoxeroides, Hydrilla verticillata*. Mississippi State: Miss. State Univ. Coop. Ext. Serv. Inf. Sheet. 1034.

Lepidium

Miller, G. K., J. A. Young, and R. A. Evans. 1986. Germination of seeds of perennial pepperweed (*Lepidium latifolium*). Weed Sci. 34:252–255.

Renz, M. J. 1999. The biology, ecology and control of perennial pepperweed (*Lepidium latifolium* L.). PhD diss., University of California, Davis.

Young, J. A., C. E. Turner, and L. F. James. 1995. Perennial pepperweed. Rangelands 17:121–123.

Limnobium

Cook, C. D. K., and K. Urmi-Konig. 1983. A revision of the genus *Limnobium* including *Hydromystria* (Hydrocharitaceae). Aquatic Bot. 17:1–27.

Lythrum

Blossey, B. 1997. Hungry herbivores feast on purple plague. CABI—Biocontrol News and Information 18:2–3. http://pest.cabweb.org/Journals/BNI/BNI18-3/Genews.htm

Hight, S. D., B. Blossey, J. Laing, and R. DeClerck-Floate. 1995. Establishment of insect biological control agents from Europe against *Lythrum salicaria* in North America. Environ. Entom. 24:967–977.

Lindgren, C. J., and R. T. Clay. 1994. Crossability of naturalized and cultivated *Lythrum* taxa. Can. J. Bot. 72:337–341.

Ottenbreit, K. A. 1993. Fertility of 'Morden Pink' *Lythrum virgatum* L. transplanted into wild stands of *L. salicaria* L. in Manitoba. HortScience 28:954.

Rees, N. E., P. C. Quimby Jr., G. L. Piper, E. C. Coombs, C. E. Turner, N. R. Spencer, and L. Knutson. 1996. Biological control of weeds in the west. 1st ed. Bozeman, MT: Western Society of Weed Science.

Melilotus

Turkington, R. A., P. B. Cavers, and E. Rempel. 1978. The biology of Canadian weeds. 29. *Melilotus alba* Desr. and *M. officinalis* (L.) Lam. Can. J. Plant Sci. 58:523–537.

Myriophyllum

Aiken, S. G. 1980. The discovery of *Myriophyllum exalbescens* Fernald (Haloragaceae) in Europe and the typification of *M. spicatum* L. and *M. verticillatum* L. Bot. J. Linnean Soc. 80:213–222.

———. 1981. A conspectus of *Myriophyllum* (Haloragaceae) in North America. Brittonia 33(1):57–69.

Aiken, S. G., P. R. Newroth, and I. Wile. 1979. The biology of Canadian weeds. 34. *Myriophyllum spicatum* L. Can. J. Plant Sci. 59:201–215.

Aiken, S. G., and R. R. Picard. 1980. The influence of substrate on the growth and morphology of *Myriophyllum exalbescens* and *Myriophyllum spicatum*. Can. J. Bot. 58:1111–1118.

Ceska, O., and A. Ceska. 1985. *Myriophyllum* Haloragaceae species in British Columbia: problems with identification. Proc. 1st Intern. Sym. on Watermilfoil (*Myriophyllum spicatum*) and Related Haloragaceae Species. 39–50.

Coble, T. A., and B. D. Vance. 1987. Seed germination in *Myriophyllum spicatum* L. J. Aquatic Plant Manage. 25:8–10.

Couch, R., and E. Nelson. 1985. *Myriophyllum spicatum* in North America. Proc. 1st Int. Sym. on Watermilfoil (*Myriophyllum spicatum*) and Related Haloragaceae Species. 8–18.

Creed, R. P. Jr. 1998. A biogeographic perspective on Eurasian watermilfoil declines: Additional evidence for the role of herbivorous weevils in promoting declines? J. Aquat. Plant Manage. 36:16–20.

Hartleb, C. F., J. D. Madsen, and C. W. Boylen. 1993. Environmental factors affecting seed germination in *Myriophyllum spicatum* L. Aquatic Bot. 45:15–25.

Kimbel, J. C., and S. R. Carpenter. 1981. Effects of mechanical harvesting on *Myriophyllum spicatum* L. regrowth and carbohydrate allocation to roots and shoots. Aquatic Bot. 11:121–127.

Nichols, S. A. 1984. Phytochemical and morphological differentiation between *Myriophyllum spicatum* L. and *Myriophyllum exalbescens* Fern in two Wisconsin lakes. Trans. Wisc. Acad. Sci. Arts Let. 72:153–156.

Orchar, A. E. 1981. A revision of South American *Myriophyllum* (Haloragaceae), and its repercussions on some Australian and North American species. Brunonia 4:27–65.

Sutton, D. L. 1985. Biology and ecology of *Myriophyllum aquaticum*. Proc. 1st Int. Sym. on Watermilfoil (*Myriophyllum spicatum*) and Related Haloragaceae Species. 59–71.

Najas

Haynes, R. R. 1979. Revision of North and Central American *Najas* (Najadaceae). Sida 8:34–56.

Nuphar, Nymphaea, Nymphoides

Conard, H. S. 1905. The waterlilies: A monograph of the genus *Nymphaea*. Washington: Carnegie Institute of Washington.

Padgett, D. J. 1997. A biosystematic monograph of the genus *Nuphar* Sm. (Nymphaeaceae). Ph.D. diss. Durham: University of New Hampshire.

Smits, A. M., and A. M. Wetzels. 1986. Germination studies on three nymphaeid species (*Nymphaea alba* L., *Nuphar lutea* (L.) Sm. and *Nymphoides peltata* (Gmel.) O. Kuntze). Proc. 7th Int. Sym. Aquatic Weeds. 315–320.

Welker, W. V., and D. N. Riemer. 1982. Fragrant waterlily (*Nymphaea odorata*) control with multiple applications of glyphosate. Weed Sci. 30:145–146.

Paspalum

Fajardo, F. F., and K. Moody. 1987. Effect of land preparation on control of *Paspalum distichum*. Int. Rice Res. Newslet. 12:50.

Phalaris

Kennedy, P. B. 1917. New grasses for California, *Phalaris stenoptera* Hack. Univ. Publ. Agric. Sci. 3:1–24.

Lamp, C., and F. Collet. 1989. Weeds in Australia. 3rd ed. Melbourne: Inkata Press.

Oram, R. N., and J. P. Edlington. 1996. Breeding non-toxic phalaris (*Phalaris aquatica* L.). Proc. 8th Austr. Agron. Conf., Toowoomba, Queensland, Australia. 450–453.

Skerritt, J. H., S. L. Guihot, S. E. McDonald, and R. A. Culvenor. 2000. Development of immunoassays for tyramine and tryptamine toxins of *Phalaris aquatica* L. J. Agr. Food Chem. 48:27–32.

Wilding, J. L., A. G. Barnett, and R. L. Amor. 1986. Crop Weeds. Melbourne: Inkata Press.

Pistia

Pieterse, A. H., L. D. Lange, and L. Verhagen. 1981. A study on certain aspects of seed germination and growth of *Pistia stratiotes* L. Acta Botanica Neerlandica 30:47–57.

Thawil, B. N., and B. L. Mercado. 1975. The life cycle of water lettuce (*Pistia stratiotes* L.). Philippine Weed Sci. Bull. 2:11–15.

Polygonum

Grime, J. P., J. G. Hodgson, and R. Hunt. 1988. Comparative plant ecology: A functional approach to common British species. London: Unwin Hyman.

Salisbury, E. 1961. Weeds and aliens. London: Collins.

Williams, J. B., and J. R. Morrison. 1987. ADAS color atlas of weed seedlings. London: Wolfe.

Potamogeton, Ruppia

Hellquist, C. B., and G. E. Crow. 1980. Aquatic vascular plants of New England: Part 1. Zosteraceae, Potamogetonaceae, Zannichelliaceae, Najadaceae. Durham: Univ. of New Hampshire Agric. Exp. Stat., Stat. Bull. 515.

Preston, C. D. 1995. Pondweeds of Great Britain and Ireland. London: Botanical Society of the British Isles.

Rotala

Bailey, L. H. 1945. *Rubus* in North America. [5]. Ithaca: The Bailey Hortorium, Cornell University.

Ceska, A. 1999. *Rubus armeniacus*—A correct name for Himalayan blackberries. British Columbia Botanical Electronic News ISSN 1188-603X [no. 230]. http://www.ou.edu/cas/botany-micro/ben

Crandall, P. C. 1995. Bramble production: The management and marketing of raspberries and blackberries. New York: Food Products Press.

Reed, C. F. 1977. Economically important foreign weeds: Potential problems in the United States. USDA Agric. Hdbk. No. 498.

Salix

Brinkman, K. A. 1974. *Salix* L., Willow. In C. S. Schopmeyer, ed., Seeds of woody plants in the United States. Washington, D.C.: USDA Forest Service. 746–750.

Salvinia

Chikwenhere, G. P., and C. L. Keswani. 1997. Economics of biological control of Kariba weed (*Salvinia molesta* Mitchell) at Tengwe in north-western Zimbabwe—A case study. Int. J. Pest Manage. 43:109–112.

Harley, K. S., and D. S. Mitchell. 1981. The biology of Australian weeds. 6. *Salvinia molesta* D.S. Mitchell. J. Austr. Inst. Agric. Sci. 47:67–76.

Lemon, G. D., and U. Posluszny. 1997. Shoot morphology and organogenesis of the aquatic floating fern *Salvinia molesta* D.S. Mitchell, examined with the aid of laser scanning confocal microscopy. Int. J. Plant Sci. 158:693–703.

Mitchell, D. S. 1972. The Kariba weed: *Salvinia molesta*. Brit. Fern Gaz. 10:251–252.

Room, P. M. 1986. Biological control is solving the world's *Salvinia molesta* problems. Proc. 7th Int. Sym. Aquatic Weeds. 271–276.

Room, P. M. 1993. Biological control of floating weeds in the Pacific: History and status. Micronesica 41–47.

Whiteman, J. B., and P. M. Room. 1991. Temperatures lethal to *Salvinia molesta* Mitchell. Aquatic Bot. 40:27–35.

Scirpus

Smith, S. G. 1995. New combinations in North American *Schoenoplectus*, *Bolboschoenus*, *Isolepis*, and *Trichophorum* (Cyperaceae). Novon 5:97–102.

Sesbania

Godfrey, R. K. 1988. Trees, shrubs, and woody vines of northern Florida and adjacent Georgia and Alabama. Athens: University of Georgia Press.

Graaf, J. L., and J. V. Staden. 1984. The germination characteristics of two *Sesbania* species. S. African J. Bot. 3:59–62.

Hoffmann, J. H., and V. C. Moran. 1998. The population dynamics of an introduced tree, in South Africa, in response to long-term damage caused by different combinations of three species of biological control agents. Oecologia 114:343–348.

Johnston, S. K., R. H. Walder, and D. S. Murray. 1979. Germination and emergence of hemp sesbania (*Sesbania exaltata*). Weed Sci. 27:290–293.

Spartina

Anttila, C. K., C. C. Daehler, N. E. Rank, and D. R. Strong. 1998. Greater male fitness of a rare invader (*Spartina alterniflora*; Poaceae) threatens a common native (*Spartina foliosa*) with hybridization. Am. J. Bot.

Daehler, C. C. 1998. Variation in self-fertility and the reproductive advantage of self-fertility for an invading plant (*Spartina alterniflora*). Evolutionary Ecol. 12:553–568.

———. 1999. Inbreeding depression in smooth cordgrass (*Spartina alterniflora*, Poaceae) invading San Francisco Bay. Am. J. Bot. 86:131–139.

Daehler, C. C., and D. R. Strong. 1997. Hybridization between introduced smooth cordgrass (*Spartina alterniflora*; Poaceae) and native California cordgrass (*S. foliosa*) in San Francisco Bay, California, USA. Am. J. Bot. 84:607–611.

Daehler, C. C., D. R. Strong, J. R. Carey, P. Moyle, M. Rejmanek, and G. J. Vermeij. 1994. Status, prediction and prevention of introduced cordgrass *Spartina* spp. invasions in Pacific estuaries, USA. Biol. Conserv. Spec. Issue: Biological Invasions 78:51–58.

McClung, C. R., P. Berkum, V, R. E. Davis, and C. Sloger. 1983. Enumeration and localization of N_2-fixing bacteria associated with roots of *Spartina alterniflora* Loisel. Appl. Environ. Microbiology 45:1914–1920.

Melvin, S. L., and J. W. J. Webb. 1998. Differences in the avian communities of natural and created *Spartina alterniflora* salt marshes. Wetlands 18:59–69.

Mobberley, D. G. 1956. Taxonomy and distribution of the genus *Spartina*. Iowa State College J. Sci. 30:471–574.

Plyler, D. B., and T. E. Proseus. 1996. A comparison of the seed dormancy characteristics of *Spartina patens* and *Spartina alterniflora* (Poaceae). Am. J. Bot. 83:11–14.

Simenstad, C. A., and R. M. Thom. 1995. *Spartina alterniflora* (smooth cordgrass) as an invasive halophyte in Pacific Northwest estuaries. Hortus Northwest 6:9–40.

Walsh, G. E. 1990. Anatomy of the seed and seedling of *Spartina alterniflora* Lois. (Poaceae). Aquatic Bot. 38:177–193.

Tamarix

Baum, B. R. 1978. The genus *Tamarix*. Jerusalem: Israel Acad. Sci. Hum.

Benson, L., and R. A. Darrow. 1981. Trees and shrubs of the southwestern deserts. 3rd ed. Tucson: University of Arizona Press.

Dirr, M. A. 1997. Dirr's hardy trees and shrubs. Portland: Timber Press.

DiTomaso, J. M. 1998. Impact, biology, and ecology of saltcedar (*Tamarix* spp.) in the southwestern United States. Weed Technol. 12:326–336.

Typha

Ekstam, B., and A. Forseby. 1999. Germination response of *Phragmites australis* and *Typha latifolia* to diurnal fluctuations in temperature. Seed Sci. Res. 9:157–163.

Grace, J. B., and J. S. Harrison. 1986. The biology of Canadian weeds. 73. *Typha latifolia* L., *Typha angustifolia* L. and *Typha* ×*glauca* Godr. Can. J. Plant Sci. 66:361–379.

van der Merwe, C. G., H. J. Schoonbee, and J. Pretorius. 1990. Observations on concentrations of the heavy metals zinc, manganese, nickel and iron in the water, in the sediments and in two aquatic macrophytes, *Typha capensis* (Rohrb.) N.E. Br. and *Arundo donax* L., of a stream affected by gold-mine and industrial effluents. Water S. Africa 16:119–124.

Veronica

Teketay, D. 1998. The joint role of alternating temperatures and light quality in the germination of *Veronica anagallis-aquatica* and *V. javanica*. Tropical Ecol. 39:179–184.

Zannichellia

Crow, J. H. 1979. Distribution and ecological characteristics of *Zannichellia palustris* L. along the Alaska Pacific coast. Bull. Torrey Bot. Club 106:346–349.

Jurik, T. W., S. C. Wang, and A. G. van der Valk. 1994. Effects of sediment load on seedling emergence from wetland seed banks. Wetlands 14:159–165.

Index

Bold type indicates the accepted common name. Major discussions are indicated with page ranges, e.g., 118–119. Synonyms are indicated with regular type and single page numbers.

Aeschynomene spp. (**jointvetch**)
    natans, 207
    rudis, 207–210
African pyle (*Salvinia* spp.), 57
Agrostis spp. (polypogon)
    alopecuroides, 297
    semiverticillata, 302
    viridis, 302
Alisma spp. (burhead)
    berteroi, 144
    rostratum, 144
Alisma spp. (**waterplantain**)
    generally, 143, 146, 151
    americanum, 137
    brevipes, 137
    lanceolatum, 140–143
    plantago-aquatica, 137–143
    subcordatum, 137
alligatorweed (*Alternanthera philoxeroides*), 152–155
Alopecurus spp. (polypogon)
    aristatus, 297
    monspeliensis, 297
Alternanthera philoxeroides (**alligatorweed**), 152–155
American frogbit (*Limnobium spongia*), 56
American pondweed (*Potamogeton nodosus*), 118, 123–124, 125
American speedwell (*Veronica americana*), 368
American waterplantain (*Alisma* spp.), 137
ammannia (*Ammannia* spp.)
    long-leaved, 228
    purple, 228–236
Ammannia spp. (**ammannia**)
    auriculata, 229
    coccinea, 228–229
    nana, 228
    peploides, 228
    robusta, 228–236
    sanguinolenta, 228
Amorpha spp. (**indigobush**)
    fruticosa, 219–220
    occidentalis, 219
amphibious bistort (*Polygonum* spp.), 314

anabaena (*Anabaena* spp.), 74–76
Anacharis spp. (egeria/elodea)
    canadensis, 96
    densa, 96
annual beardgrass (*Polypogon* spp.), 297
apple mint (*Mentha suaveolens*), 226–227
Argentine vervain (*Verbena* spp.), 387
arrowhead (*Sagittaria* spp.)
    generally, 142–143, 146
    California, 147–151
    giant, 147
    Gregg, 150–151
    hooded, 147
    longbarb, 150
arroyo willow (*Salix lasiolepis*), 353–358
Arundo spp. (**reed**)
    donax, 254–262
    glauca, 254
    latifolia, 254
    sativa, 254
    versicolor, 254
athel pine (*Tamarix* spp.), 369
athel tamarisk (*Tamarix aphylla*), 369–377
athel tree (*Tamarix* spp.), 369
Atlantic cordgrass (*Spartina* spp.), 305
Azolla spp. (**mosquitofern**)
    generally, 44–47, 51, 154
    filiculoides, 44, 45–47
    mexicana, 44
    pinnata, 44

Baccharis spp. (**seepwillow**)
    glutinosa, 162
    salicifolia, 162–164, 358
    viminea, 162
bacopa (*Bacopa* spp.), 358
Bacopa spp. (**waterhyssop**)
    eisenii, 359–364
    monnieri, 361–362
    nobsiana, 362
    repens, 362–363
    rotundifolia, 362–364
bahiagrass (*Paspalum notatum*), 284–285, 288–289

banana waterlily (*Nymphaea* spp.), 114
barnyardgrass (*Echinochloa* spp.)
  generally, 263–275
  rough, 270, 271
  small, 263
beaked tasselweed (*Ruppia* spp.), 128
bearded sprangletop (*Leptochloa fascicularis*), 276–280
beardgrass (*Polypogon* spp.)
  annual, 297
  tawny, 297
bistort, amphibious (*Polygonum* spp.), 314
bitter dock (*Rumex* spp.), 329
blackberry (*Rubus* spp.)
  cutleaf, 348–352
  cut-leaved, 348
  elmleaf, 352
  evergreen, 348
  Himalaya, 348–352
  Himalayan, 348
black willow, Goodding's (*Salix gooddingii*), 353–358
bladderpod (*Sesbania* spp.), 214
blue vervain (*Verbena* spp.), 387
blunt spikerush (*Eleocharis obtusa*), 185–187
Bolboschoenus spp. (bulrush)
  generally, 189
  fluviatilis, 191
  glaucus, 193
  maritimus, 191
  robustus, 191
bottlebrush (*Equisetum* spp.), 202
bouquet-violet (*Lythrum* spp.), 237
Brasenia schreberi (**watershield**), 111–113
brassbuttons (*Cotula coronopifolia*), 165–167
Brazilian egeria (*Egeria densa*), 96–105
Brazilian elodea (*Egeria* spp.), 96
Brazilian watermilfoil (*Myriophyllum* spp.), 86
Brazilian waterweed (*Egeria* spp.), 96
brittlewort (*Nitella* spp.), 66
broadleaf cattail (*Typha* spp.), 378
broadleaf dock (*Rumex obtusifolius*), 329–341
broad-leafed pondweed (*Potamogeton* spp.), 118
broad-leaved cattail (*Typha* spp.), 378
broad waterweed (*Elodea* spp.), 96
brown flatsedge (*Cyperus* spp.), 182

bulbous canarygrass (*Phalaris* spp.), 290
bulrush (*Scirpus* spp.)
  comparison table, 198
  California, 191, 193–194, 198
  cosmopolitan, 191, 194–195, 198
  great, 189
  hardstem, 189–191, 198
  Pacific coast, 191
  ricefield, 193, 197, 198
  river, 190, 191, 192–193, 198
  roughseed, 193
  southern, 191
  sturdy, 191, 195–196, 198
  tuberous, 193, 196, 198
burhead (*Echinodorus* spp.)
  creeping, 142
  upright, 142–146, 151
butterfly fern (*Salvinia* spp.), 57

cabomba (*Cabomba caroliniana*), 80, 95
Cabomba caroliniana (cabomba), 80
Cabomba caroliniana (**fanwort**), 80–82, 95
California arrowhead (*Sagittaria montevidensis*), 147–151
California bulrush (*Scirpus californicus*), 191, 193–194, 198
California cordgrass (*Spartina foliosa*), 306, 308–310, 313
California loosestrife (*Lythrum californicum*), 244, 247
California waterprimrose (*Ludwigia* spp.), 249
Canadian pondweed (*Elodea* spp.), 96
Canadian waterweed (*Elodea* spp.), 96
canarygrass (*Phalaris* spp.)
  bulbous, 290
  Carolina, 293–295
  reed, 292–294, 296
  short-spike, 293–295
  tuberous, 290
cane (*Arundo* spp.)
  reed, 254
  wild, 254
Cardaria spp. (**cress/whitetop**)
  generally, 175
  draba, 174–175
  draba spp. *chalepensis*, 175
  latifolium, 171
  pubescens, 175
Carolina canarygrass (*Phalaris caroliniana*), 293–295

Castalia flava (Mexican waterlily), 114
cattail (*Typha* spp.)
  broadleaf, 378
  broad-leaved, 378
  common, 378–386
  narrowleaf, 382–386
  southern, 384–386
caulerpa (*Caulerpa taxifolia*), 64–65
Caulinia guadalupensis (southern naiad),
  106
Ceratophyllum spp. (**coontail**)
  apiculatum, 78
  asperum, 78
  cornutum, 78
  demersum, 78–85, 95
  oxyacanthum, 78
  tricuspidatum, 78
  tuberculatum, 78
  unicorne, 78
chain speedwell (*Veronica catenata*),
  367–368
chara (*Chara* spp.), 66–68
Chara spp. (**chara**)
  generally, 66–68
  globularis, 66
  zeylonica, 67
Chilean polypogon (*Polypogon australis*),
  300–302, 304
Chinese tamarisk (*Tamarix chinensis*),
  376–377
cladophora (*Cladophora* spp.), 71–73
closed-leaved pondweed (*Potamogeton*
  spp.), 118
clover (*Melilotus* spp.)
  honey, 211
  tree, 211
clover (*Trifolium* spp.), 47
cluster dock (*Rumex conglomeratus*),
  333–334, 338, 341
clustered saltgrass (*Leptochloa* spp.), 276
cluster-flowered verbena (*Verbena* spp.),
  387
cocksfoot panicum (*Echinochloa* spp.),
  263
cockspur, Gulf (*Echinochloa crus-pavonis*),
  270
cockspur grass (*Echinochloa* spp.), 263
coffeeweed (*Sesbania* spp.), 214, 218
Coleogeton pectinatus (sago pondweed),
  118
common cattail (*Typha latifolia*), 378–386

common cordgrass (*Spartina anglica*),
  311–313
common duckweed (*Lemna minor*),
  49–51
common elodea (*Elodea canadensis*),
  96–105
common floating pondweed (*Potamogeton*
  spp.), 118
common horsetail (*Equisetum* spp.), 202
common knotweed (*Polygonum* spp.), 314
common reed (*Phragmites australis*),
  258–261
common scouringrush (*Equisetum* spp.),
  202
common spikerush (*Eleocharis* spp.), 184
common spikesage (*Eleocharis* spp.), 184
common waterplantain (*Alisma plantago-
  aquatica*), 137–143
common waterweed (*Egeria* spp.), 96
coontail (*Ceratophyllum demersum*),
  78–85, 95
cordgrass (*Spartina* spp.)
  comparison table, 313
  Atlantic, 305
  California, 306, 308–310, 313
  common, 311–313
  dense-flowered, 308, 310–311, 313
  saltmarsh, 305
  salt-meadow, 310–313
  saltwater, 305
  small, 311–312
  smooth, 305–313
cosmopolitan bulrush (*Scirpus maritimus*), 191, 194–195, 198
cow parsnip (*Heracleum lanatum*), 158
Coyote willow (*Salix exigua*), 201,
  353–358
creeping burhead (*Echinodorus* spp.), 142
creeping primrose-willow (*Ludwigia* spp.),
  249
creeping spikerush (*Eleocharis
  macrostachya*), 184–188
creeping waterhyssop (*Bacopa repens*),
  362–363
creeping waterprimrose (*Ludwigia
  peploides*), 249–253
cress, hoary (*Cardaria draba*), 174, 175
crispate-leaved pondweed (*Potamogeton*
  spp.), 118
crisped-leaved pondweed (*Potamogeton*
  spp.), 118

crisped pondweed (*Potamogeton* spp.), 118

curled dock (*Rumex* spp.), 329

curled-leaved pondweed (*Potamogeton* spp.), 118

curltop ladysthumb (*Polygonum* spp.), 314

curly dock (*Rumex crispus*), 329–341

curlyleaf pondweed (*Potamogeton crispus*), 118, 119–120, 121, 123–124, 125

curly-leaved dock (*Rumex* spp.), 329

curlytop knotweed (*Polygonum* spp.), 314

cutleaf blackberry (*Rubus laciniatus*), 348–352

cut-leaved blackberry (*Rubus* spp.), 348

Cynodon donax (giant reed), 254

cyperus, tall (*Cyperus* spp.), 176

Cyperus spp. (**sedge**)
   difformis, 176–183
   eragrostis, 176–183
   erythrorhizos, 180–183
   flavicomus, 181–183
   fuscus, 182
   halei, 182
   lateriflorus, 176
   monandrus, 176
   serrulatus, 176
   vegetus, 176

daisy, false (*Eclipta* spp.), 168

dallisgrass (*Paspalum dilatatum*), 281–289

Daubentonia punicea (rattlebrush), 214

dense-flowered cordgrass (*Spartina densiflora*), 308, 310–311, 313

dense waterweed (*Egeria* spp.), 96

devil's shoestring (*Polygonum* spp.), 314

Dichotophyllum demersum (coontail), 78

Digitaria spp. (dallisgrass/knotgrass)
   dilatata, 281
   disticha, 281
   paspalodes, 281
   paspaloides, 281

Dimorphostachys oaxacensis (dallisgrass/knotgrass), 281

Diplachne spp. (sprangletop)
   fascicularis, 276
   verticillata, 276

disc waterhyssop (*Bacopa rotundifolia*), 362–364

ditchgrass, spiral (*Ruppia cirrhosa*), 128–129

ditchgrass (*Paspalum* spp.), 281

ditch-grass (*Ruppia* spp.), 128

ditch polypogon (*Polypogon interruptus*), 299–301, 304

dockleaf smartweed (*Polygonum* spp.), 314

dock (*Rumex* spp.)
   bitter, 329
   broadleaf, 329–341
   cluster, 333–334, 338, 341
   curled, 329
   curly, 329–341
   curly-leaved, 329
   fiddleleaf, 339–341
   green, 338
   Kerner's, 336–341
   narrowleaf, 329
   narrow-leaved, 329
   sour, 329
   toothed, 335–336, 338–339, 341
   yellow, 329

Donax arundinaceus (giant reed), 254

dotted smartweed (*Polygonum punctatum*), 326–328

duckmeat (*Spirodela* spp.), 49, 51

ducksalad (*Heteranthera limosa*), 342–347

duckweed, tropical (*Pistia* spp.), 42

duckweed (*Lemna* spp.)
   generally, 45
   common, 49–51

duckweed (*Spirodela* spp.)
   generally, 45
   giant, 49, 51

dwarf spikerush (*Eleocharis parvula*), 185–188

early tamarisk (*Tamarix* spp.), 369

early watergrass (*Echinochloa oryzoides*), 271–275

Echinochloa spp. (**junglerice/barnyardgrass**)
   colona, 263–275
   colonum, 263
   crus-galli, 263–275
   crus-pavonis, 270
   muricata, 270, 271
   oryzicola, 270–275
   oryzoides, 271–275

phyllopogon, 271
 zonalis, 263
Echinodorus spp. (**upright burhead**)
 berteroi, 142–146, 151
 cordifolius, 144
 lanceolatus, 144
 rostratus, 144
eclipta (*Eclipta prostrata*), 168–170
Eclipta spp. (**eclipta**)
 alba, 168–170
 erecta, 168
 prostrata, 168
eel-grass pondweed (*Potamogeton* spp.), 127
egeria, Brazilian (*Egeria densa*), 96–105
Eichhornia spp. (**water hyacinth**)
 crassipes, 42, 52–56, 58, 347
 speciosa, 52
Eisen waterhyssop (*Bacopa eisenii*), 359–364
Eleocharis spp. (**spikerush**)
 acicularis, 185–186, 188
 coloradoensis, 186
 macrostachya, 184–188
 mamillata, 184
 obtusa, 185–187
 palustris, 184–188
 parvula, 185–188
 perlonga, 184
elephant grass (*Arundo* spp.), 254
elmleaf blackberry (*Rubus ulmifolius*), 352
elodea (*Egeria* spp.)
 Brazilian, 96
 leafy, 96
elodea (*Elodea* spp.)
 American, 96
 common, 96–105
elodea (*Hydrilla* spp.)
 Florida, 96
Elodea spp. (Brazilian egeria)
 densa, 96
Elodea spp. (**common elodea**)
 brandegae, 96
 canadensis, 96–105
 ioensis, 96
 linearis, 96
 planchonii, 96
Elodea spp. (hydrilla)
 verticillata, 96
Emerus puniceus (rattlebrush), 214

Enydria aquatica (watermilfoil), 86
Equisetum spp. (**horsetail/scouringrush**)
 arvense, 202–206
 boreale, 202
 braunii, 205
 calderi, 202
 campestre, 202
 fustoni, 205
 hiemale, 202
 hyemale, 202–206
 kansanum, 205
 laevigatum, 205–206
 praealtum, 202
 riparium, 202
 robustum, 202
 saxicola, 202
 telmateia, 205–206
Erianthus ravennae (ravennagrass), 261
Eurasian watermilfoil (*Myriophyllum spicatum*), 82, 84, 86–93, 95
European pennyroyal (*Mentha* spp.), 224
European speedwell (*Veronica beccabunga*), 367–368
European wand loosestrife (*Lythrum virgatum*), 247
evergreen blackberry (*Rubus* spp.), 348

fairy moss (*Azolla* spp.), 44
false daisy (*Eclipta* spp.), 168
false indigo, western (*Amorpha* spp.), 219
fanwort (*Cabomba caroliniana*), 80–82, 95
fennel-leaf pondweed (*Potamogeton* spp.), 118
fern, horsetail (*Equisetum* spp.), 202
fern (*Salvinia* spp.)
 butterfly, 57
 water, 60
Festuca spp. (sprangletop)
 fascicularis, 276
 polystachya, 276
 texana, 276
fiddleleaf dock (*Rumex pulcher*), 339–341
field horsetail (*Equisetum arvense*), 202–206
fingergrass (*Echinochloa* spp.), 263
five-stamen tamarisk (*Tamarix* spp.), 369
flatsedge (*Cyperus* spp.)
 brown, 182
 redroot, 180–183
 tall, 176

flatsedge, cont.
variable, 176
whitemargined, 181–183
flatstem pondweed (*Potamogeton zosteri-formis*), 127
floatingheart, yellow (*Nymphoides peltata*), 116, 117
floatingleaf pondweed (*Potamogeton natans*), 118, 121–123, 125
floating marshpennywort (*Hydrocotyle spp.*), 159
floating pennywort (*Hydrocotyle ranunculoides*), 159–161
floating pondweed, common (*Potamogeton spp.*), 118
Florida elodea (*Hydrilla spp.*), 96
fox-tail rush (*Equisetum spp.*), 202
fragrant waterlily (*Nymphaea odorata*), 115–117
French tamarisk (*Tamarix gallica*), 376–377
frogbit (*Limnobium spp.*)
American, 56
smooth, 55–56

garden loosestrife (*Lysimachia vulgaris*), 246–248
giant arrowhead (*Sagittaria spp.*), 147
giant duckweed (*Spirodela polyrrhiza*), 49, 51
giant hogweed (*Heracleum mantegazzianum*), 156–158
giant horsetail (*Equisetum telmateia*), 205
giant reed (*Arundo donax*), 254–262
giant salvinia (*Salvinia molesta*), 57–61
giant white weed (*Lepidium spp.*), 171
Gila River waterhyssop (*Bacopa spp.*), 359
Goodding's black willow (*Salix gooddingii*), 353–358
grand redstem (*Ammannia spp.*), 228
grass poly (*Lythrum spp.*), 237
grassy naiad (*Najas graminea*), 105, 107–108
grassy pondweed (*Potamogeton spp.*), 127
great bulrush (*Scirpus spp.*), 189
great water speedwell (*Veronica spp.*), 365
green dock (*Rumex spp.*), 338
Gregg arrowhead (*Sagittaria longiloba*), 150–151
Gulf cockspur (*Echinochloa crus-pavonis*), 270

hairy pepperwort (*Marsilea vestita*), 45, 47–48
hairy water-clover (*Marsilea spp.*), 45
hairy whitetop (*Cardaria pubescens*), 175
Harding grass (*Phalaris aquatica*), 290–296
hardstem bulrush (*Scirpus acutus*), 189–191, 198
hardy pampasgrass (*Saccharum spp.*), 261
heart-weed (*Polygonum spp.*), 314
Heliocharis macrostachya (spikerush), 184
hemp sesbania (*Sesbania exalta*), 210, 217–219
Heracleum spp. (hogweed/cow parsnip)
lanatum, 158
mantegazzianum, 156–158
Herzog salvinia (*Salvinia herzogii*), 57
Heteranthera spp. (ducksalad)
alismoides, 342
limosa, 342–347
rotundifolia, 342
Heteranthera formosa (water hyacinth), 52, 58
Himalaya blackberry (*Rubus armeniacus*), 348–352
Himalayan blackberry (*Rubus spp.*), 348
hoary cress (*Cardaria draba*), 174, 175
hogweed, giant (*Heracleum mantegazzianum*), 156–158
hollyleaf naiad (*Najas marina*), 108
honey clover (*Melilotus spp.*), 211
hooded arrowhead (*Sagittaria spp.*), 147
horned pondweed (*Zannichellia palustris*), 108–109, 125–127, 129, 132–134
hornwort (*Ceratophyllum spp.*), 78
horsepipes (*Equisetum spp.*), 202
horsetail (*Equisetum spp.*)
common, 202
fern, 202
field, 202–206
giant, 205
scouringrush, 202
hyacinth, water (*Eichhornia crassipes*), 42, 52–56, 58, 347
hydraulthele, western (*Bacopa spp.*), 358
hydrilla (*Hydrilla verticillata*), 86, 96–105, 117, 186

Hydrilla spp. (**hydrilla**)
  lithuanica, 96
  verticillata, 86, 96–105, 117, 186
Hydrocotyle spp. (**floating pennywort**)
  adoensis, 159
  batrachioides, 159
  natans, 159
  ranunculoides, 159–161
  umbellata, 161
  verticillata, 161
Hydrophace minor (common duckweed), 49
hyssop loosestrife (*Lythrum hyssopifolium*), 237–248
hyssop lythrum (*Lythrum* spp.), 237

Illinois pondweed (*Potamogeton illinoensis*), 118–119, 121–122, 125, 127
Indian toothcup (*Rotala indica*), 228–236
indigo, western false (*Amorpha* spp.), 219
indigobush (*Amorpha fruticosa*), 219–220
indigobush, false (*Amorpha* spp.), 219
indigoweed (*Sesbania* spp.), 214
iris (*Iris* spp.)
  paleyellow, 221
  yellow flag, 221
  yellowflag, 221–223
Iris spp. (**iris**)
  acoriformis, 221
  bastardi, 221
  curtopetala, 221
  lutea, 221
  paludosa, 221
  pseudacorus, 221–223
iron weed (*Lepidium* spp.), 171
Isolepis spp. (bulrush), 189

Japanese kelp (*Undaria pinnatifida*), 64–65
jointgrass (*Paspalum* spp.), 281
jointvetch (*Aeschynomene* spp.)
  rough, 207–210
  zigzag, 207
junglerice (*Echinochloa colona*), 263–275
Jussiaea spp. (waterprimrose)
  californica, 249
  glabrescens, 249
  grandiflora, 253
  patibilcensis, 249
  polygonoides, 249
  repens, 249, 253
  uruguayensis, 253

karibaweed (*Salvinia* spp.), 57
kelp, Japanese (*Undaria pinnatifida*), 64–65
kelp (*Polygonum* spp.), 314
Kerner's dock (*Rumex kerneri*), 336–341
knotgrass (*Paspalum distichum*), 281–289
knotweed (*Polygonum* spp.)
  common, 314
  curlytop, 314
  spotted, 314
  swamp, 314
  water, 314
koi kandy (*Salvinia* spp.), 57

ladysthumb (*Polygonum persicaria*), 314–328
ladysthumb, curltop (*Polygonum* spp.), 314
Lamcosoa coronopifolia (brassbuttons), 165
lanceleaved waterplantain (*Alisma lanceolatum*), 140–143
largeleaf pondweed (*Potamogeton amplifolius*), 120, 127
large white waterlily (*Nymphaea* spp.), 115
large yellow loosestrife (*Lysimachia* spp.), 248
late tamarisk (*Tamarix* spp.), 369
late watergrass (*Echinochloa oryzicola*), 270–275
leafy elodea (*Egeria* spp.), 96
leafy pondweed (*Potamogeton foliosus*), 118–119, 120, 122, 125, 127
Lemna spp. (**common duckweed**)
  generally, 45, 121
  minor, 49–51
  minuscula, 49, 50
lens-podded whitetop (*Cardaria draba*), 175
lentil, water (*Lemna* spp.), 49
Lepidium latifolium (**perennial pepperweed**), 171–175
Leptanthus ovalis (ducksalad), 342
Leptochloa spp. (**bearded/Mexican sprangletop**)
  fascicularis, 276–280
  fusca, 276
  imbricata, 276

Leptochloa spp., cont.
  polystachya, 276
  tracyi, 276
  uninervia, 276–280
Limnantheumum peltatum (yellow floatingheart), 117
Limnobium spp. (**frogbit**)
  laevigatum, 55–56
  spongia, 56
Limnophila X *ludoviciana* (**marshweed**),
  82–83
longbarb arrowhead (*Sagittaria* spp.), 150
longleaf pondweed (*Potamogeton* spp.), 118
long-leaved pondweed (*Potamogeton*
  spp.), 118
longroot smartweed (*Polygonum* spp.),
  314
loose-flowered sprangletop (*Leptochloa*
  spp.), 276
loosestrife (*Lysimachia* spp.)
  dotted, 248
  garden, 246–248
  large yellow, 248
loosestrife (*Lythrum* spp.)
  California, 244, 247
  European wand, 247
  hyssop, 237–248
  purple, 237–248
  spatulaleaf, 243, 245
  threebract, 242, 245
Lophotocarpus spp. (arrowhead)
  californicus, 147
  calycinus, 147
  depauperatus, 147
lovegrass sedge (*Cyperus eragrostis*),
  176–183
lover's pride (*Polygonum* spp.), 314
Ludwigia spp. (**waterprimrose**)
  glabrescens, 249
  hexapetala, 155, 251–253
  major, 253
  montevidensis, 249, 251, 252
  palustris, 253
  peploides, 249–253
  uruguayensis, 253
Lysimachia spp. (loosestrife)
  generally, 247–248
  punctata, 248
  vulgaris, 247–248
lythrum (*Lythrum* spp.)
  hyssop, 237
  purple, 237

Lythrum spp. (**loosestrife**)
  adsurgens, 237
  californicum, 244, 247
  gracilior, 237
  hyssopifolium, 237–248
  portula, 243, 245
  salicaria, 237–248
  tomentosum, 237
  tribracteatum, 242, 245
  virgatum, 247
  vulgare, 237

marshpennywort, floating (*Hydrocotyle*
  spp.), 159
marshpepper smartweed (*Polygonum*
  hydropiper), 322–323, 327–328
marsh smartweed (*Polygonum* spp.), 314
marshweed (*Limnophila* X *ludoviciana*),
  82–83
Marsilea spp. (**hairy pepperwort**)
  mucronata, 45
  oligospora, 45
  vestita, 45, 47–48
meadow-pine (*Equisetum* spp.), 202
Mediterranean polypogon (*Polypogon*
  maritimus), 299, 301, 304
Megastachya uninervia (Mexican sprangletop), 276
melilot, white (*Melilotus* spp.), 211
Melilotus albus (**white sweetclover**),
  211–213
Mentha spp. (**pennyroyal**)
  daghestanica, 224
  pulegium, 224–227
  spicata, 226–227
  suaveolens, 226–227
mercer grass (*Paspalum* spp.), 281
Mexican mosquitofern (*Azolla mexicana*),
  44
Mexican sprangletop (*Leptochloa uninervia*), 276–280
Mexican waterlily (*Nymphaea mexicana*),
  112, 114–117
mild smartweed (*Polygonum hydropiperoides*), 325, 328
Milium spp. (junglerice/knotgrass)
  colona, 263
  distichum, 281
millet, spreading (*Leptochloa* spp.), 276
mint, apple (*Mentha suaveolens*), 226–227
Molina salicifolia (seepwillow), 162

Monnier waterhyssop (*Bacopa monnieri*), 361–362
monochoria (*Monochoria vaginalis*), 342–347
Monochoria spp. (**monochoria**)
   africana, 342
   brevipetiolata, 342
   linearis, 342
   plantaginia, 342
   vaginalis, 342–347
mosquitofern (*Azolla* spp.)
   generally, 44–47, 51, 154
   Mexican, 44
   Pacific, 44, 45–47
   pinnate, 44
moss, fairy (*Azolla* spp.), 44
mudplantain (*Heteranthera* spp.)
   blue, 342
   longleaf, 342
mule fat (*Baccharis* spp), 162
muskgrass (*Chara* spp.), 66
Myriophyllum spp. (**watermilfoil**)
   aquaticum, 86–89, 91, 93
   brasiliense, 86
   exalbescens, 93
   hippuroides, 93, 94
   proserpinacoides, 86
   sibiricum, 82, 84, 87, 92, 93, 95
   spicatum, 82, 84, 86–93, 95
   verticillatum, 93

naiad (*Najas* spp.)
   generally, 126–127, 129, 134
   grassy, 105, 107–108
   hollyleaf, 108
   southern, 105–109
   spiny, 108
Najas spp. (**naiad**)
   generally, 126–127, 129, 134
   flexilis, 106
   floridana, 106
   gracilis, 108
   graminea, 105, 107–108
   guadalupensis, 105–109
   latifolia, 108
   major, 108
   marina, 108
   muenscheri, 106
   olivacea, 106
narrowleaf cattail (*Typha angustifolia*), 382–386

narrowleaf dock (*Rumex* spp.), 329
narrow-leafed oleaster (*Elaeagnus* spp.), 199
narrowleaf willow (*Salix* spp.), 353
narrow-leaved dock (*Rumex* spp.), 329
needle spikerush (*Eleocharis acicularis*), 185–186, 188
nitella (*Nitella* spp.), 66–70
Nitella spp. (**Nitella**)
   generally, 66–68
   clavata, 69
   flexilis, 70
   furcata, 69
   gracilis, 70
nodding smartweed (*Polygonum* spp.), 314
northern watermilfoil (*Myriophyllum spicatum*), 82, 84, 87, 92, 93, 95
northern waterplantain (*Alisma* spp.), 137
nostoc (*Nostoc* spp.), 74–76
Nuphar spp. (**yellow pondlily**)
   lutea, 110
   luteum, 110
   polysepala, 110–112, 117
   polysepalum, 110
Nymphaea spp. (**waterlily**)
   generally, 111–112
   mexicana, 112, 114–117
   odorata, 115–117
   polysepalum, 110
Nymphoides (**yellow floatingheart**)
   nymphaeoides, 117
   peltata, 116, 117
Nymphozanthus polysepalus (yellow pondlily), 110

oleaster (*Elaeagnus* spp.), 199
olive (*Elaeagnus* spp.)
   Russian, 199–201
   wild, 199
Oplismenus spp. (junglerice)
   colona, 263
   crusgalli, 263
Oxalis spp. (sorrel), 47

Pacific coast bulrush (*Scirpus* spp.), 191
Pacific mosquitofern (*Azolla filiculoides*), 44, 45–47, 46–47
pale persicaria (*Polygonum* spp.), 314
pale smartweed (*Polygonum lapathifolium*), 314–328

pale spikerush (*Eleocharis* spp.), 184
pale spikesage (*Eleocharis* spp.), 184
paleyellow iris (*Iris* spp.), 221
pampasgrass, hardy (*Saccharum* spp.), 261
panicum, cocksfoot (*Echinochloa* spp.), 263
Panicum spp. (dallisgrass/knotgrass)
   digitarioides, 281
   platense, 281
Panicum spp. (junglerice/barnyardgrass)
   colona, 263
   crusgalli, 263
   grossum, 263
   incertum, 263
   prorepens, 263
   zonale, 263
parrotfeather (*Myriophyllum aquaticum*), 86–89, 91, 93
parsnip, cow (*Heracleum lanatum*), 158
paspalum (*Paspalum* spp.), 281
Paspalum spp. (**dallisgrass/knotweed**)
   digitaria, 281
   dilatatum, 281–289
   distichum, 281–289
   eriophorum, 281
   lanatum, 281
   notatum, 284–285, 288–289
   ovatum, 281
   paspalodes, 281
   paspaloides, 281
   pedunculare, 281
   platense, 281
   urvillei, 284–285, 287–288
payal (*Salvinia* spp.), 57
Pennsylvania smartweed (*Polygonum pensylvanicum*), 324, 327–328
pennyroyal (*Mentha pulegium*), 224–227
pennyroyal, European (*Mentha* spp.), 224
pennywort (*Hydrocotyle* spp.)
   floating, 159–161
   water, 161
   whorled, 161
Peplis indica (Indian toothcup), 228
peppercress, perennial (*Lepidium* spp.), 171
peppergrass, perennial (*Lepidium* spp.), 171
peppergrass, slender perennial (*Lepidium* spp.), 171
pepperweed (*Lepidium* spp.)
   broadleaf, 171

broadleaved, 171
   perennial, 171–175
pepperwort, hairy (*Marsilea vestita*), 45, 47–48
perennial peppercress (*Lepidium* spp.), 171
perennial peppergrass (*Lepidium* spp.), 171
perennial pepperweed (*Lepidium latifolium*), 171–175
persicaria (*Polygonum* spp.)
   pale, 314
   swamp, 314
Persicaria spp. (smartweed)
   amphibia, 314
   coccinea, 314
   lapathifolia, 314
   maculata, 314
   muhlenbergii, 314
   persicaria, 314
   ruderalis, 314
   vulgaris, 314
persicary (*Polygonum* spp.), 314
Phalaris spp. (**Harding grass/canarygrass**)
   aquatica, 290–296
   arundinacea, 294–296, 298
   brachystachys, 293–296
   caroliniana, 293–296
   commutata, 290
   hirtiglumis, 290
   stenoptera, 290
   tuberosa, 290
Philotria densa (Brazilian egeria), 96
Philotria spp. (common elodea)
   canadensis, 96
   linearis, 96
Phleum spp. (polypogon)
   crinitum, 297
   monspeliense, 297
Phragmites spp. (**common reed**)
   australis, 258–261
   communis, 258
Piaropus crassipes (water hyacinth), 52
pinegrass (*Equisetum* spp.), 202
pinnate mosquitofern (*Azolla pinnata*), 44
Piscidia spp. (rattlebrush)
   ovalifolia, 214
   punicea, 214
Pistia stratiotes (**waterlettuce**), 42–43
pistie (*Pistia* spp.), 42

Poa uninervia (Mexican sprangletop), 276
polished willow (*Salix* spp.), 353
Polygonum spp.(**smartweed/ladysthumb**)
   amphibium, 155, 314–328
   coccineum, 314
   dubium, 314
   emersum, 314
   fusiforme, 314
   hydropiper, 322–323, 327–328
   hydropiperoides, 325, 328
   lapathifolium, 314–328
   minus, 314
   muhlenbergii, 314
   nodosum, 314
   pensylvanicum, 324, 327–328
   persicaria, 314–328
   punctatum, 326–328
   puritanorum, 315
   stipulaceum, 315
polypogon (*Polypogon* spp.)
   comparison table, 304
   Chilean, 300–302, 304
   ditch, 299–301, 304
   Mediterranean, 299, 301, 304
   rabbitfoot, 297–304
   streambank, 301–302, 304
Polypogon spp. (**polypogon**)
   comparison table, 304
   australis, 300–302, 304
   crinitus, 297
   elongatus, 301–302, 304
   flavescens, 297
   interruptus, 299–301, 304
   lutosus, 301
   maritimus, 299, 301, 304
   monspeliensis, 297–304
   semiverticillata, 302
   viridis, 302–304
pond lily, Indian (*Nuphar* spp.), 110
pond-lily, Rocky Mountain (*Nuphar* spp.),
   110
pondlily, yellow (*Nuphar polysepala*),
   110–112, 117
pondweed (*Potamogeton* spp.)
   generally, 108–109, 118–127, 130–131,
      134
   American, 118, 123–124, 125
   broad-leafed, 118
   close-leaved, 118
   common floating, 118
   crispate-leaved, 118

   crisped, 118
   crisped-leaved, 118
   curled-leaved, 118
   curlyleaf, 118, 119, 121, 123–124, 125
   eel-grass, 127
   fennel-leaf, 118
   flatstem, 127
   floatingleaf, 118, 121–123, 125
   grassy, 127
   Illinois, 118–119, 121–122, 125, 127
   largeleaf, 120, 127
   leafy, 118–119, 120, 122, 125, 127
   longleaf, 118
   long-leaved, 118
   ribbonleaf, 127
   Richardson's, 127
   shining, 118
   small, 118, 123–124, 125, 127
   small-leafed, 118
   threadleaf, 127
   variable, 127
   waterthread, 127
   whitestem, 127
   ziz's, 118
pondweed, Canadian (*Elodea* spp.), 96
pondweed, horned (*Zannichellia*
      palustris), 108–109, 125–127, 129,
      132–134
pondweed, sago (*Stuckenia pectinatus*),
      109, 118–119, 123, 124, 125,
      126–127, 130
Pontederia crassipes (water hyacinth), 52
Pontederia spp. (ducksalad/monochoria)
   limosa, 342
   vaginalis, 342
Potamogeton spp. (**pondweed**)
   generally, 108–109, 118–127, 129–131,
      134
   americanus, 118
   amplifolius, 120, 127
   angustifolius, 118
   crispus, 118, 119–120, 121, 123–124,
      125
   diversifolius, 127
   epihydrus, 127
   filiformis, 127
   foliosus, 118–119, 120, 122, 125, 127
   gramineus, 127
   illinoensis, 118–119, 121–122, 125, 127
   lonchites, 118
   lucens, 118

Potamogeton spp., cont.
  natans, 118, 121–123, 125
  nodosus, 118, 123–124, 125
  panormitanus, 118
  pectinatus, 118
  perfoliatus, 127
  praelongus, 127
  pusillus, 118, 123–124, 125, 127
  richardsonii, 127
  zizii, 118
  zosteriformis, 127
primrose-willow (*Ludwigia* spp.)
  creeping, 249
  floating, 249
Pulegium spp. (pennyroyal)
  daghestanicum, 224
  vulgare, 224
purple ammannia (*Ammannia robusta*),
  228–236
purple loosestrife (*Lythrum salicaria*),
  237–248
purple lythrum (*Lythrum* spp.), 237
purple sesban (*Sesbania* spp.), 214
purple-top vervain (*Verbena* spp.), 387
pyle, African (*Salvinia* spp.), 57

rabbitfootgrass (*Polypogon* spp.), 297
rabbitfoot polypogon (*Polypogon monspeliensis*), 297–304
rabbitsfootgrass (*Polypogon* spp.), 297
Rabdochloa imbricata (Mexican sprangletop), 276
Ranunculus aquatilis (**white waterbuttercup**), 84–85
rattlebox (*Sesbania* spp.), 214
rattlebrush (*Sesbania punicea*), 214–220
ravennagrass (*Saccharum ravennae*),
  260–262
raygrass (*Leptochloa* spp.), 276
redberry (*Ammannia* spp.), 228
redroot flatsedge (*Cyperus erythrorhizos*),
  180–183
red shanks (*Polygonum* spp.), 314
redstem (*Ammannia coccinea*), 228–229
redstem, grand (*Ammannia* spp.), 228
red willow (*Salix laevigata*), 353–358
reed (*Arundo* spp.)
  bamboo, 254
  donax, 254
  giant, 254–262
  Spanish, 254

reed, **common** (*Phragmites australis*),
  258–261
reed canarygrass (*Phalaris arundinacea*),
  292–294, 296
reed cane (*Arundo* spp.), 254
reed grass (*Arundo* spp.), 254
rhizoclonium (*Rhizoclonium* spp.), 71–73
ribbonleaf pondweed (*Potamogeton epihydrus*), 127
ricefield bulrush (*Scirpus mucronatus*),
  193, 197, 198
Richardson's pondweed (*Potamogeton
  richardsonii*), 127
river bulrush (*Scirpus fluviatilis*), 190,
  191, 192–193, 198
Rotala spp. (**Indian toothcup/toothcup**)
  indica, 228–236
  ramosior, 233–236
rough barnyardgrass (*Echinochloa muricata*), 270, 271
rough jointvetch (*Aeschynomene rudis*),
  207–210
roughseed bulrush (*Scirpus* spp.), 193
Rubus spp. (**blackberry**)
  armeniacus, 348–352
  discolor, 348
  fruticosus, 348
  laciniatus, 348–352
  procerus, 348
  ulmifolius, 348
  vulgaris, 348
Rumex spp. (**dock**)
  conglomeratus, 333–334, 338, 341
  crispus, 329–341
  dentatus, 334–335, 338–339, 341
  folius, 329–341
  kerneri, 336–341
  obtusifolius, 329–341
  pulcher, 339–341
Ruppia spp. (**widgeongrass**)
  generally, 108–109, 125–127, 125–131,
    134
  cirrhosa, 128–129
  maritima, 127–130
  pectinata, 128
rush, fox-tail (*Equisetum* spp.), 202
Russian olive (*Elaeagnus angustifolia*),
  199–201

Saccharum ravennae (**ravennagrass**),
  260–262

Sagittaria spp. (**arrowhead**)
  generally, 142–143, 146
  calycina, 147
  longiloba, 150–151
  montevidensis, 147–151
  pugioniformis, 147
sago pondweed (*Stuckenia pectinatus*), 109,
      118–119, 123, 124, 125, 126–127,
      130
Salix spp. (**willow**)
  generally, 164, 201, 358
  agrophylla, 353
  babylonica, 357–358
  bakeri, 353
  congesta, 353
  exigua, 201, 353–358
  gooddingii, 353–358
  hindsiana, 353
  laevigata, 353–358
  lasiolepis, 353–358
  leucodendroides, 353
  linearifolia, 353
  lutea, 353
  nevadensis, 353
  nigra, 353
  parishiana, 353
  sessifolia, 353
  thurberi, 353
  tracyi, 353
  vallicola, 353
saltcedar (*Tamarix ramosissima*), 369–377
saltgrass, clustered (*Leptochloa* spp.), 276
saltmarsh cordgrass (*Spartina* spp.), 305
salt-meadow cordgrass (*Spartina patens*),
      310–313
saltwater cordgrass (*Spartina* spp.), 305
salvinia complex (*Salvinia* spp.)
  generally, 57–61
  giant, 57–61
  Herzog, 57
  water fern, 60
  water sprangles, 60
Salvinia spp. (**salvinia**)
  auriculata, 60
  herzogii, 57
  hispida, 57
  minima, 60
  molesta, 57–61
  natans, 57
  rotundifolia, 57
sandbar willow (*Salix* spp.), 353
Santia monspeliense (polypogon), 297

scale grass (*Leptochloa* spp.), 276
Schoenoplectus spp. (**bulrush**)
  acutus, 189
  californicus, 191
  fluviatilis, 191
  mucronatus, 193
  occidentalis, 189
  robustus, 191
  rubiginosus, 189
Scirpus spp. (**bulrush**)
  comparison table, 198
  acutus, 189–198
  californicus, 191, 193–194, 198
  fluviatilis, 190, 191, 192–193, 198
  glaucus, 193, 196, 198
  lacustris, 189
  maritimus, 191, 194–195, 198
  mucronatus, 193, 197, 198
  occidentalis, 189–198
  robustus, 191, 195–196, 198
  rubiginous, 189
  tuberosus, 193
Scirpus palustris (spikerush), 184
Scolochloa ssp. (giant reed)
  arundinacea, 254
  donax, 254
scouringrush (*Equisetum* spp.)
  generally, 202–206
  common, 202
  horsetail, 202
  smooth, 205–206
  western, 202
seashore vervain (*Verbena litoralis*),
      387–392
sedge (*Cyperus* spp.)
  lovegrass, 176–183
  smallflower umbrella, 176–183
seepwillow (*Baccharis salicifolia*), 162–164,
      358
Serpicula verticullata (elodea), 96
Sertula albus (white sweetclover), 211
sesban, purple (*Sesbania* spp.), 214
Sesbania spp. (hemp sesbania)
  herbacea, 218
  macrocarpa, 218
Sesbania spp. (**rattlebrush**)
  exaltata, 210, 217–219
  punicea, 214–220
  tripetii, 214
shanks, red (*Polygonum* spp.), 314
shavegrass (*Equisetum* spp.), 202
shining pondweed (*Potamogeton* spp.), 118

short-spike canarygrass (*Phalaris brachystachys*), 293–295
short-spike watermilfoil (*Myriophyllum* spp.), 93
Siberian watermilfoil (*Myriophyllum sibiricum*), 93
silverberry (*Elaeagnus* spp.), 199
slender perennial peppergrass (*Lepidium* spp.), 171
small cordgrass (*Spartina maritima*), 311–312
smallflower tamarisk (*Tamarix parviflora*), 369–377
smallflower umbrella sedge (*Cyperus difformis*), 176–183
small-leafed pondweed (*Potamogeton* spp.), 118
small pondweed (*Potamogeton pusillus*), 118, 123–124, 125, 127
smartweed (*Polygonum* spp.)
    dockleaf, 314
    dotted, 326–328
    longroot, 314
    marsh, 314
    marshpepper, 322–323, 327–328
    mild, 325, 328
    nodding, 314
    pale, 314–328, 328
    Pennsylvania, 324, 327–328
    spotted, 314
    swamp, 155, 314–328
    water, 314, 315
    willow, 314
smooth cordgrass (*Spartina alterniflora*), 305–313
smooth frogbit (*Limnobium laevigatum*), 55–56
snake-grass (*Equisetum* spp.), 202
sorrel (*Oxalis* spp.), 47
sour dock (*Rumex* spp.), 329
South American waterweed (*Egeria* spp.), 96
southern bulrush (*Scirpus* spp.), 191
southern cattail (*Typha domingensis*), 384–386
southern naiad (*Najas guadalupensis*), 105–109
southern waternymph (*Najas* spp.), 106
Spartina spp. (**cordgrass**)
    comparison table, 313
    alterniflora, 305–313

anglica, 311–313
brasiliensis, 305
densiflora, 308, 310–311, 313
foliosa, 306, 308–310, 313
glabra, 305
maitima, 305
maritima, 311–312
patens, 310–313
pilosa, 305
stricta, 305, 311–312
spatterdock (*Nuphar* spp.), 110
spatulaleaf loosestrife (*Lythrum portula*), 243, 245
spearmint (*Mentha spicata*), 226–227
speedwell (*Veronica* spp.)
    American, 368
    chain, 367–368
    European, 367–368
    great water, 365
    water, 365–368
spikerush (*Eleocharis* spp.)
    blunt, 185–187
    common, 184
    creeping, 184–188
    dwarf, 185–188
    needle, 185–186, 188
    pale, 184
spikesage (*Eleocharis* spp.)
    common, 184
    pale, 184
spike watermilfoil (*Myriophyllum* spp.), 86
spiny naiad (*Najas* spp.), 108
spiny waternymph (*Najas* spp.), 108
spiral ditchgrass (*Ruppia cirrhosa*), 128–129
Spirodela spp. (duckweed)
    generally, 45, 49
    polyrrhiza, 49, 51
sponge plant (*Limnobium laevigatum*), 55
spotted knotweed (*Polygonum* spp.), 314
spotted smartweed (*Polygonum* spp.), 314
sprangles, water (*Salvinia minima*), 60
sprangletop (*Leptochloa* spp.)
    bearded, 276–280
    loose-flowered, 276
    Mexican, 276–280
spreading millet (*Leptochloa* spp.), 276
stonewort (*Chara* spp.), 66
stonewort (*Nitella* spp.), 66

streambank polypogon (*Polypogon elongatus*), 301–302, 304

Stuckenia spp. (**sago pondweed**)
  generally, 109, 118, 134
  filiformis, 127
  pectinatus, 118–119, 123, 124, 125, 126–127, 130

sturdy bulrush (*Scirpus robustus*), 191, 195–196, 198

summergrass (*Echinochloa* spp.), 263

swamp knotweed (*Polygonum* spp.), 314

swamp persicaria (*Polygonum* spp.), 314

swamp smartweed (*Polygonum amphibium*), 155, 314–328

sweetclover, white (*Melilotus albus*), 211–213

sweetclover, white (*Sertula* spp.), 211

tall cyperus (*Cyperus* spp.), 176

tall flatsedge (*Cyperus* spp.), 176

tall vervain (*Verbena bonariensis*), 387–392

tamarisk (*Tamarix* spp.)
  athel, 369–377
  Chinese, 376–377
  early, 369
  five-stamen, 369
  French, 376–377
  late, 369
  smallflower, 369–377

Tamarix spp. (**tamarisk/saltcedar**)
  africana, 369
  altaica, 369
  aphylla, 369–377
  articulata, 369
  chinensis, 369–370
  cretica, 369
  ewersmannii, 369
  gallica, 369, 376–377
  lucronensis, 369
  odessana, 369
  orientalis, 369
  pallasii, 369
  parviflora, 369–377
  pentandra, 369
  petteri, 369
  ramosissima, 369–377
  rubella, 369
  tetranda, 369

tanweed (*Polygonum* spp.), 314

tasselweed, beaked (*Ruppia* spp.), 128

tawny beardgrass (*Polypogon* spp.), 297

threadleaf pondweed (*Potamogeton filiformis*), 127

thread-of-life (*Myriophyllum* spp.), 86

threebract loosestrife (*Lythrum tribracteatum*), 242, 245

Thuja aphylla (athel tamarisk), 369

toothcup (*Rotala ramosior*), 233–236

toothcup, Indian (*Rotala indica*), 228–236

toothed dock (*Rumex dentatus*), 335–336, 338–339, 341

toowoomba grass (*Phalaris* spp.), 290

Trachynotia alterniflora (smooth cordgrass), 305

Tracy's willow (*Salix* spp.), 353

tree clover (*Melilotus* spp.), 211

Trichophorum spp. (bulrush), 189

Trifolium spp. (clover), 47

tropical duckweed (*Pistia* spp.), 42

tuberous bulrush (*Scirpus glaucus*), 193, 196, 198

tuberous canarygrass (*Phalaris* spp.), 290

tule (*Scirpus* spp.), 189

Typha spp. (**cattail**)
  angustifolia, 382–386
  domingensis, 384–386
  latifolia, 378–386

umbrellaplant (*Cyperus* spp.), 176

umbrella sedge, smallflower (*Cyperus difformis*), 176–183

umbrellasedge, tall (*Cyperus* spp.), 176

Undaria pinnatifida (**wakeme**), 64–65

upright burhead (*Echinodorus berteroi*), 142–146, 151

Uralepis spp. (sprangletop)
  composita, 276
  verticillata, 276

Uralepsis spp. (sprangletop)
  composita, 276
  verticillata, 276

Uruguay waterprimrose (*Ludwigia hexapetala*), 155, 251–253

variable flatsedge (*Cyperus* spp.), 176

variable pondweed (*Potamogeton gramineus*), 127

vaseygrass (*Paspalum urvillei*), 284–285, 287

velvet, water (*Azolla* spp.), 44

verbena, cluster-flowered (*Verbena* spp.), 387

Verbena spp. (**vervain**)
  generally, 392
  bonariensis, 387–392
  brasiliensis, 387
  caracasana, 387
  hansenii, 387
  litoralis, 387–392
  littoralis, 387

Verbesina spp. (eclipta)
  alba, 168
  prostrata, 168

Veronica spp. (**speedwell**)
  americana, 368
  anagallis, 365
  anagallis-aquatica, 365–368
  beccabunga, 367–368
  catenata, 367
  connata, 367
  cosmosa, 367

vervain (*Verbena* spp.)
  Argentine, 387
  blue, 387
  purple-top, 387
  seashore, 387–392
  tall, 387–392

wakeme (*Undaria pinnatifida*), 64–65
wand loosestrife, European (*Lythrum virgatum*), 247
water bent (*Polypogon viridis*), 302–304
waterbuttercup, white (*Ranunculus aquatilis*), 84–85
water-clover, hairy (*Marsilea* spp.), 45
water fern (*Azolla* spp.), 44
water fringe (*Nymphoides* spp.), 117
watergrass (*Echinochloa* spp.)
  generally, 263, 267, 269, 275
  early, 271–275
  late, 270–275
water grass (*Paspalum* spp.), 281
water hyacinth (*Eichhornia crassipes*), 42, 52–56, 58, 347
waterhyssop (*Bacopa* spp.)
  creeping, 362–364
  disc, 362–364
  Eisen, 359–364
  Gila River, 359
  Monnier, 361–362
water knotweed (*Polygonum* spp.), 314

water lentil (*Lemna* spp.), 49
waterlettuce (*Pistia stratiotes*), 42–43
waterlily (*Nymphaea* spp.)
  generally, 111–112
  banana, 114
  fragrant, 115–117
  large white, 115
  Mexican, 112, 114–117
  yellow, 114
watermeal (*Wolffia* spp.), 45, 49, 51
watermilfoil (*Myriophyllum* spp.)
  Brazilian, 86
  Eurasian, 82, 84, 86–93, 95
  northern, 82, 84, 87, 92, 93, 95
  parrotfeather, 86
  short-spike, 93
  Siberian, 93
  spike, 86
  western, 93, 94
  whorled, 93
watermoss (*Salvinia* spp.)
  aquarium, 57
  eared, 57
waternymph (*Najas* spp.)
  southern, 106
  spiny, 108
water pennywort (*Hydrocotyle umbellata*), 161
waterplantain (*Alisma* spp.)
  generally, 143, 146, 151
  American, 137
  common, 137–143
  lanceleaved, 140–143
  northern, 137
waterprimrose (*Ludwigia* spp.)
  California, 249
  creeping, 249–253
  Uruguay, 155, 251–253
waterpurslane (*Ludwigia palustris*), 253
watershield (*Brasenia schreberi*), 111–113
water smartweed (*Polygonum* spp.), 314, 315
water speedwell (*Veronica anagallis-aquatica*), 365–368
water speedwell, great (*Veronica* spp.), 365
water sprangles (*Salvinia minima*), 60
waterthread pondweed (*Potamogeton diversifolius*), 127
waterthyme (*Hydrilla* spp.), 86, 96
water velvet (*Azolla* spp.), 44

water-wally (*Baccharis* spp), 162
water-weed, yellow (*Ludwigia* spp.), 249
waterweed (*Egeria* spp.)
    Brazilian, 96
    common, 96
    dense, 96
    South American, 96
waterweed (*Elodea* spp.)
    broad, 96
    Canadian, 96
weeping willow (*Salix babylonica*),
    357–358
western false indigo (*Amorpha* spp.), 219
western hydraulthele (*Bacopa* spp.), 358
western watermilfoil (*Myriophyllum hip-
    puroides*), 93, 94
whitemargined flatsedge (*Cyperus flavico-
    mus*), 181–183
white melilot (*Melilotus* spp.), 211
whitestem pondweed (*Potamogeton prae-
    longus*), 127
white sweetclover (*Melilotus albus*),
    211–213
white sweetclover (*Sertula* spp.), 211
whitetop (*Cardaria* spp.)
    hairy, 175
    lens-podded, 175
white waterbuttercup (*Ranunculus
    aquatilis*), 84–85
white waterlily, large (*Nymphaea* spp.), 115
white weed, giant (*Lepidium* spp.), 171
whorled pennywort (*Hydrocotyle verticil-
    lata*), 161
whorled watermilfoil (*Myriophyllum ver-
    ticillatum*), 93
widgeongrass (*Ruppia* spp.), 108–109,
    125–131, 134
wild cane (*Arundo* spp.), 254
wild olive (*Elaeagnus* spp.), 199
willow (*Salix* spp.)
    generally, 164, 201, 358
    arroyo, 353–358

    Coyote, 201, 353–358
    Goodding's, 353
    Goodding's black, 353–358
    narrowleaf, 353
    polished, 353
    red, 353–358
    sandbar, 353
    Tracy's, 353
    weeping, 357–358
willow smartweed (*Polygonum* spp.), 314
willow-weed (*Polygonum* spp.), 314
wiregrass (*Eleocharis* spp.), 184
wiregrass (*Paspalum* spp.), 281
wireweed (*Polygonum* spp.), 314
wisteria tree, scarlet (*Sesbania* spp.), 214
wokas (*Nuphar* spp.), 110
Wolffia spp. (**watermeal**), 45, 49, 51

yellow dock (*Rumex* spp.), 329
yellowflag iris (*Iris pseudacorus*),
    221–223
yellow flag iris (*Iris* spp.), 221
yellow floatingheart (*Nymphoides pelta-
    ta*), 116, 117
yellow loosestrife, large (*Lysimachia* spp.),
    248
yellow pondlily (*Nuphar polysepala*),
    110–112, 117
yellow waterlily (*Nymphaea* spp.), 114
yellow water-weed (*Ludwigia* spp.), 249

Zannichellia spp. (**horned pondweed**)
    major, 132
    palustris, 108–109, 125–127, 129,
        132–134
    repens, 132
    stenophylla, 132
Z-grass (*Zannichellia* spp.), 132
zigzag jointvetch (*Aeschynomene* spp.),
    207
ziz's pondweed (*Potamogeton* spp.), 118

Authors and Contributors

Joseph M. DiTomaso received the BS degree in wildlife and fisheries biology from the University of California, Davis, in 1977 and the MS degree specializing in plant taxonomy from Humboldt State University in 1981. He completed doctoral research at UC Davis in 1986 in weed science, specializing in plant physiology, and was a faculty member for seven years at Cornell University in Ithaca, New York, where he coauthored *Weeds of the Northeast*. Since 1995, he has been a noncrop weed specialist at UC Davis, focusing on the biology, ecology, and management of invasive weeds.

Evelyn Healy received the BS degree in botany from the University of California, Davis, in 1995, with emphasis in plant identification, ecology, and plant systematics.

Jack Kelly Clark, principal photographer in the Division of Agricultural and Natural Resources at the University of California, provided many of the photographs in this book, particularly the submerged aquatics and seeds.

Ellen Dean, director of the Tucker Herbarium at the University of California, Davis, provided important identifications, assisted in the development of the keys, and advised the authors on several aspects related to the production of the book.